INTRODUCTION TO MATHEMATICS

INTRODUCTION TO

MATHEMATICS

BRUCE E. MESERVE

Professor of Mathematics
University of Vermont

MAX A. SOBEL

Professor of Mathematics
Montclair State College

Prentice-Hall, Inc., Englewood Cliffs, N. J.

PREFACE

This book has been written with a number of different audiences in mind. The subject matter is suitable for the undergraduate college student who has had moderate secondary school training in mathematics, one who is not a mathematics major, but who wishes to acquire a basic understanding of the nature of mathematics. Many students seeking a knowledge of basic mathematics are so included. Frequently, prospective elementary-school teachers will be among such students. This book is also appropriate for in-service courses for elementary-school and junior high school teachers. To this end, the emphasis throughout the book is on key concepts and the structure of mathematics, without undue concern over the mechanical procedures.

As the title of the first chapter suggests, mathematics can be fun! The authors have embarked with this idea and have gone ahead to introduce a variety of interesting and timely topics without a major emphasis upon the so-called practical applications. This point of view, it is felt, will leave the reader with a better picture of the true meaning and beauty of mathematics as opposed to a traditional approach with a major emphasis on abstract manipulations.

Very little mathematical background is required of the reader. It is expected that he will have had some secondary school introduction to algebra and geometry, but no working knowledge of any of the skills normally taught in these subjects is presupposed. Maturity, on the other hand, is expected; and interest in the subject is anticipated.

The subject matter presented in this text is sufficient for a three semester hour college course for the above-mentioned type of student. Chapters 1 through 7 may be used for a two-semester hour course. Preliminary editions of these chapters have been used for the past two years at Montclair State College in a two semester hour course for college juniors who were prospective teachers of subjects other than mathematics. Chapters 8, 9, and 10 enable the teacher of a three-semester hour course to include more thorough introductions to algebra, logic, and geometry. The authors recommend the sequence of chapters as they are ordered in the book. However, Chapters 1, 2, 3, 4, and 9 may be studied independently; the dependence of the other chapters is shown in the following array:

$$
\begin{array}{ccccc}
& & & 5\text{—}10 & \\
& & & \diagup & \\
1, & 2, & 3, & 4\text{—}6 & , \quad 9. \\
& & & \diagdown & \\
& & & 7\text{—}8 &
\end{array}
$$

Note that Chapter 4 on "Sets of Elements" provides a basis for most of the remaining chapters of the book.

The authors wish to express their appreciation of the assistance of numerous students who participated actively in college courses at Montclair State College and used the materials that provided a basis for this book. In particular, they appreciate the suggestions of Mr. Jack Ott and Mr. Martin Cohen, who along with the authors taught courses using these materials. The authors also appreciate the cooperation of Prentice-Hall in preparing preliminary paperback editions of much of this material for classroom testing purposes.

The famous French mathematician René Descartes concluded his famous *La Géométrie* with the statement: "I hope that posterity will judge me kindly, not only as to the things which I have explained, but also as to those which I have intentionally omitted so as to leave to others the pleasure of discovery." The authors have attempted to provide a great deal of exposition in this text. They have, however, left a great deal for the reader so that he may experience the true beauty of mathematics through discovery.

BRUCE E. MESERVE
MAX A. SOBEL

CONTENTS

Contents

INTRODUCTION TO MATHEMATICS

CHAPTER

ONE

FUN WITH MATHEMATICS - ha

Mathematics has numerous practical applications ranging from everyday usage to the charting of astronauts through outer space. Mathematics also interests many just by the sheer beauty of its structure. We hope in this text to examine some of the beauty without unduly emphasizing the practical values. Thus, we hope to show that mathematics can be studied just for one's interest in it—that is, just for fun. Accordingly, this chapter contains a smorgasbord variety of items served up to whet the reader's appetite for the main course that follows.

1-1 Mathematical Patterns

Mathematicians love to search for patterns and generalizations in all branches of their subjects—in arithmetic, in algebra, and in geometry. A search for such patterns may not only be interesting but may also help one develop insight into mathematics as a whole.

1

Multiples of nine

Many patterns that often escape notice may be found in the structure of arithmetic. For example, consider the multiples of 9:

$$1 \times 9 = 9,$$
$$2 \times 9 \doteqdot 18,$$
$$3 \times 9 = 27,$$
$$4 \times 9 = 36,$$
$$5 \times 9 = 45,$$
$$6 \times 9 = 54,$$
$$7 \times 9 = 63,$$
$$8 \times 9 = 72,$$
$$9 \times 9 = 81.$$

What patterns do you notice in the column of multiples on the right? You may note that the sum of the digits in each case is always 9. You should also see that the units digit decreases $(9, 8, 7, \ldots)$, whereas the tens digit increases $(1, 2, 3, \ldots)$. What lies behind this pattern?

Consider the product
$$5 \times 9 = 45.$$

To find 6×9 we need to add 9 to 45. Instead of adding 9, we may add 10 and subtract 1.

$$\begin{array}{r} 45 \\ +10 \\ \hline 55 \end{array} \qquad \begin{array}{r} 55 \\ -1 \\ \hline 54 \end{array} = 6 \times 9$$

That is, by adding 1 to the tens digit, 4, of 45, we are really adding 10 to 45. We then subtract 1 from the units digit, 5, of 45 to obtain 54 as our product.

$$+10 \ +\left(\begin{array}{c} 45 \\ 9 \\ \hline 54 \end{array}\right) \ -1$$

A similar explanation can be given for each of the other multiples in the table.

Finger multiplication

The number 9, incidentally, has other fascinating properties. Of special interest is a procedure for multiplying by 9 on one's fingers. For example, to multiply 9 by 3, place both hands together as in the figure, and bend the third finger from the left. The result is read as 27.

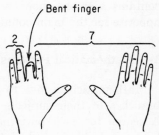

Bent finger

$3 \times 9 = 27$

The next figure shows the procedure for finding the product 7 × 9. Note that the seventh finger from the left is bent, and the result is read in terms of the tens digit, to the left, and the units digit to the right of the bent finger.

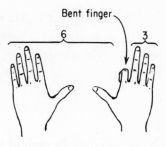

7 x 9 = 63

What number fact is shown in the next figure?

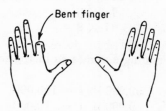

Patterns of numbers

Here is one more pattern related to the number 9. You may, if you wish, verify that each of the following is correct:

$$
\begin{aligned}
1 \times 9 + 2 &= 11, \\
12 \times 9 + 3 &= 111, \\
123 \times 9 + 4 &= 1{,}111, \\
1{,}234 \times 9 + 5 &= 11{,}111, \\
12{,}345 \times 9 + 6 &= 111{,}111.
\end{aligned}
$$

Try to find a correspondence of the number of 1's in the number symbol on the right with one of the numbers used on the left. Now, see if you can supply the answers, without computation, to the following:

$$
\begin{aligned}
123{,}456 \times 9 + 7 &= \text{?} \\
1{,}234{,}567 \times 9 + 8 &= \text{?}
\end{aligned}
$$

Now, let's see *why* this pattern works. To do so we shall examine just one of the statements. A similar explanation can be offered for each of the other statements. Consider the statement:

$$
12{,}345 \times 9 + 6 = 111{,}111.
$$

We can express 12,345 as a sum of five numbers as follows:

$$
\begin{array}{r}
11,111 \\
1,111 \\
111 \\
11 \\
\underline{1} \\
12,345
\end{array}
$$

Next we multiply each of the five numbers by 9:

$$
\begin{aligned}
11,111 \times 9 &= 99,999, \\
1,111 \times 9 &= 9,999, \\
111 \times 9 &= 999, \\
11 \times 9 &= 99, \\
1 \times 9 &= 9.
\end{aligned}
$$

Finally, we add 6 by adding six ones as in the following array, and find the total sum:

$$
\begin{aligned}
99,999 + 1 &= 100,000 \\
9,999 + 1 &= 10,000 \\
999 + 1 &= 1,000 \\
99 + 1 &= 100 \\
9 + 1 &= 10 \\
1 &= \underline{1} \\
& 111,111
\end{aligned}
$$

Here is another interesting pattern. After studying the pattern, see if you can add the next three lines to the table.

$$
\begin{aligned}
1 \times 1 &= 1 \\
11 \times 11 &= 121 \\
111 \times 111 &= 12,321 \\
1,111 \times 1,111 &= 1,234,321 \\
11,111 \times 11,111 &= 123,454,321
\end{aligned}
$$

Geometric patterns

In the study of geometry we frequently jump to conclusions on the basis of a small number of examples, together with an exhibited pattern. Consider, for example, the problem of determining the number of triangles that can be formed from a given polygon by drawing diagonals from a given vertex, P. First we draw several figures and consider the results in tabular form as follows.

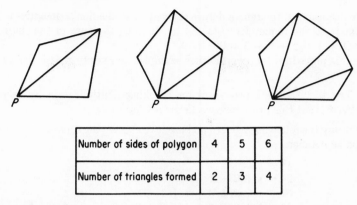

Number of sides of polygon	4	5	6
Number of triangles formed	2	3	4

From the pattern of entries in the table it appears that the number of triangles formed is two less than the number of sides of the polygon. Thus we expect that we can form 10 triangles from a dodecagon, a polygon with 12 sides, from a given vertex. In general then, for a polygon with n sides, called an n-gon, we can form $n - 2$ triangles.

This is reasoning by induction. We formed a generalization on the basis of several specific examples and an obvious pattern. It does not however, constitute a proof. To *prove* that $n - 2$ triangles can be formed we must observe that two of the n sides of the polygon intersect at the common point of the diagonals and each of the other $n - 2$ sides is used to form a different triangle.

Exercises

1. Verify that the process for finger multiplication shown in this section will work for each of the multiples of nine from 1×9 through 9×9.

2. Follow the procedure outlined in this section and show that $1,234 \times 9 + 5 = 11,111$.

3. An addition problem can be checked by a process called "casting out nines." To do this, you first find the sum of the digits of each of the addends (that is, numbers that are added), divide by 9, and record the remainder. The sum of these remainders is then divided by 9 to find a final remainder. This should be equal to the remainder found by considering the sum of the addends (that is, the answer), adding its digits, dividing the sum of these digits by 9, and finding the remainder. Here is an example:

Addends	*Sum of digits*	*Remainders*
4,378	22	4
2,160	9	0
3,872	20	2
1,085	14	5
11,495		11

When the sum of the remainders is divided by 9, the final remainder is 2. This corresponds to the remainder obtained by dividing the sum of the digits in the answer $(1 + 1 + 4 + 9 + 5 = 20)$ by 9.

Try this procedure for several other examples and verify that it works in each case.

4. Try to discover a procedure for checking multiplication by casting out nines. Verify that this procedure works for several cases.

5. Study the following pattern and use it to express the squares of 6, 7, 8, and 9 in the same manner.

$$1^2 = 1$$
$$2^2 = 1 + 2 + 1$$
$$3^2 = 1 + 2 + 3 + 2 + 1$$
$$4^2 = 1 + 2 + 3 + 4 + 3 + 2 + 1$$
$$5^2 = 1 + 2 + 3 + 4 + 5 + 4 + 3 + 2 + 1$$

6. Study the entries that follow and use the pattern that is exhibited to complete the last three rows.

$$1 + 3 = 4 \text{ or } 2^2$$
$$1 + 3 + 5 = 9 \text{ or } 3^2$$
$$1 + 3 + 5 + 7 = 16 \text{ or } 4^2$$
$$1 + 3 + 5 + 7 + 9 = ?$$
$$1 + 3 + 5 + 7 + 9 + 11 = ?$$
$$1 + 3 + 5 + 7 + 9 + 11 + 13 = ?$$

7. There is a procedure for multiplying a two-digit number by 9 on one's fingers provided that the tens digit is smaller than the ones digit. The accompanying diagram shows how to multiply 28 by 9. Reading from the left, put a space after the second finger and bend the eighth finger. Read the product in groups of fingers as 252.

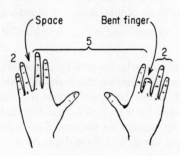

Use this procedure to find:

(a) $9 \times 47;$ **(b)** $9 \times 36;$ **(c)** $9 \times 18;$ **(d)** $9 \times 29.$

Check each of the answers you have obtained.

8. Take a piece of notebook paper and fold it in half. Then fold it in half again and cut off a corner that does not involve an edge of the original piece of paper.

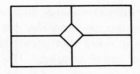

Step 1   Step 2

Your paper, when unfolded, should look like the accompanying sketch.

That is, with two folds we produced one hole. Repeat the same process but this time make three folds before cutting off an edge. Try to predict the number of holes that will be produced. How many holes will be produced with four folds? With n folds?

9. A famous mathematician named Gauss is said to have found the sum of the first 100 counting numbers at a very early age by the following procedure:

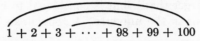

$$1 + 2 + 3 + \cdots + 98 + 99 + 100$$

He reasoned that there would be 50 pairs of numbers, each with a sum of 101 ($100 + 1$, $99 + 2$, $98 + 3$, etc.). Thus, the sum would be 50×101 or 5050. Use this procedure to find:

(a) the sum of the first 50 counting numbers;

(b) the sum of the first 200 counting numbers;

(c) the sum of all the odd numbers from 1 through 49;

(d) the sum of all the odd numbers from 1 through 99;

(e) the sum of all the even numbers from 2 through 200.

10. Use the results obtained in Exercise 9 and try to find a formula for the sum of:

(a) the first n counting numbers [that is, $1 + 2 + 3 + \cdots + (n - 1) + n$];

(b) the first n odd numbers [that is, $1 + 3 + 5 + \cdots + (2n - 3) + (2n - 1)$].

1-2 Finite and Infinite

In modern times all of us have become familiar with very large numbers merely by observing the national budget and the national debt. The number "one million" no longer seems exceptionally large, but have you ever stopped to consider just how big this number really is?

Just for fun, can you estimate how long it would take you to count to a million? Assume that you count at the rate of one number per second with no time off to eat, rest, or sleep. (Don't do any computation yet; merely estimate.) Would you guess that it would take you less than an hour? A few hours? A day? A few days? More than a week? A month?

Let's find out how long it would take to count to a million. At the rate we suggested it would take a million seconds. There are 3,600 seconds in an hour, so it would take $1,000,000 \div 3,600$ or approximately 278 hours. This is equivalent to about $11\frac{1}{2}$ days, counting night and day without rest, to reach one million!

Yes, one million is a large number, but it is **finite**; that is, it is countable. In this sense we also consider the number "one trillion" as finite even though we would not want to actually count to it.

Is there a largest number? The answer is clearly "no," for if someone claimed to be in possession of the world's largest number, you would merely have to add one to this number and then you would be in possession of a larger number.

One of the largest numbers ever named is a **googol**. This has been defined as 1 followed by one hundred zeros:

100000000000000000000000000000000000000000000000000000000000000
00000000000000000000000000000000000000.

This number is larger than what is considered to be the total number of protons or electrons in the universe! A googol can be expressed, using exponents, as

$$10^{100}.$$

Even larger than a googol is a **googolplex**, defined as 1 followed by a googol of zeros. One famous mathematician claimed that there would not even be room between the earth and the moon to write all the zeros in a googolplex!

Although large beyond human comprehension, these numbers are still finite. The question one might well ask is whether or not there are numbers that are **infinite**—that is, beyond the finite. To answer this we turn to the procedure used by man in ancient times.

When ancient man wished to count the number of animals he owned he did so by placing a pebble on the ground for each animal. Then the number of pebbles was the same as the number of animals. He had established a **one-to-one correspondence** between the set of animals that he owned and a set of pebbles; for each pebble there was an animal, and for each animal there was a pebble.

When we wish to count today we make use of the set of numbers 1, 2, 3, 4, 5, and so on. We place the things which we count in a one-to-one correspondence with members of this set of numbers. The last number used tells the size of the collection. For example, to count the numbers of letters in the word "Thursday" we proceed as follows:

$$
\begin{array}{cccccccc}
T & h & u & r & s & d & a & y \\
\updownarrow & \updownarrow & \updownarrow & \updownarrow & \updownarrow & \updownarrow & \updownarrow & \updownarrow \\
1 & 2 & 3 & 4 & 5 & 6 & 7 & 8
\end{array}
$$

We say that the **cardinality** of the set of letters in the word is 8. A number used to denote the size of a collection is called a **cardinal number**. (Actually when we write "8" we are writing a **numeral** and not a number. Numbers are abstract concepts which cannot be written on paper. However, here,

and in later work, we shall distinguish between a number and a numeral
only when it proves helpful to do so.)

Whenever two sets are such that their members may be placed in a
one-to-one correspondence with each other we say that the two sets are
equivalent. Thus the set of letters in the word "Thursday" is equivalent to
the set of the first eight counting numbers. In a similar manner, the following two sets are equivalent.

$$1 \quad 2 \quad 3 \quad 4 \quad 5$$
$$\updownarrow \quad \updownarrow \quad \updownarrow \quad \updownarrow \quad \updownarrow$$
$$2 \quad 4 \quad 6 \quad 8 \quad 10$$

Also, the set of even numbers greater than zero is equivalent to the set of
counting numbers.

$$1 \quad 2 \quad 3 \quad 4 \quad 5 \quad 6 \; \ldots \; n \; \ldots$$
$$\updownarrow \quad \updownarrow \quad \updownarrow \quad \updownarrow \quad \updownarrow \quad \updownarrow \qquad \updownarrow$$
$$2 \quad 4 \quad 6 \quad 8 \quad 10 \; 12 \; \ldots \; 2n \; \ldots$$

Each counting number, n, can be matched with an even counting number,
$2n$.

It appears strange to be able to say that these two sets are equivalent.
We are really saying that there are just as many even counting numbers
as there are counting numbers altogether! This puzzled mathematicians
for centuries until, at the turn of the twentieth century, a German mathematician named Georg Cantor developed an entire theory of infinite
sets of numbers. This is essentially what he did.

He assigned a cardinal number to the set of counting numbers, namely,
$\aleph_0$. This is read **"aleph-null"** and is really a **transfinite** (beyond the finite)
cardinal number. It is correct then to say that there are $\aleph_0$ counting
numbers, just as you might say that there are 7 days of the week or 10 fingers on your hands. Furthermore, any set that can be matched in a one-to-
one correspondence with the set of counting numbers is also of size $\aleph_0$.

The discussion of transfinite numbers gives rise to some very interesting
apparent paradoxes. One of the most famous of these is the story of the
infinite house. This is a house that contains an infinite number of rooms,
numbered 1, 2, 3, 4, 5, and so on. Each room is occupied by a single
tenant. That is, there is a one-to-one correspondence between rooms and
occupants. There are $\aleph_0$ rooms, and $\aleph_0$ occupants. One day a stranger
arrived at the house and asked to be admitted. The caretaker was an
amateur mathematician and was able to accommodate this visitor in the
following manner. He asked the occupant of room 1 to move to room 2,
the occupant of room 2 to move to room 3, the occupant of room 3 to
move to room 4, and in general the occupant of room n to move to room
$n + 1$. Now everyone had a room and room number 1 was available for
the visitor! In other words we have demonstrated the interesting fact

$$\aleph_0 + 1 = \aleph_0.$$

Several days later an infinite number of visitors arrived at the house, all demanding individual rooms! Again the caretaker was able to accommodate them. He merely asked each tenant to move to a room number which was double his current room number. That is, the occupant of room 1 moved to room 2, the occupant of room 2 moved to room 4, room 3 to room 6, and room n to room $2n$. After this move was made, the new arrivals were placed in rooms 1, 3, 5, and so forth. Here we have an example of another interesting fact in the language of transfinite arithmetic:

$$\aleph_0 + \aleph_0 = \aleph_0.$$

As another example of this last fact note that the set of even counting numbers is of size $\aleph_0$, and the set of odd counting numbers is also of size $\aleph_0$. But the even counting numbers together with the odd counting numbers form the set of all counting numbers, which we have agreed is of size $\aleph_0$. Therefore, again, we see that $\aleph_0 + \aleph_0 = \aleph_0$.

Exercises

1. Estimate how long it would take you to count to one billion at the rate of one number per second. Then compute this to the nearest day.

2. You are offered a job that pays 1¢ the first day, 2¢ the second day, 4¢ the third day, and so forth. That is, your wages are doubled each day. First estimate, then compute, your salary for the thirtieth day on the job.

3. (a) Estimate the number of seconds that elapse in a century. **(b)** Find this number to the nearest million.

4. How long would it take you to spend one million dollars if you spent one dollar every minute for eight hours every day?

5. Show that there are just as many multiples of five (5, 10, 15, 20, . . .), as there are counting numbers.

6. Estimate how many pennies it would take to make a stack one inch high. Approximately how high would a stack of one million pennies be?

†**7.** How many zeros are there in the number represented as a googol times a googol? Express this number using exponents. Is this number smaller or larger than a googolplex?

†**8.** Place a half-dollar, a quarter, and a nickel in one position, A, as in the figure. Then try to move these coins, one at a time, to position C. Coins may also be placed in position B. At no time may a larger coin be placed on a smaller coin. This can be accomplished in $2^3 - 1$, that is, 7 moves.

---

† Whenever an exercise is preceded by a dagger, it shall indicate that the exercise is more difficult or challenging than the others.

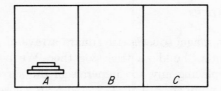

Next add a penny to the pile and try to make the change in $2^4 - 1$, that is, 15 moves.

This is an example of a famous problem called the **Tower of Hanoi.** The ancient Brahman priests were to move a pile of 64 such discs of decreasing size, after which the world would end. This would require $2^{64} - 1$ moves. Try to estimate how long this would take at the rate of one move per second.

1-3 Mathematical Recreations

The popularity of mathematics as a means of recreation and pleasure is evidenced by the frequency with which it is found in popular magazines and newspapers. In this section we shall explore several of these recreational aspects of mathematics.

Magic squares

How many of us have ever failed to be impressed by a magic square? The magic square shown here is arranged so that the sum of the numbers in any row, column, or diagonal is always 34.

Although there are formal methods to complete such an array we will not go into them here. Suffice it to say that such arrangements have fascinated man for many centuries. Indeed, the first known example of a magic square is said to have been found on the back of a tortoise by the Emperor Yu in about 2200 B.C.! This was called the "lo-shu" and appeared as an array of numerals indicated by knots in strings as in the figure on the left below. Black knots were used for even numbers and white ones for odd numbers. In modern times this appears as a magic square of third order. The sum along any row, column, or diagonal is 15 as in the figure on the right below.

1	12	7	14
8	13	2	11
10	3	16	5
15	6	9	4

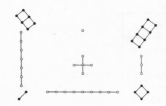

4	9	2
3	5	7
8	1	6

Mathematical tricks

Closely akin to magic squares are square arrays of numbers useful in "mathemagic." Let's "build" a trick together. We begin by forming a square array and placing any six numerals in the surrounding spaces as in the figure. The numbers 3, 4, 1, 7, 2, and 5 are chosen arbitrarily.

+	3	4	1
7			
2			
5			

Next find the sum of each pair of numbers as in a regular addition table.

+	3	4	1
7	10	11	8
2	5	6	3
5	8	9	6

Now we are ready to perform the trick. Have someone circle any one of the nine numerals in the box, say 10, and then cross out all the other numerals in the same row and column as 10.

+	3	4	1
7	(10)	11	8
2	5	6	3
5	8	9	6

Next circle one of the remaining numerals, say 3, and repeat the process. Circle the only remaining numeral, 9. The sum of the circled numbers is 10 + 3 + 9 = 22.

+	3	4	1
7	(10)	11	8
2	5	6	(3)
5	8	(9)	6

The interesting item here is that the sum of the three circled numbers will always be equal to 22, regardless of where you start on the first row! Furthermore, note that 22 is the sum of the six numbers outside the square. Try to explain why this trick works, and build a table with 16 entries.

Another type of mathematical trick which is quite popular is the "think of a number" type. Follow these instructions:

> Think of a number.
> Add 3 to this number.
> Multiply your answer by 2.
> Subtract 4 from your answer.
> Divide by 2.
> Subtract the number with which you started.

If you follow these instructions carefully, your answer will always be 1, regardless of the number with which you start. We can explain why this trick works by using algebraic symbols or by drawing pictures, as shown below.

Think of a number:	n	☐	(Number of coins in a box)
Add 3:	$n+3$	☐ ○ ○ ○	(Number of original coins plus three)
Multiply by 2:	$2n+6$	☐ ○ ○ ○ / ☐ ○ ○ ○	(Two boxes of coins plus six)
Subtract 4:	$2n+2$	☐ ○ / ☐ ○	(Two boxes of coins plus two)
Divide by 2:	$n+1$	☐ ○	(One box of coins plus one)
Subtract the original number, n:	$(n+1)-n=1$	○	(One coin is left)

Try to make up a similar trick of your own.

Optical illusions

Optical illusions are vivid reminders of the fact that we can not always trust our eyes. Can you trust yours? Test yourself and see. First guess which of the segments, AB or CD, appears to be the longer in the four parts of the following figure. Then use a ruler and check your estimate.

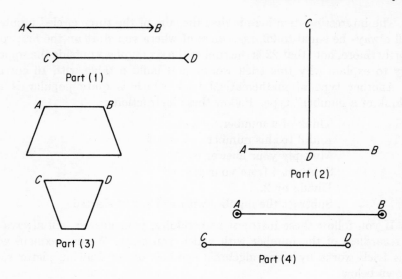

Part (1)

Part (2)

Part (3)

Part (4)

Now see whether you can guess which lines are parallel, if any, in the three parts of the next figure.

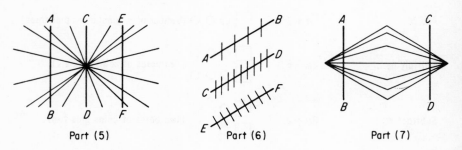

Part (5)   Part (6)   Part (7)

You should have found, in both cases, that looks can be deceiving. In each of the first four drawings, the segments are equal in length; in each of the last three they are parallel!

Fallacies

Mathematical fallacies may range from absurdity to intricacy. As an example of the former type, consider the following.

                1 cat has 1 tail
                0 cat has 8 tails   (that is, *no* cat has 8 tails)

Therefore, by addition, 1 cat has 9 tails.

Here is another arithmetic fallacy to puzzle you. You might even consider trying this on your local banker. First you need to deposit $50 in the bank and then make withdrawals in the following manner:

Withdraw $20, leaving a balance of $30.
Withdraw $15, leaving a balance of $15.
Withdraw $ 9, leaving a balance of $ 6.
Withdraw $ 6, leaving a balance of $ 0.
Adding, we have: $50 $51

The total withdrawal is $50, whereas the total of the balances is $51. Can you therefore go to the bank to demand an extra dollar?

Here is a "proof" that $1 = 2$. Even though you may have forgotten the algebra you need to follow this, don't let it stop you; see if you can discover the fallacy.

Let $a = b$. Then

$$a^2 = b^2 = b \cdot b.$$

Since $a = b$, we may write $b \cdot b$ as $a \cdot b$. Thus

$$a^2 = a \cdot b$$

Subtract b^2:

$$a^2 - b^2 = a \cdot b - b^2.$$

Factor:

$$(a + b)(a - b) = b(a - b).$$

Divide by $a - b$:

$$\frac{(a + b)(a - b)}{(a - b)} = \frac{b(a - b)}{(a - b)}.$$

Thus

$$a + b = b.$$

Since $a = b$, we may write this as

$$b + b = b \qquad \text{or} \qquad 2b = b.$$

Divide by b:

$$\frac{2b}{b} = \frac{b}{b}.$$

Therefore

$$2 = 1.$$

Many people enjoy solving interesting or amusing puzzles. A variety of these, many of which are old-timers, appear in the exercises that follow.

Exercises

1. All of the following puzzles have logical answers, but they are not strictly mathematical. See how many you can answer.

(a) How many four-cent postal cards are there in a dozen?

(b) How many telephone poles are needed in order to reach the moon?

(c) How far can you walk into a forest?

(d) Two United States coins total 55¢ in value, yet one of them is not a nickel.

Can you explain this?

(e) How much dirt is there in a hole which is 3 feet wide, 4 feet long, and 2 feet deep?

(f) There was a blind beggar who had a brother, but this brother had no brothers. What was the relationship between the two?

2. A farmer has to get a fox, a goose, and a bag of corn across a river in a boat which is only large enough for him and one of these three items. Now if he leaves the fox alone with the goose, the fox will eat the goose. If he leaves the goose alone with the corn, the goose will eat the corn. How does he get all items across the river?

3. Three Indians and three missionaries need to cross a river in a boat big enough only for two. The Indians are fine if they are left alone or if they are with the same number or with a larger number of missionaries. They are dangerous if they are left alone in a situation where they outnumber the missionaries. How do they all get across the river without harm?

4. A bottle and cork cost $1.50 together. The bottle costs one dollar more than the cork. How much does each cost?

5. A cat is at the bottom of a 30-foot well. Each day she climbs up three feet; each night she slides back two feet. How long will it take for the cat to get out of the well?

6. If a cat and a half eats a rat and a half in a day and a half, how many days will it take for 100 cats to eat 100 rats?

7. Place the numerals 1, 2, 3, 4, 5, and 6 in the circles in the figure so that the sum of the three numbers along each side of the triangle is 12. Each number may be used only once.

8. Place the numerals 1, 2, 3, 4, 5, 6, 8, 9, 10, and 12 in the circles in the figure so that the sum of the four numbers along each line is 24.

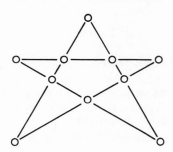

9. A sailor lands on an island inhabited by two types of people. The A's always lie, and the B's always tell the truth. The sailor meets three inhabitants on the beach and asks the first of these: "Are you an A or a B?" The man answers, but the sailor doesn't understand him and asks the second person what he had said. The man replies: "He said that he was a B. He is, and so am I." The third inhabitant then says: "That's not true. The first man is an A and I'm a B." Can you tell who was lying and who was telling the truth?

10. A man goes to a well with three cans whose capacities are 3 gallons, 5 gallons, and 8 gallons. Explain how he can obtain exactly 4 gallons of water from the well.

11. Here is a mathematical trick you can try on a friend. Ask someone to place a penny in one of his hands, and a dime in the other. Then tell him to multiply the value of the coin in the right hand by 6, multiply the value of the coin held in the left hand by 3, and add. Ask for the result. If the number given is even you then announce that the penny is in the right hand; if the result is an odd number then the penny is in the left hand and the dime is in the right hand. Can you figure out why this trick works?

Cabinet		Desk
Television set	Sofa	Bookcase

12. Consider a house with six rooms and furniture arranged as in the accompanying figure. We wish to interchange the desk and the bookcase, but in such a way that there is never more than one piece of furniture in a room at a time. Can you do this? Try it using coins or other objects to represent the furniture.

13. Three men enter a hotel and rent a suite of rooms for $30. After they are taken to their rooms the manager discovers he overcharged them; the suite only rents for $25. He thereupon sends a bellhop upstairs with the $5 change. The dishonest bellhop decides to keep $2 and only returns $3 to the men. Now the rooms originally cost $30, but the men had $3 returned to them. This means that they only paid $27 for the room. The bellhop kept $2. $27 + $2 = $29. What happened to the extra dollar?

14. A man went into a shoestore and bought a $5 pair of shoes, paying for them with a $20 bill. The shoestore owner went next door to the grocer to get change for the bill and then gave the customer his $15 change. Later the grocer discovered that the $20 bill was counterfeit and the shoestore had to replace it with a good bill. How much did the shoestore lose in terms of money and merchandise in this whole transaction?

15. Write the numbers from 1 through 10 using four 4's for each. Here are the first three completed for you:

$$\frac{44}{44} = 1; \qquad \frac{4}{4} + \frac{4}{4} = 2; \qquad \frac{4 + 4 + 4}{4} = 3.$$

16. Arrange two pennies and two dimes as shown below. Try to interchange the coins so that the pennies are at the right and the dimes at the left. You may move only one coin at a time, you may jump over only one coin, and pennies may be moved only to the right while dimes may be moved only to the left. No two coins may occupy the same space at the same time. What is the minimum number of moves required to complete the game?

17. Repeat Exercise 16 for three pennies and three dimes using seven blocks. What is the minimum number of moves required to complete the game?

1-4 Impossible and Unsolved Problems

Before you are led to the false conclusion that mathematicians know everything, we will conclude this chapter with a discussion of things that mathematicians do not know!

There are some problems in mathematics that are impossible. That is, mathematicians have *proved* that certain problems cannot be done. An outstanding example of this is the problem of angle trisection. It has been proved that it is not possible to divide any given angle (that is, all possible angles) into three equal parts using only an unmarked straight edge and a compass. Nevertheless each year there are numerous reports of "angle trisectors" who wish to claim fame by asserting they have solved the problem. They are wasting their time; the problem has been solved—it cannot be done.

In another category are those problems which remain unsolved to this date despite the efforts of mathematicians for centuries. Many of these are of interest in that they are very easy to state so that the nonmathematician can understand them. Here are several for which no solution is yet available.

Fermat's last theorem

We know that there are many replacements for x, y, and z such that $x^2 + y^2 = z^2$. For example, $3^2 + 4^2 = 5^2$ and $5^2 + 12^2 = 13^2$. (Can you find several others?) It is conjectured that it is not possible to find replacements for x, y, and z such that $x^n + y^n = z^n$ where n is greater than 2 and where x, y, and z are counting numbers. For example, we cannot find replacements for x, y, and z so that $x^3 + y^3 = z^3$. A great mathematician named Pierre de Fermat (1601–1665) wrote in the margin of his book that he had a proof of the impossibility of this problem, but that he had no room to write it there. No mathematician since has been able to prove or disprove this conjecture, although it has been proved for values of n up to 4,002.

Goldbach's conjecture

An integer greater than 1 which is divisible only by 1 and by itself is called a **prime number**. Some examples of prime numbers are

$$2, 3, 5, 7, 11, 13, 17, 19, 23.$$

A mathematician named Goldbach conjectured that every even number greater than 2 could be written as the sum of two primes; e.g., $12 = 5 + 7$, $20 = 7 + 13$, and $30 = 13 + 17$. No one has ever been able to find a number that cannot be so expressed, nor has anyone been able to prove that every even number can be written as the sum of two prime numbers.

There are other unproved statements concerning prime numbers. Pairs of primes like 3 and 5, 11 and 13, 41 and 43, and 101 and 103 are called **twin primes**. Are there an infinite number of pairs of primes that differ by two? No one knows!

No one has ever been able to invent a formula that would always produce a prime number. One effort produced the formula

$$n^2 - n + 41.$$

If you substitute the numbers $1, 2, 3, \ldots, 40$ in this formula for n, a prime number will be produced. However, for $n = 41$ we do not get a prime number. Pierre de Fermat thought he had a formula, the expression

$$2^{2^n} + 1.$$

Prime numbers are produced for $n = 1, 2, 3,$ and 4. About a century later another mathematician discovered that for $n = 5$ this formula gives the number 4,294,967,297, which is not a prime number. To date no formula has been discovered, nor has anyone been able to prove that such a formula is impossible.

The four-color problem

About the middle of the nineteenth century a problem related to map making was proposed and remains unsolved to this date. This problem, known as the four-color problem, involves the coloring of maps using at most four colors. When two countries have common boundaries, they must have different colors. When two countries have only single points in common they may use the same color. The figure gives two examples of these restrictions.

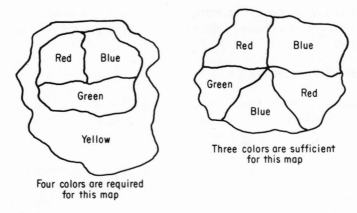

Four colors are required
for this map

Three colors are sufficient
for this map

No one has ever been able to produce a map that would require more than four colors, but no one has been able to prove that four colors are sufficient for all maps. However, it has been proved that if a map could be drawn that would require five colors, there would have to be at least 36 countries on it. It has also been proved that five colors are sufficient for all maps, but may not be necessary.

Infinite decimals

Every real number can be represented by a decimal. In particular $\sqrt{2} = 1.4142.$ . . . This is a nonrepeating, nonterminating decimal; we may carry out the decimal to as many places as desired. However there does not seem to be any way to answer such questions as these regarding the decimal expansion for $\sqrt{2}$:

(a) Will there ever be five consecutive 5's?
(b) Are there infinitely many 1's?
(c) Will the sequence 1, 2, 3, 4, 5 ever appear?

Thus you see that there is room for you, the reader, to claim fame by solving some of these problems—or else by proposing other problems that mathematicians cannot solve! The problems proposed in the following set of exercises call for some discovery on your part. All of them are solvable, although for some the solution may be that they are impossible. You should try to find answers for the possible and to identify the impossible.

Exercises

1. A diagonal of a polygon is a line segment connecting two nonadjacent vertices. For example, in the accompanying figure AC and BD are two diagonals.

(a) How many diagonals can be drawn in a pentagon? (A pentagon is a five-sided polygon.)

(b) How many diagonals can be drawn in a hexagon, a six-sided polygon?

(c) In general, write a formula for D, the number of diagonals in an n-gon, a polygon of n sides.

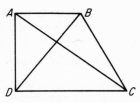

2. We wish to color each of the pyramids in the accompanying figure so that no two of the sides (faces) that have a common edge are of the same color.

 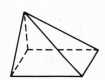 

(a) What is the minimum number of colors required for each pyramid?

†(b) What is the relationship between the minimum number of colors required and the number of faces in a pyramid?

3. Note each of the following relationships.

$$25^2 = 2 \times 300 + 25 = 625$$

$$35^2 = 3 \times 400 + 25 = 1,225$$

$$45^2 = 4 \times 500 + 25 = 2,025$$

(a) State a shortcut for squaring a two-digit number whose units digit is 5.

†(b) Find an algebraic explanation for this shortcut.

4. Try to draw lines to show how three houses located at A, B, and C can be connected to three utilities at X, Y, and Z so that no two lines intersect.

$\circ A$ $\circ B$ $\circ C$

$\circ X$ $\circ Y$ $\circ Z$

5. A three-inch cube (three inches long, three inches wide, and three inches high) is painted red and then cut into 27 one-inch cubes.

(a) What is the smallest number of cuts that can be used to divide the original cube into 27 pieces? (You are not allowed to move the pieces after you start to make a cut.)

(b) How many of these one-inch cubes will have red paint on none of their faces? On one of their faces? On two of their faces? On three of their faces? On more than three of their faces?

6. Answer the question in Exercise 5 (b) for a four-inch cube that is painted red and then cut into 64 one-inch cubes. Repeat the same procedure for a five-inch cube. Do you see any emerging pattern?

7. You wish to travel from A to B on the accompanying figure.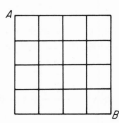
In how many ways can this be done if you are permitted to
move neither to the left nor up?

8. Repeat Exercise 7 for each of the following figures.

(a)   **(b)**

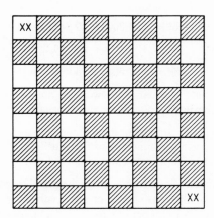

†**9.** How many line segments can be drawn between n points, no three of which
are on a line?

10. You are given a checkerboard and a set of dominoes. The size of each
domino is such that it is able to cover two squares on the board. Can you arrange
the dominoes in such a way that all of the board is covered with the exception
of two squares in opposite corners? (That is, you are to leave uncovered the two
squares marked **XX** in the figure.)

CHAPTER

TWO

SYSTEMS OF NUMERATION

We habitually take for granted the use of our system of notation as well as our computational procedures. However, these represent the creative work of man through the ages. We can gain a better appreciation of our own system of numeration and methods of computation by examining other systems. This chapter is devoted to such an examination.

2-1 Egyptian Numeration

First we distinguish between a *number* and a *numeral*. A number is an abstract concept; a **numeral** is the name of a number. We write numerals; we cannot write numbers. From a similar point of view, when you see the word "cat" on a piece of paper, you see the name of an animal rather than the animal itself.

We shall make this distinction between a number and a numeral in this book only where it proves helpful in understanding some concept. As an example, consider the number which represents the size of the following collection of symbols:

$$x \quad x \quad x \quad x \quad x$$
$$x \quad x \quad x \quad x \quad x$$

We would write this, in our system of notation, as 10. The ancient Egyptians used the symbol ∩. The ancient Babylonians used the symbol ◀. The Romans used X. All of these symbols—and there are others—are merely numerals; that is, they are different ways of representing (providing a name for) the same number.

23

Let us explore one system, the one used by the ancient Egyptians, in greater detail. They used a new symbol for each power of ten. Here are some of their symbols, a description of the physical objects they are supposed to represent, and the number they represent as expressed in our notation:

ǀ	Vertical staff	1
∩	Heel–bone	10
ℰ	Scroll	100
ℓ	Lotus flower	1000
⁊	Pointing finger	10,000

This Egyptian system is said to have a **base** of ten, but has no place value. The "base" ten is due to the use of powers of ten. We call our system of numeration a **decimal system** to emphasize our use of powers of ten. The absence of a place value means that the position of the symbols does not affect the number represented. For example, in our decimal system of numeration, 23 and 32 represent different numbers. In the Egyptian system ∩ǀ and ǀ∩ are different ways of writing eleven, that is, different names or numerals for the same number. (The former notation is the one normally found in their hieroglyphics.) Here are some other comparisons of decimal and ancient Egyptian number symbols.

$$25 \; \cap\cap \; \mathsf{I\ I\ I\ I\ I}$$
$$142 \; \mathcal{C}\cap\cap\cap\cap \; \mathsf{I\ I}$$
$$12{,}321 \; \text{⁊} \, \ell\ell \; \mathcal{C} \; \mathcal{CC} \cap\cap \, \mathsf{I}$$

Computation in the ancient Egyptian system is possible, although tedious. For example, we use these steps to add 27 and 35.

Observe that, in this Egyptian system, an indicated collection of ten ones was replaced by a symbol for ten before the final computation took place. In our decimal system we mentally perform a similar exchange of ten ones for a ten when we express $(7 + 5)$ as one ten and two ones. We exchange kinds of units in a similar manner in subtraction.

Exchange

32   ∩∩⟨∩⟩II   ∩∩ II
− 17   − ∩ II II II   − ∩ II II II
  15   ∩ II II II

Exercises

Write in ancient Egyptian notation:

1. 25.   **2.** 138.   **3.** 1,426.   **4.** 40.   **5.** 12,407.

Write in decimal notation:

6. ∩∩II   **7.** ℮℮∩I   **8.** 𝒻℮II

9. 𝒻𝒻℮℮∩I   **10.** 𝒻℮℮℮∩∩IIII

Write in ancient Egyptian notation and perform the indicated operation in that system:

11. 42   **12.** 153   **13.**   238   **14.**   431   **15.** 1,243
      +21   +62   −135   −213   −137

†**16.** The Egyptians did not have a symbol for zero. Why do we need such a symbol in our system of numeration? Why did they find it unnecessary to invent such a symbol in order to have symbols for other numbers?

2-2 Other Methods of Computation

There exist numerous examples of the ways in which ancient man performed his computations. Some of these may prove of interest to the reader. The method of multiplication which appeared in one of the first published arithmetic texts in Italy, the *Treviso Arithmetic* (1478), is an interesting one. Let us use it to find the product of 457 and 382 considered in ordinary decimal notation. (We shall refer to this process here as "galley" multiplication, although it was called "Gelosia" multiplication in the original text.)

First prepare a "galley" with three rows and three columns, and draw the diagonals as in the figure. Our choice for the number of rows and columns was based on the fact that we are to multiply two three-digit numerals.

Place the digits 4, 5, and 7 in order from left to right at the top of the columns. Place the digits 3,

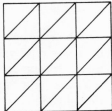

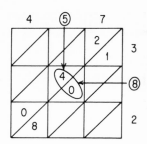

8, and 2 in order from top to bottom at the right of the rows. Then each product of a digit of 457 and a digit of 382 is called a **partial product** and is placed at the intersection of the column and row of the digits. The diagonal separates the digits of the partial product (tens digit above units digit). For example, $3 \times 7 = 21$, and this partial product is placed in the upper right-hand corner of the "galley"; $5 \times 8 = 40$, and this partial product is placed in the center of the galley; $4 \times 2 = 8$, and this partial product is entered as 08 in the lower left-hand corner of the galley. See if you can justify each of the entries in the completed array shown below.

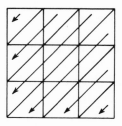

After all partial products have been entered in the galley, we add along diagonals, starting in the lower right-hand corner and carrying where necessary. The next diagram indicates this pattern.

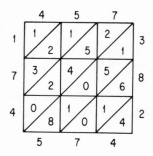

The completed problem appears in the following form:

We read the final answer, as indicated by the arrow in the figure, as 174,574. Note that we read the digits in the opposite order to that in which they were obtained.

EXAMPLE 1. Use galley multiplication and multiply 372 by 47.

Solution:

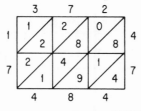

Answer: 17,484

This procedure works because we are really listing all partial products before we add. Compare the following two computations.

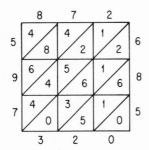

$$872$$
$$\times 685$$

$$\begin{array}{r} 10 \\ 35 \\ 40 \end{array} \Big\} \; 5 \times 872$$

$$\begin{array}{r} 16 \\ 56 \\ 64 \end{array} \Big\} \; 80 \times 872$$

$$\begin{array}{r} 12 \\ 42 \\ 48 \end{array} \Big\} \; 600 \times 872$$

$$597{,}320 = 685 \times 872$$

Note that the numerals along the diagonals correspond to those in the columns at the right.

The English mathematician, John Napier, made use of this system as he developed what proved to be one of the forerunners of the modern computing machines. His device is referred to as **Napier's rods**, or **Napier's bones**, named after the material on which he had numerals printed.

To make a set of these rods we need to prepare a collection of strips of paper, or other material, with multiples of each of the digits listed. Study the set of rods shown on the following page as Figure A.

Index	4	8	3
1	0/4	0/8	0/3
2	0/8	1/6	0/6
3	1/2	2/4	0/9
4	1/6	3/2	1/2
5	2/0	4/0	1/5
6	2/4	4/8	1/8
7	2/8	5/6	2/1
8	3/2	6/4	2/4
9	3/6	7/2	2/7

(B)

Index	1	2	3	4	5	6	7	8	9
1	0/1	0/2	0/3	0/4	0/5	0/6	0/7	0/8	0/9
2	0/2	0/4	0/6	0/8	1/0	1/2	1/4	1/6	1/8
3	0/3	0/6	0/9	1/2	1/5	1/8	2/1	2/4	2/7
4	0/4	0/8	1/2	1/6	2/0	2/4	2/8	3/2	3/6
5	0/5	1/0	1/5	2/0	2/5	3/0	3/5	4/0	4/5
6	0/6	1/2	1/8	2/4	3/0	3/6	4/2	4/8	5/4
7	0/7	1/4	2/1	2/8	3/5	4/2	4/9	5/6	6/3
8	0/8	1/6	2/4	3/2	4/0	4/8	5/6	6/4	7/2
9	0/9	1/8	2/7	3/6	4/5	5/4	6/3	7/2	8/1

(A)

Note, for example, that the rod headed by the numeral 9 lists the multiples of 9: 9, 18, 27, 36, 45, 54, 63, 72, and 81.

We can use these rods to multiply two numbers. To multiply 7 × 483, place the rods headed by numerals 4, 8, and 3 alongside the index as shown on the facing page as Figure B.

Consider the row of numerals alongside 7 on the index.

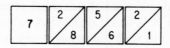

Add along the diagonals, as in "galley multiplication."

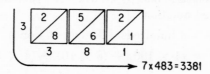

The same arrangement of rods may be used to read immediately the product of 483 and any other one-digit number. With practice one can develop skill in using these rods for rapid computation. For example, 8 × 483 = 3,864 as follows:

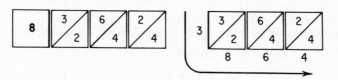

Combining the two previous results we can find the product 87 × 483:

$$
\begin{array}{rr}
483 & 7 \times 483 = 3{,}381 \\
\underline{\times 87} & \underline{80 \times 483 = 38{,}640} \\
& 87 \times 483 = 42{,}021 \\
\end{array}
$$

Note that we are able to read only products with a one-digit multiplier directly from the rods.

Exercises

Multiply, using the "galley" method:

1. 492	**2.** 2,768	**3.** 432	**4.** 607	**5.** 7,025
×37	×53	×276	×498	×398

Construct a set of Napier rods and use them to find each of the following products:

6. 427	**7.** 387	**8.** 409	**9.** 7,256	**10.** 427
×9	×5	×7	×8	×36

2-3 Decimal Notation

We now turn our attention to the **decimal system of notation**. It is a decimal system in that it is based on powers or groups of tens. Furthermore, it has place value in that the value of any digit used depends upon the position which it occupies. Thus, the two numerals 4 in 484 have quite different values.

To illustrate this latter concept we will write this number, 484, in what is known as **expanded notation**:

$$484 = 4 \text{ hundreds} + 8 \text{ tens} + 4 \text{ ones}$$
$$= (4 \times 100) + (8 \times 10) + (4 \times 1).$$

Note that one of the numerals 4 represents 4 hundreds whereas the other 4 represents 4 units; that is, 4 ones.

It is convenient to use exponents when writing a number in expanded notation. An **exponent** is a number that tells how many times another number, called the **base**, is used as a factor in a product. For example, in the expression 7^2, the numeral 2 is the exponent and 7 is the base. Note that, $7^2 = 7 \times 7 = 49$, and similarly $7^3 = 7 \times 7 \times 7 = 343$.

Using exponents to write 484 in expanded notation, we have

$$484 = (4 \times 100) + (8 \times 10) + (4 \times 1)$$
$$= (4 \times 10^2) + (8 \times 10) + (4 \times 1).$$

EXAMPLE 1. Write 2,376 in expanded notation.

Solution:

$$2,376 = (2 \times 10^3) + (3 \times 10^2) + (7 \times 10) + (6 \times 1).$$

We may use the exponent 1 to indicate that a number is to be used as a factor only once; thus $10^1 = 10$. We also define $10^0 = 1$. Using these exponents

$$2,376 = (2 \times 10^3) + (3 \times 10^2) + (7 \times 10^1) + (6 \times 10^0).$$

Negative exponents are used in writing decimals as follows:

$$10^{-1} = \frac{1}{10} = 0.1,$$

$$10^{-2} = \frac{1}{100} = 0.01,$$

$$10^{-3} = \frac{1}{1,000} = 0.001.$$

Notice that for any integer k we have $10^{-k} = \frac{1}{10^k}$. In general, $b^{-k} = \frac{1}{b^k}$. For example,

$$2^{-3} = \frac{1}{2^3} = \frac{1}{8};$$

$$5^{-2} = \frac{1}{5^2} = \frac{1}{25};$$

$$3^2 = \frac{1}{3^{-2}}.$$

Now we are able to write any number given in decimal notation in expanded notation as in the following example.

EXAMPLE 2. Write 8,027.45 in expanded notation.

Solution:

$$8,027.45 = (8 \times 10^3) + (0 \times 10^2) + (2 \times 10^1)$$
$$+ (7 \times 10^0) + (4 \times 10^{-1}) + (5 \times 10^{-2}).$$

Exercises

Write in decimal notation:

1. 5^3. **2.** 3^5. **3.** 10^{-3}. **4.** 10^{-2}.

5. 8^0. **6.** 3×10^2. **7.** 4×10^{-2}. **8.** 3×10^{-1}.

9. 2×10^3. **10.** 4×10^{-3}.

Write in expanded notation:

11. 432. **12.** 107. **13.** 4.23. **14.** 89.7.

15. 2345. **16.** 2.758. **17.** 423.83. **18.** 5,093.02

19. 0.007. **20.** 2.0301.

Write in decimal notation:

21. $(3 \times 10^3) + (2 \times 10^2) + (5 \times 10^1) + (3 \times 10^0)$.

22. $(2 \times 10^{-1}) + (3 \times 10^{-2})$.

23. $(5 \times 10^1) + (2 \times 10^0) + (1 \times 10^{-1}) + (7 \times 10^{-2}) + (3 \times 10^{-3})$.

24. $(7 \times 10^1) + (0 \times 10^0) + (0 \times 10^{-1}) + (8 \times 10^{-2})$.

25. $(2 \times 10^{-2}) + (5 \times 10^{-3})$.

2-4 Other Systems of Notation

In our decimal system of notation objects are grouped and counted in tens and powers of ten. For example, the diagram below shows how one might group and count 134 items.

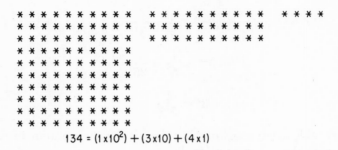

$$134 = (1 \times 10^2) + (3 \times 10) + (4 \times 1)$$

We could, however, just as easily group sets of items in other ways. In the next figure we see 23 asterisks grouped in three different ways.

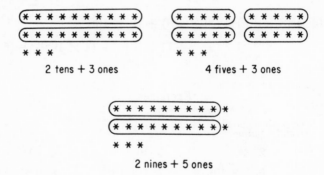

If we use a subscript to indicate our manner of grouping, we may write many different numerals (names) for the number of items in the same collection:

$$23_{\text{ten}} \qquad = \qquad 43_{\text{five}} \qquad = \qquad 25_{\text{nine}}.$$
$$(2 \; tens + 3 \; \text{ones}) \quad (4 \; fives + 3 \; \text{ones}) \quad (2 \; nines + 5 \; \text{ones})$$

Each of these numerals represents the number of asterisks in the same set of asterisks. Still another numeral for this number is 35_{six}:

$$35_{\text{six}} = 3 \; sixes + 5 \; \text{ones} = 18 + 5 = 23.$$

We call our decimal system of notation a **base ten** system; when no subscript is used, the numeral is expressed in base ten. When we group by fives we have a **base five** system of notation; that is, we name our system of notation by the manner in which the grouping is accomplished.

EXAMPLE 1. Draw a diagram for 18 objects and write the corresponding numeral **(a)** in base five and **(b)** in base eight notation.

Solution:

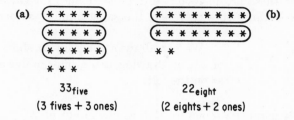

(a) 33$_{five}$	22$_{eight}$ (b)
(3 fives + 3 ones)	(2 eights + 2 ones)

Exercises

Write numerals for each of the following collections in the bases indicated by the manner of grouping.

1.   2.   3.   4.

Draw a diagram to show the meaning of each of the following:

5. 24$_{five}$.   **6.** 31$_{six}$.   **7.** 25$_{seven}$.   **8.** 41$_{nine}$.

Change to base ten notation:

9. 43$_{five}$.   **10.** 24$_{seven}$.   **11.** 32$_{eight}$.   **12.** 51$_{six}$.

13. Write, in base five notation, a numeral for 17.

14. Write, in base eight notation, a numeral for 21.

15. Write, in base six notation, a numeral for 20.

†16. Change 132$_{five}$ to base ten notation.

2-5 Base Five Numeration

In this section we will explore, in some detail, the manner of writing numerals in another number base. We will work with a base five system since it is convenient to think of numbers written in base five notation in terms of hands and fingers. Thus 23$_{five}$ may be thought of in terms of two hands and three fingers; that is, as 2 fives and 3 ones.

For convenience we will write all numbers in base five notation using the numeral 5 as a subscript, such as 23$_5$. As usual, numbers written without a subscript will be assumed to be in base ten notation. Thus it is correct to write:

$$23_5 = 13.$$

Recall that these are merely two different names for the same number. (Two fives + three ones represent the same number as one ten + three ones.)

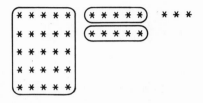 We can draw a diagram to show the meaning of 23_5 by drawing two groups of five and three ones as on the left.

In a similar manner we picture 123_5 as one group of 25, two groups of 5, and three ones.

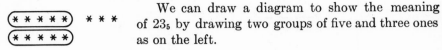

In the decimal system of notation, numbers are written in terms of powers of ten using digits 0, 1, 2, 3, 4, 5, 6, 7, 8, and 9. For example,

$$234 = (2 \times 10^2) + (3 \times 10^1) + (4 \times 10^0).$$

In base five notation, numbers are written in terms of powers of five using digits 0, 1, 2, 3, and 4. For example,

$$43_5 = (4 \times 5^1) + (3 \times 5^0);$$
$$324_5 = (3 \times 5^2) + (2 \times 5^1) + (4 \times 5^0);$$
$$2{,}143_5 = (2 \times 5^3) + (1 \times 5^2) + (4 \times 5^1) + (3 \times 5^0).$$

Note that $5^0 = 1$.

The numbers 1 to 30 are written in the base five in the following table.

Base 10	Base 5	Base 10	Base 5	Base 10	Base 5
1	1	11	21	21	41
2	2	12	22	22	42
3	3	13	23	23	43
4	4	14	24	24	44
5	10	15	30	25	100
6	11	16	31	26	101
7	12	17	32	27	102
8	13	18	33	28	103
9	14	19	34	29	104
10	20	20	40	30	110

To translate a number from base 5 notation to base 10 notation, express the number in terms of powers of 5 and simplify.

EXAMPLE 1. Write $3,214_5$ in base 10 notation.

Solution:

$$3,214_5 = (3 \times 5^3) + (2 \times 5^2) + (1 \times 5^1) + (4 \times 5^0)$$
$$= (3 \times 125) + (2 \times 25) + (1 \times 5) + (4 \times 1)$$
$$= 434.$$

EXAMPLE 2. Write 2.34_5 in base 10 notation.

Solution:

$$2.34_5 = (2 \times 5^0) + (3 \times 5^{-1}) + (4 \times 5^{-2})$$
$$= (2 \times 1) + (3 \times 1/5) + (4 \times 1/25)$$
$$= (2 \times 1) + (3 \times 2/10) + (4 \times 4/100)$$
$$= 2.76.$$

To translate from base 10 to base 5, any one of several procedures may be adopted. Consider the problem

$$339 = (\qquad)_5.$$

When a number is expressed to the base 5, it is written in terms of powers of 5:

$$5^0 = 1, \quad 5^1 = 5, \quad 5^2 = 25, \quad 5^3 = 125, \quad \dot{5}^4 = 625, \quad \ldots.$$

The highest power of 5 that is not greater than the given number is 5^3. This power of 5, namely $5^3 = 125$, can be subtracted from 339 twice. Then the remainder 89 is positive and less than 125.

$$
\begin{array}{r}
339 \\
-125 \\
\hline
214 \\
-125 \\
\hline
89
\end{array}
$$

Thus, we write 2×5^3 in the expansion of 339 to the base 5.

The next power of 5 is 5^2. This number can be subtracted from 89 three times to obtain a nonnegative remainder less than 25.

$$
\begin{array}{r}
89 \\
-25 \\
\hline
64 \\
-25 \\
\hline
39 \\
-25 \\
\hline
14
\end{array}
$$

Thus, we write 3×5^2 in the expansion.

Finally, we subtract 5 from 14 twice, write 2×5 in the expansion, and obtain 4 as a remainder.

$$\begin{array}{r} 14 \\ -5 \\ \hline 9 \\ -5 \\ \hline 4 \end{array}$$

$$\begin{aligned} 339 &= 2(125) + 3(25) + 2(5) + 4 \\ &= (2 \times 5^3) + (3 \times 5^2) + (2 \times 5^1) + (4 \times 5^0) = 2{,}324_5. \end{aligned}$$

A group of 339 elements can be considered as 2 groups of 125 elements, 3 groups of 25 elements, 2 groups of 5 elements, and 4 elements.

An alternative procedure for changing 339 to the base 5 depends upon successive division by 5:

$$\begin{aligned} 339 &= 67 \times 5 + 4; \\ 67 &= 13 \times 5 + 2; \\ 13 &= 2 \times 5 + 3. \end{aligned}$$

Next, substitute from the third equation into the second; from the second to the first; and simplify as follows:

$$\begin{aligned} 13 &= 2 \times 5 + 3; \\ 67 &= 13 \times 5 + 2 = (2 \times 5 + 3) \times 5 + 2; \\ 339 &= 67 \times 5 + 4 = [(2 \times 5 + 3) \times 5 + 2] \times 5 + 4 \\ &= 2 \times 5^3 + 3 \times 5^2 + 2 \times 5^1 + 4 \times 5^0 = 2{,}324_5. \end{aligned}$$

The arithmetical steps involved in these computations can be performed as shown in the following array (often called an algorithm).

$$\begin{array}{r|l} 5 & 339 \\ \cline{2-2} 5 & 67 - 4 \\ \cline{2-2} 5 & 13 - 2 \\ \cline{2-2} 5 & 2 - 3 \\ \cline{2-2} & 0 - 2 \end{array}$$ Read upward as $2{,}324_5$.

Note that the remainder is written after each division by 5. Then the remainders are read in reverse order to obtain the expression for the number to the base 5.

EXAMPLE 3. Write 423 in base 5 notation.

Solution:

$$\begin{array}{r|l} 5 & 423 \\ \cline{2-2} 5 & 84 - 3 \\ \cline{2-2} 5 & 16 - 4 \\ \cline{2-2} 5 & 3 - 1 \\ \cline{2-2} & 0 - 3 \end{array}$$ *Answer:* $3{,}143_5.$

Check:

$$3{,}143_5 = (3 \times 5^3) + (1 \times 5^2) + (4 \times 5^1) + (3 \times 5^0)$$
$$= 375 + 25 + 20 + 3 = 423.$$

After computations in other bases have been considered, the method of successive division by the new base may be used in changing from one base to another. For example, we will be able to use this procedure to change from base 5 to base 10, successively dividing by 20_5. The computation must be done in base 5 notation. For the present we may change from base 5 to base 10 by expressing the number in terms of powers of 5. We may also use powers of the base whenever fractional parts are involved, as in Example 2.

Exercises

Write each number in decimal notation:

1. 423_5.	**2.** 120_5.	**3.** 444_5.	**4.** $1{,}230_5$.	**5.** 321_5.
6. $4{,}103_5$.	**7.** $1{,}031_5$.	**8.** 21.3_5.	**9.** 131.42_5.	**10.** 4.023_5.

Write each number in base 5 notation:

11. 382.	**12.** 593.	**13.** 782.	**14.** 194.	**15.** 625.
16. 58.	**17.** 137.	**18.** 368.	**19.** 0.4.	**20.** 0.04.
†**21.** 0.48.	†**22.** 0.64.	†**23.** 0.008.	†**24.** 48.16.	†**25.** 379.016.

Extend the concepts of this section and write each number in decimal notation:

†**26.** 437_8.	†**27.** $2{,}013_4$.	†**28.** $1{,}011_2$.	†**29.** 321_{12}.
†**30.** 132_{20}.	†**31.** 312.3_6.	†**32.** 214.3_{15}.	†**33.** 142.2_8.

2-6 Other Bases ✓

The base 5 system has been used merely for illustrative purposes; any other positive integer greater than 1 would have served just as well as a base. For each base N, the digits used are $0, 1, 2, \ldots, N - 1$. For each base, powers of that base are used as place values for the digits.

EXAMPLE 1. Change 324_8 to base 10.

Solution:

$$324_8 = (3 \times 8^2) + (2 \times 8^1) + (4 \times 8^0) = 212.$$

EXAMPLE 2. Change $1{,}231_4$ to base 10.

Solution:

$$1{,}231_4 = (1 \times 4^3) + (2 \times 4^2) + (3 \times 4^1) + (1 \times 4^0) = 109.$$

Any number may be changed from base 10 to another base by dividing successively by the new base and using the remainders as in § 2-5. This procedure is always performed in the notation of the old base. It has already been used for the base 5 and may be adapted for other bases as well.

EXAMPLE 3. Change 354 to base 8.

Solution:

$$
\begin{array}{r}
8 \mid 354 \\
8 \mid 44 - 2 \\
8 \mid 5 - 4 \\
0 - 5
\end{array}
\qquad \text{Answer: } 542_8.
$$

Check:

$$542_8 = (5 \times 8^2) + (4 \times 8^1) + (2 \times 8^0)$$
$$= 320 + 32 + 2$$
$$= 354.$$

Exercises

Change to base 10:

1. 327_8.   **2.** $3{,}213_4$.   **3.** $5{,}440_6$.   **4.** 437_{12}.

5. $101{,}011_2$.   **6.** $1{,}121_3$.   **7.** 532_7.   **8.** 184_9.

Change to the stated base:

9. $724 = ($ $)_4$.   **10.** $396 = ($ $)_8$.   **11.** $472 = ($ $)_6$.

12. $25 = ($ $)_2$.   **13.** $171 = ($ $)_{12}$.   **14.** $257 = ($ $)_{12}$.

15. $896 = ($ $)_5$.   **16.** $114 = ($ $)_3$.

2-7 Computation in Base Five Notation ✓

We can form an addition table for the numbers in base 5 notation very easily. Consider, for example, the problem $4_5 + 3_5$. This may be written as $4_5 + 1_5 + 2_5$. Now, $(4_5 + 1_5)$ is one group of 5, or 10_5. We then add 2_5 to obtain 12_5. This is equivalent to

$$(1 \times 5^1) + (2 \times 5^0) = (1 \times 5^1) + (2 \times 1) = 5 + 2 = 7.$$

In a similar manner, $4_5 + 4_5 = 4_5 + 1_5 + 3_5$. Now $(4_5 + 1_5) = 10_5$. We then add 3_5 to obtain the sum 13_5. This result could also have been obtained by grouping: $4_5 + 4_5$ can be represented as (****) + (****), which can be regrouped as (*****) + (***)—that is, 13_5.

Shown below is a table of the number facts needed for addition problems in base 5. (You should verify each entry.)

+	0	1	2	3	4
0	0	1	2	3	4
1	1	2	3	4	10_5
2	2	3	4	10_5	11_5
3	3	4	10_5	11_5	12_5
4	4	10_5	11_5	12_5	13_5

The facts in this table may be used in finding sums of numbers, as illustrated in the following example.

EXAMPLE 1. Find the sum of 432_5 and 243_5. Then check in base 10 notation.

Solution:

$$432_5$$
$$+243_5$$
$$\overline{1,230_5}$$

Check:

$$432_5 = (4 \times 5^2) + (3 \times 5^1) + (2 \times 5^0) \qquad\qquad = 117$$
$$+243_5 = (2 \times 5^2) + (4 \times 5^1) + (3 \times 5^0) \qquad\qquad = \underline{73}$$
$$\overline{1,230_5} = (1 \times 5^3) + (2 \times 5^2) + (3 \times 5^1) + (0 \times 5^0) = 190$$

Here are the steps used in Example 1. In each case the familiar symbol 5 has been used in place of 10_{five} to help the reader recognize that powers of 5 are involved. This convention will be followed throughout this chapter.

(a) Add the column of 1's.

$$(4 \times 5^2) + (3 \times 5^1) + (2 \times 5^0)$$
$$\underline{(2 \times 5^2) + (4 \times 5^1) + (3 \times 5^0)}$$
$$10_5$$

(b) Write the sum 10_5 of the 1's as 1×5^1 in the 5's column, and add the column of 5's.

$$1 \times 5^1$$
$$(4 \times 5^2) + (3 \times 5^1) + (2 \times 5^0)$$
$$\underline{(2 \times 5^2) + (4 \times 5^1) + (3 \times 5^0)}$$
$$(13_5 \times 5^1) + (0 \times 5^0)$$

(c) Write $10_5 \times 5^1$ from the previous sum in the 5^2 column and add the column of 5^2 entries.

$$1 \times 5^2$$
$$(4 \times 5^2) + (3 \times 5^1) + (2 \times 5^0)$$
$$\underline{(2 \times 5^2) + (4 \times 5^1) + (3 \times 5^0)}$$
$$(12 \times 5^2) + (3 \times 5^1) + (0 \times 5^0) = 1{,}230_5$$

Note that we "carry" groups of five in base 5 computation, just as we "carry" groups of ten in decimal computation.

Subtraction is not difficult if it is thought of as the inverse of addition. The table of addition facts in base 5 may again be used.

EXAMPLE 2. Subtract in base 5 and check in base 10: $211_5 - 142_5$.

Solution: Think of 211_5 as $(2 \times 5^2) + (1 \times 5^1) + (1 \times 5^0)$; then, as $(1 \times 5^2) + (11_5 \times 5^1) + (1 \times 5^0)$; then, as $(1 \times 5^2) + (10_5 \times 5^1) + (11_5 \times 5^0)$. Thus:

$$211_5 = (1 \times 5^2) + (10_5 \times 5^1) + (11_5 \times 5^0)$$
$$\underline{-142_5 = (1 \times 5^2) + \quad(4 \times 5^1) + \quad(2 \times 5^0)}$$
$$14_5 \qquad\qquad\qquad (1 \times 5^1) + \quad(4 \times 5^0)$$

Check:

$$211_5 = 56$$
$$\underline{-142_5 = 47}$$
$$14_5 = 9$$

This problem can be solved by borrowing and thinking in base 5 in the following steps:

$$
\text{(a)}\quad
\begin{array}{r} 211_5 \\ -142_5 \\ \hline \end{array}
\qquad
\text{(b)}\quad
\begin{array}{r} 20\overset{1}{1}_5 \\ -14\,2_5 \\ \hline 4_5 \end{array}
\qquad
\text{(c)}\quad
\begin{array}{r} \overset{1}{1}\,0\overset{1}{1}_5 \\ -1\,4\,2_5 \\ \hline 1\,4_5 \end{array}
$$

Problems in multiplication can be performed either as repeated additions or in base 10 and converted to base 5.

EXAMPLE 3. Find the product of 243_5 and 4_5.

Solution: We need the following facts:

$$4 \times 3 = 12_{10} = (2 \times 5^1) + (2 \times 5^0) = 22_5,$$
$$4 \times 4 = 16_{10} = (3 \times 5^1) + (1 \times 5^0) = 31_5,$$
$$4 \times 2 = 8_{10} = (1 \times 5^1) + (3 \times 5^0) = 13_5.$$

The pattern for the computation when multiplying and "carrying" in base 5 notation is then precisely the same as that used in base 10 computation. For example, partial products are indented to represent the powers of 5 involved. In the long form, no attempt is made to "carry" mentally from one place to the next.

$$243_5 \qquad\qquad Condensed\ form:$$
$$\underline{\times 4_5} \qquad\qquad\qquad 243_5$$
$$22_5 \qquad\qquad\qquad \underline{\times 4_5}$$
$$31_5 \qquad\qquad\qquad 2{,}132_5$$
$$\underline{13_5}$$
$$2{,}132_5$$

Division can be performed in base 5 by considering it as the inverse operation of multiplication.

EXAMPLE 4. Divide 121_5 by 4_5; check by multiplication in base 5.

Solution: We need the following facts:

$$12_5 = 1_5 \times 4_5 + 3_5; \quad 12_5 - 4_5 = 3_5; \quad 31_5 = 4_5 \times 4_5.$$

The pattern for the computation when dividing in base 5 notation is then precisely the same as that used in base 10 computation.

$$\begin{array}{r} 14_5 \\ 4_5 \overline{)121_5} \\ 4_5 \\ \hline 31_5 \\ 31_5 \end{array} \qquad Check: \quad \begin{array}{r} 14_5 \\ \underline{\times 4_5} \\ 121_5 \end{array}$$

Exercises

Add in base 5 and check in base 10:

1. 31_5	2. 31_5	3. 324_5	4. $2{,}341_5$	5. 321_5
$\underline{12_5}$	$\underline{32_5}$	$\underline{233_5}$	$\underline{1{,}034_5}$	120_5
				$\underline{432_5}$

Subtract in base 5 and check in base 10:

6. 43_5	7. 43_5	8. 312_5
$\underline{-21_5}$	$\underline{-24_5}$	$\underline{-121_5}$

9. 421_5
   $\underline{-223_5}$

10. Complete the following table for the basic multiplication facts in base 5:

Multiply in base 5 and check in base 10:

11. 342_5	12. 212_5	13. 413_5
$\underline{\times 1_5}$	$\underline{\times 2_5}$	$\underline{\times 2_5}$

×	0	1	2	3	4
0					
1					
2					
3					
4					

14. 324_5 **†15.** 24_5 **†16.** 342_5
     $\times 4_5$ $\times 32_5$ $\times 24_5$

Divide in base 5 and check in base 10:

17. $4_5 \overline{\smash{)}\ 143_5}$ **18.** $3_5 \overline{\smash{)}\ 121_5}$

†19. $11_5 \overline{\smash{)}\ 143_5}$ **†20.** $32_5 \overline{\smash{)}\ 3,031_5}$

†21. Complete the following tables of addition and multiplication facts for base 4:

+	0	1	2	3
0	0	1	2	3
1	1	2	3	10
2	2	3	10	11
3	3	10	11	12

×	0	1	2	3
0	0	0	0	0
1	0	1	2	3
2	0	2	10	12
3	0	3	12	21

†22. Complete the following tables of addition and multiplication facts for base 8:

+	0	1	2	3	4	5	6	7
0								
1								
2								
3								
4								
5								
6								
7								

×	0	1	2	3	4	5	6	7
0								
1								
2								
3								
4								
5								
6								
7								

†23. Using t for 10 and e for 11, complete the following tables of addition and multiplication facts for base 12:

+	0	1	2	3	4	5	6	7	8	9	t	e
0												
1												
2												
3												
4												
5												
6												
7												
8												
9												
t												
e												

×	0	1	2	3	4	5	6	7	8	9	t	e
0												
1												
2												
3												
4												
5												
6												
7												
8												
9												
t												
e												

2-8 Binary Notation

Numbers written to the base 2 are of special interest because of their application in computers. This system of notation is called **binary notation**. Only two digits are used, namely, 0 and 1.

Each number can be written as a sequence of 0's and 1's. Computers may use a hole in a card for 1 and no hole for 0, or a closed switch for 1 and an open switch for 0. Thus, numbers in binary notation can be easily utilized by machines. The operations performed by the machines are all based on two very simple operations—addition and multiplication. Tables for addition and multiplication are relatively simple.

Base 10	Base 2		Base 10	Base 2
1	1		9	1,001
2	10		10	1,010
3	11		11	1,011
4	100		12	1,100
5	101		13	1,101
6	110		14	1,110
7	111		15	1,111
8	1,000		16	10,000

+	0	1
0	0	1
1	1	10_2

×	0	1
0	0	0
1	0	1

Exercises

Write each number in binary notation:

1. 28.   **2.** 32.   **3.** 19.   **4.** 64.   **5.** 152.

Change each number to decimal notation:

6. $110,111_2$.   **7.** $101,010_2$.

8. $100,110_2$.   **9.** $11,011,011,011_2$.

Perform the indicated operation in binary notation and check in base 10:

10. $1,101_2$
     $+1,011_2$

11. $10,011_2$
     $+10,101_2$

12. $11,011_2$
     $-10,110_2$

13. $110,101_2$
     $-10,111_2$

14. $1,101_2$
     $\times 11_2$

15. $10,110_2$
     $\times 101_2$

16. Write the number 214 in base 8 and then in base 2 notation. Can you discover a relationship between these two bases?

2-9 Just for Fun

Many recreational items are based on the binary system of notation. Consider, for example, the boxes shown below, within which the numbers 1 to 15 are placed according to the following scheme:

In box A place all numbers that have a 1 in the units place when written in binary notation. In box B place those with a 1 in the second position from the right in binary notation. In C and D are those numbers with a 1 in the third and fourth positions, respectively.

A	B	C	D
1	2	4	8
3	3	5	9
5	6	6	10
7	7	7	11
9	10	12	12
11	11	13	13
13	14	14	14
15	15	15	15

Next, ask someone to think of a number and tell you in which box or boxes it appears. You then tell that person his number by finding the sum of the first number in each box he mentions. Thus, if his number is 11, he lists boxes A, B, and D. You then find the sum $1 + 2 + 8$ as the number under discussion.

Exercises

1. Explain why the method given in § 2–9 for finding a number after knowing the boxes in which it appears works as it does.

2. Extend the boxes in § 2–9 to include all the numbers through 31. (A fifth column, E, will be necessary.)

3. Find a reference to the game of Nim and study its relationship to the binary system of notation.

4. Here is an experiment to show you how the binary system of notation may be used in the process of card sorting. First prepare a set of 16 index cards with four holes punched in each and one corner notched as in the accompanying figure. Next represent the numbers 0 through 15 in binary notation. Cut out the space above each hole to represent 0; leave the hole untouched to represent 1. Here is how several representative cards should appear.

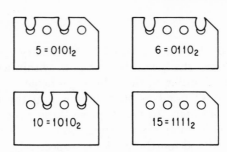

$$5 = 0101_2 \qquad 6 = 0110_2$$

$$10 = 1010_2 \qquad 15 = 1111_2$$

After all the cards have been completed in this manner, shuffle thoroughly and align them, making certain that they remain "face up." (The notched corners will help indicate when the cards are right side up.) Then, starting from the right and going to the left, perform the following operation. Stick a pencil or other similar object through the first hole and lift up. Some of the cards will come up, namely those in which the holes have not been cut through to the edge of the card. (That is, those cards representing numbers whose units digit in binary notation is 1. Why?)

Place the cards that lift up to the rear of the pile and repeat the same operation for the remaining holes. When you have finished, the cards should be in numerical order, 0 through 15. Can you explain why this works?

5. Repeat Exercise 4 with a set of 32 cards to represent the numbers 0 through 31. Here five holes are needed on each card and five "lifting" operations are necessary to place the set in numerical order.

CHAPTER THREE

FINITE MATHEMATICAL SYSTEMS

In the preceding chapter we discussed various systems of numeration as well as operations with elements in each of these systems. Much of mathematics is concerned with the study of basic principles. In this chapter we shall explore some of these basic principles while studying a collection of abstract, but interesting, systems.

3-1 What Is a Mathematical System? *I haven't the slightest idea*

A mathematical system involves a set of elements (such as the set of integers), one or more operations (such as addition, subtraction, multiplication, and division), one or more relations (such as the equality $2 \times 3 = 6$), and some axioms (rules) which the elements, operations, and relations satisfy. For example, we assume that every system involves the relation of equality and the axiom that $a = a$; that is, any quantity is equal to itself. Actually you have been working with mathematical systems ever since you started school. Let us look at a specific example of a mathematical system.

Let us assume that we have a set D of integers from 1 through 10:

$$D = \{1, 2, 3, 4, 5, 6, 7, 8, 9, 10\};$$

together with the operation of addition, the relation of equality, and their usual properties. We now have a mathematical system and can explore some of the properties of this system. We find, for example, that addition

47

is not always possible if we are restricted to this collection of numbers. For example, there is no element of the set D which is equal to $5 + 7$.

Next consider the same set D together with the operation of multiplication. Is multiplication always possible if the product must be an element of D? If not, you should be able to give an example showing that it is not.

The system just described includes one element, 1, that has an important special property. If we multiply any number in the set D by 1 that number remains unchanged. For example, $3 \times 1 = 3$, $8 \times 1 = 8$, etc. Later we shall give a special name to an element of a set that has this particular property.

Let us enlarge the set under discussion to include all the numbers that we use for counting:

$$C = \{1, 2, 3, 4, 5, \ldots\}.$$

We call this collection the set C of **counting numbers** and use the three dots to indicate that the elements of the set cannot all be listed; that is, that C is an infinite set. In general, any set of elements that cannot be counted is said to be an **infinite set**; a set of elements that can be counted is said to be a **finite set**.

If we consider the set C of counting numbers and the operation of addition, we can find many interesting properties of this system; we shall do so in detail later in this text. We now enumerate just two of these properties:

1. *The set C is closed under the operation of addition*. That is, the sum of any two elements of the set C is always an element of the set C.

2. *Addition is commutative*. That is, the sum of any two elements of the set C is the same regardless of the order in which the elements are added. Thus $5 + 7 = 7 + 5$, $8 + 3 = 3 + 8$, etc.

In the next section we consider mathematical systems with elements that are not numbers. The operations are well-defined **binary operations**; that is, they associate one and only one element (which may or may not be an element of the given set) with any two elements of the given set taken in order. The relation of equality and its properties is assumed to be a part of all mathematical systems. When the set of elements used is finite, the system is called a **finite mathematical system**.

3-2 An Abstract System

Let us define an abstract system composed of the set of elements:

$$\{*, \#, \Sigma, [\ \ ]\}.$$

For ease of notation we shall call this set Y; that is,

$$Y = \{*, \#, \Sigma, [\ \ ]\}.$$

Next we define an operation which we call "multition" and denote this with the symbol $\sim$. The operation is defined by means of the following table:

$\sim$	$*$	$\#$	Σ	$[\ \ ]$
$*$	$*$	$\#$	Σ	$[\ \ ]$
$\#$	$\#$	Σ	$[\ \ ]$	$*$
Σ	Σ	$[\ \ ]$	$*$	$\#$
$[\ \ ]$	$[\ \ ]$	$*$	$\#$	Σ

To "multify" two elements of Y, we read the first of these elements in the vertical column at the left and the second in the horizontal row across the top. The answer is found where the column and the row intersect within the table. Verify from the table that each of the following statements is correct:

$$\# \sim \Sigma = [\ \ ],$$
$$[\ \ ] \sim \# = *,$$
$$\Sigma \sim * = \Sigma.$$

The task of major importance before us is to examine this system for its basic properties. The following are some of the more important ones.

1. Whenever any two elements of the set Y are combined by the process of multition, the result is a unique element of the original collection Y of elements. In other words, there is one and only one answer whenever two elements of Y are multified and this answer is always one of the elements of Y. We say that *the set Y is closed under the operation of multition.*

In general a set S is said to be **closed** under a given binary operation if the process of performing that operation upon any two elements of the set S produces a unique result which is also an element of the set S.

2. Consider the order in which we combine any two elements of the set Y. Does $\# \sim \Sigma = \Sigma \sim \#$? Does $[\ \ ] \sim * = * \sim [\ \ ]$? In general, if a and b represent any two elements of the set Y, does $a \sim b = b \sim a$? We find the answer to be in the affirmative in each case and summarize this property by saying that *the elements of set Y satisfy the commutative property for multition.*

In general, a set of elements is said to satisfy the **commutative property** for a particular operation if the result obtained by combining any two elements of the set under that operation does not depend upon the order in which these elements are combined.

3. Next we combine three elements of the set Y. Can you find the answer for $\Sigma \sim [\ \ ] \sim \#$? Here we see that two possibilities exist. We could combine Σ and $[\ \ ]$ first and then combine the result with $\#$, or we could combine $[\ \ ]$ and $\#$ first and then combine Σ with the result obtained. Let us try both ways:

$$(\Sigma \sim [\ \ ]) \sim \# = \# \sim \# = \Sigma,$$
$$\Sigma \sim ([\ \ ] \sim \#) = \Sigma \sim * = \Sigma.$$

We obtain the same result in both cases and will do so for any choice of three members of the set Y. We call this the **associative property** for multition, and write, in symbols:

$\left(a+b \right) + c = a + \left(b+c \right)$ $a \sim (b \sim c) = (a \sim b) \sim c,$

where a, b, and c may be replaced by any elements of the set Y.

4. The set Y contains a unique element, $*$, which leaves every other element unchanged with respect to multition. For example:

$$* \sim * = *, \quad \# \sim * = \#, \quad \Sigma \sim * = \Sigma \quad \text{and} \quad [\ \ ] \sim * = [\ \ ].$$

The element with this property is called the **identity element** for multition.

In ordinary arithmetic what is the identity element for addition? That is, what can we add to 7 to obtain 7? Does $9 + 0 = 9$? Do you see that 0 is the identity element for addition? What is the identity element for multiplication?

5. We examine one more property of the set Y. Replace each blank in the following by an element of the set Y to obtain a correct statement:

$$* \sim \underline{\ \ *\ \ } = *,$$
$$\# \sim \underline{\ \ \ \ \ } = *,$$
$$\Sigma \sim \underline{\ \ \ \ \ } = *,$$
$$[\ \ ] \sim \underline{\ \ \ \ \ } = *.$$

The correct answers are, respectively, $*$, $[\ \ ]$, Σ, and $\#$. We find that for each element of the set Y there is another element of Y such that the first "multified" by the second produces the identity element $*$. Each of these second elements is called the **inverse** of the first element of the statement in which it was used. Thus the inverse of $*$ is $*$, the inverse of $\#$ is $[\ \ ]$, the inverse of Σ is Σ, and the inverse of $[\ \ ]$ is $\#$. Note that $*$ and Σ serve as their own inverses.

In an arithmetic where positive and negative numbers are admitted, every number has an inverse under addition. Complete the blank spaces in each of the following:

$$5 + \underline{} = 0.$$
$$-3 + \underline{} = 0.$$
$$0 + \underline{} = 0.$$
$$\tfrac{2}{3} + \underline{\phantom{-\tfrac{2}{3}}} = 0.$$

Inverse + no. = 0

The inverse of 5 is -5 in that $5 + (-5) = 0$. Similarly the inverse of -3 is 3, the inverse of 0 is 0, and the inverse of $\tfrac{2}{3}$ is $-\tfrac{2}{3}$.

In summary, the set Y:

(a) is closed with respect to multition,
(b) is commutative with respect to multition,
(c) is associative with respect to multition,
(d) contains an identity element with respect to multition, and
(e) contains an inverse for each of its elements with respect to multition.

We may summarize all five of these properties by saying that the elements of the set Y form a **commutative group** under multition.

Exercises

Find the answer to each of the following from the table given in this section:

1. $\# \sim *$.   2. $* \sim \Sigma$.   3. $[\ \ ] \sim [\ \ ]$.   4. $\Sigma \sim \#$.

Verify that each of the following is true and state the name of the property that each illustrates:

5. $\Sigma \sim \# = \# \sim \Sigma$.   6. $[\ \ ] \sim (\# \sim \Sigma) = ([\ \ ] \sim \#) \sim \Sigma$.

7. $\# \sim * = \#$.   8. $\# \sim [\ \ ] = *$.

9. $(\# \sim \Sigma) \sim * = \# \sim (\Sigma \sim *)$.   10. $[\ \ ] \sim * = [\ \ ]$.

11. $[\ \ ] \sim \# = *$.   12. $[\ \ ] \sim * = * \sim [\ \ ]$.

Answer Exercises 13 through 21 by using the following table which defines an operation $\odot$ for the elements of the set $\{\triangle, \square, Q\}$.

$\odot$	$\triangle$	$\square$	Q
$\triangle$	Q	$\triangle$	$\square$
$\square$	$\triangle$	$\square$	Q
Q	$\square$	Q	$\triangle$

13. Find $\triangle \odot \square$.   **14.** Find $Q \odot \triangle$.

15. Does $Q \odot \square = \square \odot Q$?   **16.** Does $\triangle \odot Q = Q \odot \triangle$?

17. Does $(Q \odot \square) \odot \triangle$ **18.** Does $\square \odot (Q \odot \triangle)$
$\qquad\qquad = Q \odot (\square \odot \triangle)$? $= (\square \odot Q) \odot \triangle$?

19. Does an affirmative answer to the two preceding exercises prove that the set satisfies the associative property with respect to $\odot$?

20. Is there an identity element for $\odot$? If so, what is it?

21. Does each element have an inverse with respect to $\odot$? If so, name each.

22. Summarize the properties of the set $\{\triangle, \square, Q\}$ with respect to the operation $\odot$.

Answer Exercises 23 through 26 by using the following table which defines an operation $\boxtimes$ for the set $\{\cdot, [, !, \$\}$.

$\boxtimes$	$\cdot$	$[$	$!$	$\$$
$\cdot$	$\cdot$	$[$	$!$	$\$$
$[$	$[$	$!$	$\circ$	$\sim$
$!$	$!$	$\circ$	$\sim$	$[$
$\$$	$\$$	$[$	$!$	$\cdot$

23. Is the set closed with respect to $\boxtimes$? Justify your answer.

24. Does the set satisfy the commutative property for $\boxtimes$? Explain.

25. Does the set contain an identity element for $\boxtimes$? If so, what is it?

26. Which elements of the set have inverses with respect to $\boxtimes$? Name each of these inverses.

3-3 The Distributive Property

See if you can discover the meaning of the operations Q and Z from the following examples:

$$\begin{aligned}
5\,Q\,3 &= 5, & 8\,Z\,3 &= 8, \\
2\,Q\,8 &= 8, & 0\,Z\,3 &= 0, \\
3\,Q\,7 &= 7, & 6\,Z\,1 &= 6, \\
4\,Q\,4 &= 4, & 3\,Z\,3 &= 3.
\end{aligned}$$

You should have discovered the following meanings of Q and Z:

Q: select the larger number of the two if the numbers are different, select that number if both are the same;

Z: select the first number of the two.

Thus $5\,Q\,9 = 9$ because 9 is larger than 5, whereas $5\,Z\,9 = 5$ because 5 is the first of the two numbers in the given expression. Note that where both numbers were the same we wrote $4\,Q\,4 = 4$.

We may also combine both operations and determine the meaning of expressions such as

$$a\,Q\,(b\,Z\,c) \qquad \text{and} \qquad (a\,Q\,b)\,Z\,(a\,Q\,c),$$

where a, b, and c represent any of the numbers of ordinary arithmetic. For example, let $a = 3$, $b = 5$, $c = 1$; then the first expression becomes

$$3\,Q\,(5\,Z\,1) = 3\,Q\,5 = 5.$$

Using the same values in the second expression, we have

$$(3\,Q\,5)\,Z\,(3\,Q\,1) = 5\,Z\,3 = 5.$$

Thus we find

$$3\,Q\,(5\,Z\,1) = (3\,Q\,5)\,Z\,(3\,Q\,1).$$

In general, we may write

$$a\,Q\,(b\,Z\,c) = (a\,Q\,b)\,Z\,(a\,Q\,c)$$

for all replacements of a, b, and c. We state, formally, that Q is **distributive** with respect to Z. This property, known as the **distributive property**, may be somewhat easier to visualize for the numbers of arithmetic. We say that *multiplication is distributive with respect to addition*, since

$$a\,(b + c) = ab + ac$$

for all replacements of a, b, and c. For example:

$$3(5 + 8) = 3(13) = 39;$$
$$(3)(5) + (3)(8) = 15 + 24 = 39;$$

so that

$$3(5 + 8) = (3)(5) + (3)(8).$$

Note that addition is *not* distributive with respect to multiplication since, for example,

$$3 + (5 \times 8) \neq (3 + 5) \times (3 + 8);$$

that is, $3 + 40 \neq 8 \times 11$.

Exercises

For Exercises 1 through 6, let $ mean "select the smaller of the two given numbers," and let $\otimes$ mean "select the first of two given numbers."

1. Find $3\,\$\,8$, $8\,\$\,3$, $3 \otimes 7$, $7 \otimes 3$.

2. Find $3\,\$\,(5\,\$\,2)$, $(3\,\$\,5)\,\$\,2$.

3. Find $7 \otimes (2 \otimes 3)$, $(7 \otimes 2) \otimes 3$.

4. Find $5 \$ (1 \otimes 3)$, $(5 \$ 1) \otimes (5 \$ 3)$.

5. Find $3 \otimes (2 \$ 7)$, $(3 \otimes 2) \$ (3 \otimes 7)$.

†**6.** Show that $a \otimes (b \$ c) = (a \otimes b) \$ (a \otimes c) = a$ for all replacements of a, b, and c. Does $a \$ (b \otimes c) = (a \$ b) \otimes (a \$ c)$?

In each of Exercises 7 through 12 try to discover the meaning of the operation #
from the examples given. (It has a different meaning in each.)

7. $3 \# 4 = 7$, $2 \# 0 = 2$, $5 \# 1 = 6$, $2 \# 2 = 4$.

8. $2 \# 4 = 3$, $5 \# 7 = 6$, $8 \# 10 = 9$, $0 \# 2 = 1$.

9. $5 \# 3 = 9$, $2 \# 4 = 7$, $0 \# 3 = 4$, $1 \# 5 = 7$.

10. $2 \# 3 = 7$, $3 \# 4 = 13$, $1 \# 5 = 6$, $0 \# 3 = 1$.

11. $3 \# 4 = 2$, $4 \# 3 = 5$, $5 \# 1 = 9$, $1 \# 1 = 1$.

12. $3 \# 5 = 2$, $4 \# 5 = 1$, $2 \# 8 = 0$, $1 \# 6 = 3$.

13. $8 \# 6 = 12$, $4 \# 4 = 6$, $5 \# 5 = 8$, $6 \# 5 = 9$.

14. In ordinary arithmetic is addition distributive with respect to addition? That is, does $a + (b + c) = (a + b) + (a + c)$ for all possible replacements of a, b, and c?

15. In ordinary arithmetic is multiplication distributive with respect to multiplication? That is, does $a \times (b \times c) = (a \times b) \times (a \times c)$ for all possible replacements of a, b, and c?

3-4 Clock Arithmetic

Let us create another finite mathematical system to firmly establish the ideas presented thus far. If it is now 9 P.M. as you begin to read this section, what time will it be in 5 hours? (We hope it won't take you that long to complete your reading!) Do you see that the statement

$$9 + 5 = 2$$

is a correct statement if we are talking about positions on a 12-hour clock?

Let us consider the numerals 1 through 12 on a 12-hour clock as the elements of a set T and consider addition on this clock to be based upon counting in a clockwise direction. Thus to find the sum $9 + 5$ we start at 9 and count 5 units in a clockwise direction to obtain the result 2.

Verify that each of the following is correct:

$$8 + 7 = 3 \quad \text{(on a 12-hour clock)},$$
$$5 + 12 = 5 \quad \text{(on a 12-hour clock)},$$
$$3 + 11 = 2 \quad \text{(on a 12-hour clock)}.$$

We may make a table of addition facts on a 12-hour clock as follows:

+	1	2	3	4	5	6	7	8	9	10	11	12
1	2	3	4	5	6	7	8	9	10	11	12	1
2	3	4	5	6	7	8	9	10	11	12	1	2
3	4	5	6	7	8	9	10	11	12	1	2	3
4	5	6	7	8	9	10	11	12	1	2	3	4
5	6	7	8	9	10	11	12	1	2	3	4	5
6	7	8	9	10	11	12	1	2	3	4	5	6
7	8	9	10	11	12	1	2	3	4	5	6	7
8	9	10	11	12	1	2	3	4	5	6	7	8
9	10	11	12	1	2	3	4	5	6	7	8	9
10	11	12	1	2	3	4	5	6	7	8	9	10
11	12	1	2	3	4	5	6	7	8	9	10	11
12	1	2	3	4	5	6	7	8	9	10	11	12

Note that regardless of where we start on the clock, we shall always be at the same place 12 hours later. Thus for any element t of set T we have:

$$t + 12 = t \qquad \text{(on the 12-hour clock)}.$$

Let us attempt to define several other operations for this arithmetic on the 12-hour clock. What does multiplication mean? Multiplication by an integer may be considered as repeated addition. For example, 3×5 on the 12-hour clock is equivalent to $5 + 5 + 5$. Since $5 + 5 = 10$ and $10 + 5 = 3$, we know that $3 \times 5 = 3$ on the 12-hour clock.

Verify that each of the following is correct:

$$4 \times 5 = 8 \qquad \text{(on the 12-hour clock)},$$
$$3 \times 9 = 3 \qquad \text{(on the 12-hour clock)},$$
$$3 \times 7 = 9 \qquad \text{(on the 12-hour clock)}.$$

The following examples provide further illustrations of clock arithmetic.

EXAMPLE 1. Solve the equation $t + 6 = 2$ for t where t may be replaced by any one of the numerals on a 12-hour clock.

Solution: On the 12-hour clock $8 + 6 = 2$; therefore $t = 8$. Note that we may also solve for t by starting at 6 on the clock and counting, in a clockwise direction, until we reach 2.

EXAMPLE 2. Using the numerals on a 12-hour clock, find a replacement for t such that $9/7 = t$.

Solution: We may rewrite the given equation in the form $9 = 7t$. Thus we need to know how many groups of 7 we need to produce 9 on the 12-hour clock. From a multiplication table, or by trial and error, we find that $7 \times 3 = 9$; thus $t = 3$.

EXAMPLE 3. What is $3 - 7$ on the 12-hour clock?

Solution: If t represents a numeral on the 12-hour clock, we may write:

$$\text{"}3 - 7 = t\text{" is equivalent to "}t + 7 = 3.\text{"}$$

From the table of addition facts we find that t must be 8.

From a slightly different point of view we may solve Example 3 by counting in a clockwise direction from 12 to 3, and then counting 7 units in a counterclockwise direction. We complete this process at 8. Thus $3 - 7 = 8$ (on the 12-hour clock).

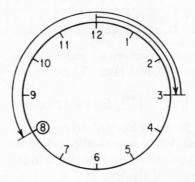

Exercises

1. Is the set of numbers used in clock arithmetic closed **(a)** with respect to addition? **(b)** with respect to multiplication?

2. Make and complete a table of multiplication facts on the 12-hour clock.

3. Do the set of numbers on the clock contain identity elements with respect to addition and multiplication? If so, what are they?

4. List the numbers of clock arithmetic in a column. Beside each number list the inverse with respect to addition and the inverse with respect to multiplication, if one exists. (Thus the inverse of 3, with respect to addition, is 9, whereas 3 does not have an inverse with respect to multiplication.)

Solve each problem as on a 12-hour clock:

5. $8 + 7.$ **6.** $3 + 11.$ **7.** $9 - 12.$ **8.** $5 - 8.$

9. 3×9.   **10.** 5×4.   **†11.** $1 \div 5$.   **†12.** $2 \div 7$.

Solve each equation where t may be replaced by any one of the numerals on a 12-hour clock:

13. $t + 7 = 5$.   **14.** $t - 3 = 11$.   **15.** $3 + t = 2$.

16. $2 - t = 10$.   **17.** $3 \times t = 3$.   **18.** $7 \times t = 4$.

†19. $t/5 = 8$.   **†20.** $t/7 = 9$.   **†21.** $2/t = 3$.

†22. $2 + t = 2 - t$.   **†23.** $t + 12 = t$.   **†24.** $3 - t = 5 + t$.

3-5 Modular Arithmetic

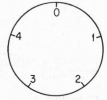

Let us next consider a mathematical system based on a clock for five hours, numbered 0, 1, 2, 3, and 4 as in the accompanying figure. Addition on this clock may be performed by counting as on an ordinary clock. However, it seems easier to think of addition as rotations in a clockwise direction. Thus $3 + 4$ indicates that one is to start at 0 and move 3 units, then 4 more. The result is 2.

We interpret 0 to mean no rotation as well as to designate a position on the clock. Then we have such facts as:

$$3 + 0 = 3 \quad \text{(on a five-hour clock)},$$
$$4 + 1 = 0 \quad \text{(on a five-hour clock)}.$$

Verify that the following table of addition facts on a five-hour clock is correct:

+	0	1	2	3	4
0	0	1	2	3	4
1	1	2	3	4	0
2	2	3	4	0	1
3	3	4	0	1	2
4	4	0	1	2	3

Multiplication on the five-hour clock is defined as repeated addition, as in § 3-4. For example, 3×4 on the five-hour clock is equivalent to $4 + 4 + 4$. Since $4 + 4 = 3$, and $3 + 4 = 2$, we see that $3 \times 4 = 2$ on the five-hour clock.

We define subtraction and division using equivalent statements as follows:

Subtraction: Since the statements "$a - b = x$" and "$a = b + x$" are equivalent, we define $a - b = x$ *if and only if* $b + x = a$.

Division: Since the statements "$a \div b = x$" and "$a = b \times x$" are equivalent, we define $a \div b = x$ *if and only if* $b \times x = a$.

Regardless of where we start on this five-hour clock, we shall always be at the same place five hours later. We describe this situation by saying that arithmetic around this clock is modulo 5. Formally, specific facts in this mathematical system are written as follows:

$3 + 4 \equiv 2$ (mod 5), read "3 + 4 is congruent to 2, modulo 5";
$4 \times 2 \equiv 3$ (mod 5), read "4 × 2 is congruent to 3, modulo 5."

In general, two numbers are **congruent modulo 5** if and only if they differ by a multiple of 5. Thus 3, 8, 13, and 18 are all congruent to each other modulo 5. We may write, for example:

$\equiv$ *means*
    congruent

$$18 \equiv 13 \text{ (mod 5)};$$
$$8 \equiv 3 \text{ (mod 5)}.$$

Notice that every integer in ordinary arithmetic is congruent modulo 5 to exactly one element of the set F where $F = \{0, 1, 2, 3, 4\}$. Indeed the set F is the set of all possible remainders when any number is divided by 5. The elements of F are the elements of arithmetic modulo 5.

EXAMPLE 1. Solve for x where x may be replaced by any element in arithmetic modulo 5: $2 - 3 = x$. $x = 4$

Solution: The statement "$2 - 3 = x$" is equivalent to "$3 + x = 2$." We note that $3 + 4 = 2$; therefore $x = 4$.

EXAMPLE 2. Solve for x in arithmetic modulo 5: $2/3 = x$.

Solution: The statement "$2/3 = x$" is equivalent to "$3 \times x = 2$." Since $3 \times 4 = 2$, $x = 4$.

Let us explore the properties of the mathematical system based upon the set $F = \{0, 1, 2, 3, 4\}$ and the operation addition as defined in this section. The following properties are of special interest.

1. *The set F of elements in arithmetic modulo 5 is closed with respect to addition.* That is, for any pair of elements, there is a unique element which represents their sum and which is also a member of the original set. We note, for example, that there is one and only one entry in each place of the table given in this section, and that each entry is an element of the set F.

2. *The set F of elements in arithmetic modulo 5 satisfies the commutative property for addition.* That is,

$$a + b = b + a,$$

where a and b are any elements of the set F. Specifically, we see that $3 + 4 = 4 + 3, 2 + 3 = 3 + 2$, etc.

3. *The set F of elements in arithmetic modulo 5 satisfies the associative property for addition.* That is,

$$(a + b) + c = a + (b + c),$$

for all elements a, b, and c of the set F.

As a specific example we evaluate $3 + 4 + 2$ in two ways:

$$(3 + 4) + 2 \equiv 2 + 2 \text{ or } 4, \text{ modulo } 5;$$
$$3 + (4 + 2) \equiv 3 + 1 \text{ or } 4, \text{ modulo } 5.$$

4. *The set F of elements in arithmetic modulo 5 includes an identity element for addition.* That is, the set contains an element 0, such that the sum of any given element and 0 is the given element. That is:

$$0 + 0 = 0, \quad 1 + 0 = 1, \quad 2 + 0 = 2, \quad 3 + 0 = 3, \quad 4 + 0 = 4.$$

5. *Each element in arithmetic modulo 5 has an inverse with respect to addition.*

The inverse of 0 is 0; $0 + 0 \equiv 0 \pmod 5$.
The inverse of 1 is 4; $1 + 4 \equiv 0 \pmod 5$.
The inverse of 2 is 3; $2 + 3 \equiv 0 \pmod 5$.
The inverse of 3 is 2; $3 + 2 \equiv 0 \pmod 5$.
The inverse of 4 is 1; $4 + 1 \equiv 0 \pmod 5$.

Exercises

Each of the following is based upon the set of elements in arithmetic modulo 5. Make and complete a table of multiplication facts and use this to answer the following questions.

1. Verify that the commutative law for multiplication holds for at least two specific instances.

2. Verify that the associative law for multiplication holds for at least two specific instances.

3. What is the identity element with respect to multiplication?

4. Find the inverse of each element with respect to multiplication.

Solve each of the following for x in arithmetic modulo 5:

5. $1 - 3 = x$.

6. $1 - 4 = x$.

7. $2 - 4 = x$.

8. $3 - x = 4$.

9. $2 - x = 4$.

10. $3/4 = x$.

11. $1/2 = x$.

12. $4/3 = x$.

13. $3/x = 2$.   **14.** $2/x = 3$.

15. $2 + x = 1$.   **16.** $x + 4 = 2$.

17. $x + 3 = 2$.   **18.** $4 + x = 1$.

19. $2 \times x = 3$.   **20.** $4 \times x = 2$.

21 $4 \times x = 1$.   **22.** $3 \times x = 1$.

23. $x + 3 = x$.   **24.** $x + 1 = 3 - x$.

†**25.** Verify that arithmetic modulo 5 satisfies the distributive property for multiplication with respect to addition by using at least two specific instances.

Supplementary Exercises

1. Consider arithmetic on a clock with four elements, $(0, 1, 2, 3)$, as in the figure. Complete tables for the addition and multiplication facts for arithmetic modulo 4. Explore these systems and list as many properties as you can for each.

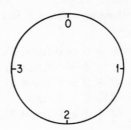

Find a replacement for x, if one exists, to make each of the following number sentences a true statement.

2. $x + 2 \equiv 0 \pmod{7}$.   **3.** $x - 3 \equiv 2 \pmod{5}$.

4. $3x \equiv 1 \pmod{7}$.   **5.** $x \times x \equiv 1 \pmod{8}$.

6. $x/4 \equiv 3 \pmod{9}$.   **7.** $7/x \equiv 15 \pmod{23}$.

8. $3 - x \equiv 4 \pmod{6}$.   **9.** $4 + x \equiv 2 \pmod{7}$.

10. $x + 3 \equiv 1 \pmod{8}$.   **11.** $2 - x \equiv 3 \pmod{6}$.

12. $2x \equiv 3 \pmod{6}$.   **13.** $2/x \equiv 3 \pmod{7}$.

14. $x - 5 \equiv 2 \pmod{7}$.   **15.** $4 + x \equiv 1 \pmod{12}$.

16. We describe the property illustrated by the equation $3 \times 4 = 0$ in arithmetic modulo 12, where the product is zero but neither number is zero, by saying that 3 and 4 are zero divisors. Are there other zero divisors in arithmetic modulo 12? If so, list them.

17. Consider a modulo 7 system where the days of the week correspond to numbers as follows: Sunday – 0; Monday – 1; Tuesday – 2; Wednesday – 3; Thursday – 4; Friday – 5; Saturday – 6. Memorial Day, May 30, is the 150th day of the year and falls on a Thursday. In that same year, on what day of the week does July 4, the 185th day of the year, fall? On what day does Christmas, the 359th day of the year, fall?

18. Take an index card and label it in each corner as shown. Also write these same letters in the corresponding corners on the reverse side of the card. Call this initial position I. Rotate the card 180° to obtain position R. Rotate the card about its horizontal axis, from the initial position, to obtain position H. Finally, rotate the card about its vertical axis, from the initial position, to obtain position V.

A	B
D	C

I

C	D
B	A

R

D	C
A	B

H

B	A
C	D

V

Use the symbol $\sim$ to mean "followed by." Thus $H \sim R$ means a rotation about the horizontal axis followed by a rotation of 180°. You should find $H \sim R = V$. Verify also that $V \sim H = R$.

Make and complete a table for this system whose horizontal and vertical headings are I, R, H, and V. List as many properties for this system as you can find.

19. Consider a soldier facing in a given direction. He is then given various commands, such as "right face," "left face," "about face," and "as you were." The last command tells him to retain whatever position he may be in at the time.

A few specific examples of his movements should clarify matters. If he is facing to the north and is given the command "about face," then in his new position he is facing to the south. If we let R represent the command "right face," A represent the command "about face," and L represent the command "left face," then R followed by A is equivalent to the single command L.

Use the symbol o to represent the operation "followed by" and verify that each of the following is correct:

$$L \circ L = A,$$
$$L \circ A = R,$$
$$A \circ R = L.$$

Now suppose our soldier makes a left turn and then we wish him to remain in that position. We make use of the command "as you were," represented by E. Thus $L \circ E = L$; also $E \circ L = L$.

(a) Make a table summarizing all possible movements, using the headings E, R, L, and A.

(b) Find $R \circ R$, $A \circ A$, $L \circ L$.

(c) Does $R \circ L = L \circ R$?

(d) Does $R \circ (L \circ A) = (R \circ L) \circ A$?

(e) Do the set of given commands appear to be commutative and associative with respect to the operation o?

(f) Find the identity element with respect to o.

(g) List the inverse of each of the elements of the set.

(h) Is the set of command closed with respect to o?

CHAPTER

FOUR

SETS OF ELEMENTS

One of the most important concepts pervading all of mathematics is that of a set. In this chapter we shall discuss the meaning of a set and examine some of the basic relationships among sets. These concepts will prove useful in later chapters.

4-1 Set Notation

A set is a collection of things which are called **elements** or **members** of the set. Thus we may speak of:

(a) the set of letters of the English alphabet;
(b) the set of states of the United States of America;
(c) the set of English names of the days of the week;
(d) the set of integers 1 through 5.

Each of the preceding sets is said to be **well-defined.** That is, from the description you can tell whether or not any given element belongs to the set. For example, we know that r, s, and t are members of the first set listed above, whereas θ and $\aleph_0$ clearly are not members. Can you tell, from the description given, which of the following numbers belong to the last of the sets previously described?

$$3, \quad 2\tfrac{1}{2}, \quad 8, \quad 1, \quad 12$$

You should note that 3 and 1 are members of the set described, whereas $2\tfrac{1}{2}$, 8, and 12 are not. The set of integers 1 through 5 is a well-defined set.

Not all sets are well-defined. See if you can explain why each set in the next list is not a well-defined one.

(a) The set of good tennis players.
(b) The set of interesting numbers.
(c) The set of beautiful movie stars.
(d) The set of well-written books.

In this text we shall be concerned primarily with well-defined sets. Furthermore, we shall agree to name a set by an arbitrarily chosen capital letter and to list the elements of the set within a pair of braces as in the following examples.

EXAMPLE 1. Write in set notation: the set W of English names of the days of the week.

Solution: $W = \{$Sunday, Monday, Tuesday, Wednesday, Thursday, Friday, Saturday$\}$.

EXAMPLE 2. List the elements in the set I of integers 1 through 5.

Solution: $I = \{1, 2, 3, 4, 5\}$.

Where it becomes tedious to list individually all of the members of a set, we frequently use three dots to indicate missing elements.

EXAMPLE 3. List the elements in the set A of letters of the English alphabet.

Solution: $A = \{a, b, c, \ldots, z\}$.

We also use three dots at the end of a sequence of elements to indicate that the set continues indefinitely in the pattern indicated; that is, that there are an infinite number of elements in the set.

EXAMPLE 4. List the elements in the set G of integers greater than 100.

Solution: $G = \{101, 102, 103, \ldots\}$.

It is interesting, at times, to seek verbal descriptions for given sets of elements which have already been listed. The next example illustrates this point.

EXAMPLE 5. Write a verbal description for the set

$$Y = \{1, 3, 5, 7, 9\}.$$

Solution: There are several correct responses that might be given. Two of these are: "The set of odd integers 1 through 9"; "The set of odd integers between 0 and 11." Note that the word "between" implies that the first and last numbers, that is 0 and 11, are not included as members of the given set.

The basic property of a set of elements is the identification of its members. A set is well-defined if its members can be identified. The sets $A = \{1, 2, 3\}$ and $B = \{3, 1, 2\}$ are the same since they have the same members. When two sets consist of precisely the same elements they are said to be **identical**. We write $\{1, 2, 3\} = \{3, 1, 2\}$ and in general $A = B$ to show that two sets consist of the same elements. We write $A \neq B$ to show that two sets do not have the same members.

Two sets, $X = \{x_1, x_2, \ldots\}$ and $Y = \{y_1, y_2, \ldots\}$ are said to be in **one-to-one correspondence** if we can find a pairing of the x's and y's such that each x corresponds to one and only one y and each y corresponds to one and only one x.

Two sets, A and B, which can be placed in a one-to-one correspondence are said to be **equivalent** (written $A \leftrightarrow B$). Thus the following two sets are equivalent:

$$A = \{1, 3, 5, 9\}, \qquad B = \{2, 4, 6, 7\}.$$

These two sets have the same **cardinality**, that is, the same number of elements in each set. When such is the case, this implies that the sets are equivalent. As another example of equivalent sets, consider the set E of even integers and the set I of positive integers. The following scheme indicates one means of placing these two sets in a one-to-one correspondence:

$$E = \{2, \quad 4, \quad 6, \quad 8, \quad \ldots, \quad 2n, \quad \ldots\},$$
$$\updownarrow \quad \updownarrow \quad \updownarrow \quad \updownarrow \qquad \updownarrow$$
$$I = \{1, \quad 2, \quad 3, \quad 4, \quad \ldots, \quad n, \quad \ldots\}.$$

Exercises

Tell whether or not each of the following sets is well-defined:

1. The set of U.S. astronauts who have orbited the earth.

2. The set of cities that are state capitals in the United States of America.

3. The set of large states in the United States.

4. The set of states in the United States and with good climates.

5. The set of states in the United States and having over 10,000,000 registered voters.

6. The set of states in the United States that are islands.

List the elements in each of the following sets, using the notation developed in this section:

7. The set of English names of the months in the year.

8. The set of letters in the English alphabet that precede h.

9. The set of integers between 0 and 10.

10. The set of integers 1 through 1,000.

11. The set of integers greater than 50.

12. The set of integers greater than 100 and less than 110.

Write a verbal description for each of the following sets:

13. $N = \{1, 2, 3, 4, 5\}$.

14. $R = \{1, 2, 3, \ldots, 99\}$.

15. $S = \{51, 52, 53, \ldots\}$.

16. $M = \{5, 10, 15, 20, \ldots\}$.

17. $K = \{10, 20, 30, \ldots, 100\}$.

18. $T = \{1, 4, 9, 16, 25, 36\}$.

†19. $P = \{0, 2, 6, 12, 20, \ldots, 90\}$.

†20. $A = \{8, 5, 4, 9, 1, 7, 6, 3, 2\}$.

†21. Are two identical sets necessarily equivalent? Are two equivalent sets necessarily identical? Explain your answer.

†22. Display a one-to-one correspondence between the set of positive odd integers and the set of positive integral multiples of 5.

4-2 Subsets

The set containing the totality of elements for any particular discussion is called the **universal set**, U, and may vary for each discussion. For example, let us agree, for the present, to talk about the set of integers 1 through 9. Then our universal set is:

$$U = \{1, 2, 3, 4, 5, 6, 7, 8, 9\}.$$

A set A is a **subset** of U if the set A has the property that each element of A is also an element of U. We write $A \subseteq U$ (read "A is included in U"). There are many subsets of U; a few of them are listed below:

$$A_1 = \{1, 2, 3\};$$
$$A_2 = \{1, 5, 7, 8, 9\};$$
$$A_3 = \{2\};$$
$$A_4 = \{1, 2, 3, 4, 5, 6, 7, 8, 9\}.$$

Note in particular that the set A_4 contains each of the elements of U and is classified as a subset of U. Any set is said to be a subset of itself. A set A is said to be a **proper subset** of U if A is a subset of U and there is at least one element of U which is not an element of A. We write $A \subset U$ (read "A is properly included in U"). Intuitively we speak of a proper subset as part of, but not all of, a given set. Each of the subsets A_1, A_2, A_3, and A_4 are subsets of U; the sets A_1, A_2, and A_3 are proper subsets of U; the set A_4 is not a proper subset of U. We may write this in symbols as follows:

$$A_1 \subset U; \quad A_2 \subset U; \quad A_3 \subset U; \quad A_4 \subseteq U.$$

EXAMPLE 1. List three proper subsets of the set R where

$$R = \{1, 2, 3, 4\}.$$

Solution: Here are three proper subsets:

$$A = \{1, 2\}; \quad B = \{1, 3, 4\}; \quad C = \{1\}.$$

Do you see that there are others? Note that the choice of letters to name each of the subsets is completely arbitrary.

The **empty** set or **null** set is the set that contains no elements and is denoted by the symbol $\varnothing$ or by the symbol $\{\ \}$. Note that the first symbol given for the empty set is not included within a pair of braces. Some examples of empty sets are:

The set of integers between 2 and 3; and

The set of states of the United States with borders on both the Atlantic Ocean and the Pacific Ocean.

By convention, the empty set is considered to be a subset of every set. Thus $\varnothing$ is a subset of set $A = \{2, 1, 3\}$ and also $\varnothing$ is a subset of itself. Since $\varnothing$ is a proper subset of A, we may write $\varnothing \subset A$; since $\varnothing$ is not a proper subset of itself, we write $\varnothing \subseteq \varnothing$.

EXAMPLE 2. List all the possible subsets for the set $U = \{1, 2\}$.

Solution: $\varnothing$, $\{1\}$, $\{2\}$, $\{1, 2\}$. Note that the subsets consist of the empty set, the elements of U taken one at a time, and the elements of U taken two at a time.

Consider a universal set $U = \{1, 2, 3, 4, 5, 6, 7\}$ and a subset $A = \{1, 2, 3, 4\}$. The set of elements of U which are not elements of A form a set, written as A' or $\overline{A}$, and is called the **complement of A relative to U**. For the example just given, $A' = \{5, 6, 7\}$.

EXAMPLE 3. Given $U = \{1, 3, 5, 7, 9\}$ and $A = \{1, 3, 7\}$, find A'.

Solution: $A' = \{5, 9\}$; these are the elements in U which are not in A.

In general, for any given universal set U, each set A has a complement A'. If $A = U$, then $A' = \varnothing$; if $A = \varnothing$, then $A' = U$. That is, the complement of the universal set is the empty set; and the complement of the empty set is the universal set.

EXAMPLE 4. How many subsets can be formed from the set

$$A = \{1, 2, 3\}?$$

Solution: We can find the answer to this question by actually listing all of the possible subsets and counting them. Here is a systematic procedure for identifying each of these subsets based on the idea that the subsets are formed by "taking" or "not taking" each of the three elements of the given set. First we adopt the symbol $\bar{1}$ to mean "not 1," $\bar{2}$ to mean "not 2," and $\bar{3}$ to mean "not 3." Then consider the accompanying diagram where each branch represents a choice to be made. For example, our first choice is to select 1 as a member of a subset or not to select 1. Finally we read along all possible branches of this diagram, called a **tree diagram**, to list the various subsets of A. There are eight such subsets as given below.

Tree diagram	Read along branches	Subsets
	$\bar{1}, \bar{2}, \bar{3}$	ϕ
	$\bar{1}, \bar{2}, 3$	$\{3\}$
	$\bar{1}, 2, \bar{3}$	$\{2\}$
	$\bar{1}, 2, 3$	$\{2,3\}$
	$1, \bar{2}, \bar{3}$	$\{1\}$
	$1, \bar{2}, 3$	$\{1,3\}$
	$1, 2, \bar{3}$	$\{1,2\}$
	$1, 2, 3$	$\{1,2,3\}$

Exercises

1. List all of the possible subsets of the set $A = \{1, 2, 3, 4\}$.

2. Repeat Exercise 1 for $B = \{1, 2, 3, 4, 5\}$.

†**3.** Use the information gained from the preceding two exercises to conjecture a formula for the number, N, of subsets which can be formed from a set consisting of n elements.

4. Give three examples of empty sets.

5. Is the set consisting of the integer, 0, equivalent to the empty set? Explain your answer.

6. Let $U = \{1, 2, 3, 4, 5\}$. List the elements in A', where A is defined as:
(a) $\{1, 2, 5\}$;   (b) $\{1\}$;   (c) $\varnothing$;   (d) $\{2, 5\}$;   (e) $\{1, 2, 3, 4, 5\}$.

7. Let U be the set of counting numbers: $\{1, 2, 3, \ldots\}$. Let A be the set of even counting numbers and describe the set A'.

†**8.** List the four subsets of $\{A, B\}$. Then list the eight subsets of $\{A, B, \varnothing\}$.

4-3 Relationships Between Sets

Let us consider two sets, A and B, defined as follows:

$$A = \{1, 2, 3, 4, 5, 6, 7\};$$
$$B = \{2, 5, 7, 8, 9\}.$$

From these two sets let us form another set, C, whose members are those elements which appear in each of the two given sets:

$$C = \{2, 5, 7\}.$$

The set C consists of the elements that the sets A and B have in common and is called the **intersection** of the sets A and B. Formally we say that the intersection of two sets A and B (written $A \cap B$) is the set of elements which are members of both of the given sets.

EXAMPLE 1. If $A = \{a, r, e\}$ and $B = \{c, a, t\}$, find $A \cap B$.

Solution: $A \cap B = \{a\}$; that is, a is the only letter that appears in each of the two given sets.

EXAMPLE 2. If $X = \{1, 2, 3, 4, 5\}$ and $Y = \{4, 5, 6, 7\}$, find $X \cap Y$.

Solution: $X \cap Y = \{4, 5\}$.

EXAMPLE 3. If $X = \{1, 2, 3\}$ and $Y = \{4, 5, 6\}$, find $X \cap Y$.

Solution: Sets X and Y have no elements in common and are said to be **disjoint**; their intersection is the null set. Thus we may write $X \cap Y = \varnothing$.

From the two given sets A and B of this section let us next form another set, D, whose members are those elements which are elements of at least one of the two given sets:

$$D = \{1, 2, 3, 4, 5, 6, 7, 8, 9\}.$$

The set D is called the **union** of sets A and B. Formally we say that the union of two sets A and B (written $A \cup B$) is the set of elements that are members of at least one of the given sets.

EXAMPLE 4. Let A represent the set of names of boys on a particular committee, $A = \{$Bill, Bruce, Max$\}$. Let B represent the set of names of boys on another committee, $B = \{$Bruce, John, Max$\}$. Find $A \cup B$.

Solution: $A \cup B = \{$Bill, Bruce, John, Max$\}$. Here the union of the two sets is the set of names of the boys who are in at least one of the two committees. Note that the names Bruce and Max appear only once in the set $A \cup B$ even though these names are listed for both committees.

EXAMPLE 5. If $A = \{1, 2, 3, 4, 5\}$ and $B = \{3, 5, 7, 9\}$, find $A \cup B$.

Solution: $A \cup B = \{1, 2, 3, 4, 5, 7, 9\}$.

EXAMPLE 6. Let
$$U = \{1, 2, 3, \ldots\}; \quad A = \{1, 2, 3, 4, 5\};$$
$$B = \{3, 4, 5, 6, 7\}.$$

List the elements in $A' \cap B'$.

Solution: Note that the universal set here consists of the set of integers greater than or equal to 1. Thus we have
$$A' = \{6, 7, 8, \ldots\}, \quad B' = \{1, 2, 8, 9, 10, \ldots\},$$
and
$$A' \cap B' = \{8, 9, 10, \ldots\}.$$

Exercises

For each of the following sets list the elements in (a) $A \cup B$; (b) $A \cap B$.

1. $A = \{1, 2, 3\}$; $B = \{1, 3, 5\}$.

2. $A = \{3, 4, 5\}$; $B = \{4, 5, 6\}$.

3. $A = \{1, 3, 5, 7\}$; $B = \{7, 9\}$.

4. $A = \{2, 4, 6, 8\}$; $B = \{4, 6, 7, 8\}$.

5. $A = \{1, 2\}$; $B = \{3, 4\}$.

6. $A = \{1, 5, 10\}$; $B = \{3, 7, 8\}$.

7. $A = \{1, 3, 5, \ldots\}$; $B = \{2, 4, 6, \ldots\}$.

8. $A = \varnothing$; $B = \{1, 2, 3, \ldots\}$.

9. $A = \{1, 2, 3, 4\}$; $B = \varnothing$.

10. $A = \{1, 2, 3, \ldots\}$; $B = \{1, 3, 5, \ldots\}$.

For each of the given universal sets list the elements in (**a**) $A' \cup B'$; (**b**) $A' \cap B'$.

11. $U = \{1, 2, 3, 4, 5\}$; $A = \{1, 2\}$; $B = \{1, 3, 5\}$.

12. $U = \{1, 2, 3, \ldots, 10\}$; $A = \{1, 3, 5, 7, 9\}$; $B = \{2, 4, 6, 8, 10\}$.

13. $U = \{1, 2, 3, \ldots\}$; $A = \{1, 3, 5, \ldots\}$; $B = \{2, 4, 6, \ldots\}$.

14. $U = \{1, 2, 3, \ldots, 100\}$; $A = \{1, 3, 5, \ldots, 99\}$; $B = \{2, 4, 6, \ldots, 100\}$

15. $U = \{1, 2, 3, 4, 5, 6, 7\}$; $A = \varnothing$; $B = \{1, 2, 3, 4, 5, 6, 7\}$.

16. $U = \{1, 2, 3, 4, 5\}$; $A = \{1, 2, 4\}$; $B = \{1, 2, 5\}$.

17. $U = \{1, 2, 3\}$; $A = \{1\}$; $B = \{3\}$.

18. $U = \{1, 2, 3, \ldots, 10\}$; $A = \{1, 3, 5, 7, 9\}$; $B = \{1, 2, 3, 4, 5\}$.

For Exercises 19 through 24, let

$$U = \{1, 2, 3, 4, 5, 6, 7, 8, 9, 10\};$$
$$A = \{1, 3, 4, 5, 7, 9\}; \quad B = \{2, 4, 5, 9, 10\}.$$

List the elements in each of the following:

19. $A' \cap B'$.   **20.** $(A \cup B)'$.   **21.** $A' \cup B$.

22. $(A' \cap B)'$.   **23.** $A \cap B$.   **24.** $(A \cup B')'$.

4-4 Venn Diagrams

An interesting way to visualize sets and relationships among sets can be given by means of figures known as **Venn diagrams**. We may represent the set of elements in the universe under discussion by the set of points of a rectangular region, that is, the points within and on the rectangle, as in the figure. We then represent various subsets of this universe as sets of points of circular regions (that is, points within or on circles) or other figures within the rectangle. The next diagram illustrates two disjoint sets, A and B, as subsets of a universal set U.

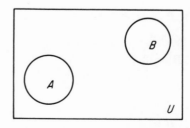

To show set A as a proper subset of B, we merely include the elements of A within B:

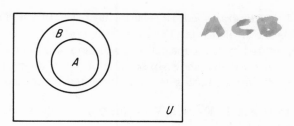

The union of sets A and B is shaded in the diagram that follows.

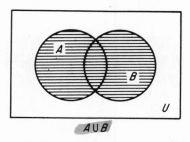

Note that $A \cup B$ includes all of the points that are in the set A as well as all of those in the set B.

The intersection of sets A and B is shaded in the next diagram.

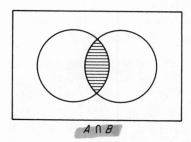

Note that $A \cap B$ includes only those points that are in both set A and set B.

We can represent the complement of a set A by shading the points in U that are outside of A.

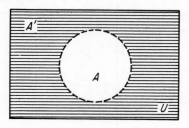

Venn diagrams can be used to show that two sets give rise to the same collection of elements. Thus two sets are said to be identical if they are represented by the same collection of points in Venn diagrams. The following two examples show, by means of Venn diagrams, that $(A \cup B)' = A' \cap B'$ in that both sets are represented by the same set of points.

EXAMPLE 1. Draw a Venn diagram to show the set of points in the set $(A \cup B)'$.

Solution: Set $A \cup B$ is shaded with horizontal lines. The complement of this set, $(A \cup B)'$, is the remaining portion of U, shaded with vertical lines.

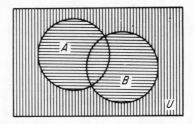

EXAMPLE 2. Draw a Venn diagram to show the set of points in the set $A' \cap B'$.

Solution: Set A' is shaded with horizontal lines; B' is shaded with vertical lines. The intersection of these sets is the subset of U which has both horizontal and vertical shading.

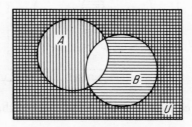

We may also use Venn diagrams to show relationships among more than two sets. For three sets we draw three circles within a rectangle. The relative positions of the three circles have been chosen so that all possible types of intersections will arise.

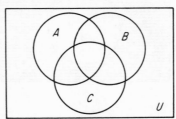

EXAMPLE 3. Show that $A \cap (B \cup C) = (A \cap B) \cup (A \cap C)$.

Solution: Set A is shaded with vertical lines; $B \cup C$ is shaded with horizontal lines. The intersection of these sets, $A \cap (B \cup C)$, is the subset of U which has both vertical and horizontal shading.

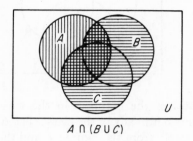

$$A \cap (B \cup C)$$

The set $A \cap B$ is shaded with horizontal lines; $A \cap C$ is shaded with vertical lines. The union of these sets is the subset of U which is shaded with lines in either or in both directions.

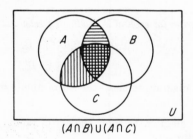

$$(A \cap B) \cup (A \cap C)$$

Note that the final results in the two diagrams are the same, thus showing the equivalence of $A \cap (B \cup C)$ and $(A \cap B) \cup (A \cap C)$.

EXAMPLE 4. In a group of 35 students, 15 are studying algebra, 22 are studying geometry, 14 are studying trigonometry, 11 are studying both algebra and geometry, 8 are studying geometry and trigonometry, 5 are studying algebra and trigonometry, and 3 are studying all three subjects. How many of these students are not taking any of these subjects? How many are taking only geometry?

Solution: This problem can easily be solved by means of a Venn diagram with three circles to represent the set of students in each of the listed subject-matter areas. It is helpful to start with the information that there are 3 students taking all three subjects. We write the number 3 in the region that is the intersection of all three circles. Then, working backwards, since 5 are taking algebra and trigonometry there must be 2 in the region representing algebra and trigonometry but *not* geometry. Continuing in this manner we enter the given data in the figure as follows:

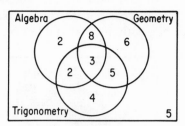

Since the total of the numbers in the various areas is 30, there must be 5 students not in any of the classes listed in the various regions. Also, reading directly from the figure we find that there are 6 students taking geometry only.

Exercises

Draw a Venn diagram for each of the following sets:

1. $A' \cup B$. **2.** $A' \cap B$.

3. $A \cap B'$. **4.** $A \cup B'$.

5. Draw a Venn diagram to show the set of points in $(A \cup B)'$ where A and B are disjoint sets.

6. Draw a Venn diagram to show the set of points in $(A \cup B \cup C)'$ where A, B, and C are disjoint sets.

Show by means of Venn diagrams:

7. $(A \cap B)' = A' \cup B'$.

†8. $A \cup (B \cup C) = (A \cup B) \cup C$.

†9. $A \cap (B \cap C) = (A \cap B) \cap C$.

†10. $A \cup (B \cap C) = (A \cup B) \cap (A \cup C)$.

11. In a survey of 50 students taking biology, chemistry, and physics, the following data were collected: 19 taking biology, 20 in chemistry, 19 in physics, 7 in physics and chemistry, 8 in biology and chemistry, 9 in biology and physics, 5 taking all three subjects. How many of the group are not taking any of the three subjects? How many are taking only chemistry? How many are taking physics and chemistry, but not biology?

12. A survey was taken of 30 students enrolled in three different clubs, A, B, and C. Show that the following data that were collected are inconsistent: 18 in A, 10 in B, 9 in C, 3 in B and C, 6 in A and B, 9 in A and C, 2 in A, B, and C.

4-5 Graphs on a Line

We shall, in this section, present a brief intuitive discussion of means of describing sets of numbers through the use of graphs on a line. (A systematic development will be given in Chapter 8.) We assume that the universe U is the set of numbers which correspond to points on a number line. We indicate that the line extends indefinitely in each of two directions by placing an arrow at each end of our figure:

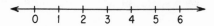

EXAMPLE 1. Draw a graph for the set A where

$$A = \{1, 2, 3, 4, 5\}.$$

Solution: We place solid dots on a number line at each of the points which correspond to a number of the set A as follows:

If we wish to draw the graph of a set that includes *all* numbers in our universe U (that is, all real numbers) rather than just integers, we draw a heavily shaded line rather than a series of dots.

We shade part of the line to graph the set of all numbers 1 through 5. The heavy dots indicate that 1 and 5 are members of the set. We use

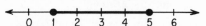

hollow dots when points are not included. For example, we graph the set of *all* numbers between 1 and 5 as in the following figure.

EXAMPLE 2. Draw the graph of the set of all numbers greater than or equal to 1.

Solution: We place a dot at 1 and draw an arrow to show that all the numbers greater than 1 are members of the set, as follows:

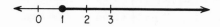

EXAMPLE 3. Draw the graph of the set of all numbers greater than 1.

Solution: Here we place a hollow dot at 1 to show that it is not to be included in the graph, and draw an arrow to the right to show that all numbers greater than 1 are members of the set.

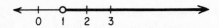

Occasionally the symbolism $[a, b]$ is used to represent a set of points on a line in the interval from a to b, with both end-points a and b included in the set. For integral points, $[2, 6] = \{2, 3, 4, 5, 6\}$. For an interval of real numbers, $[2, 6]$ represents all of the real numbers from 2 through 6 inclusive.

We use the symbolism (a, b) to represent the points on the interval from a to b, exclusive of these two end-points. A combination of these symbols may be used to indicate that one end-point is included but not the other. Thus $[a, b)$ is used to represent the points in the interval from a to b, including a but not including b.

Exercises

Draw a graph for each of the following sets:

1. $A = \{1, 2, 3\}$.   2. $B = \{1, 3, 5, 7\}$.

3. $C = \{2, 3, 5\}$.   4. $D = \{1, 2, 3, \ldots, 10\}$.

5. The set of integers 2 through 7.

6. The set of integers between 2 and 7.

7. The set of all real numbers greater than 2.

8. The set of all real numbers 2 through 7.

9. The set of all real numbers between 2 and 7.

10. The set of all real numbers greater than or equal to 2.

11. The set of all real numbers greater than 2 and less than or equal to 7.

Draw a graph for **(a)** A; **(b)** B; **(c)** $A \cup B$; *and* **(d)** $A \cap B$.

12. A: The set of integers between 2 and 5.
    B: The set of integers between 1 and 4.

13. A: The set of integers greater than 2 and less than 9.
    B: The set of integers greater than or equal to 1 and less than or equal to 7.

†14. A: The set of all numbers greater than 1.
     B: The set of all numbers less than or equal to 6.

†15. A: The set of all numbers less than or equal to 5.
     B: The set of all numbers less than 3.

Supplementary Exercises

List and then show on a number line the integral elements in each set:

1. $[2, 4] \cup [1, 5]$.   **2.** $[3, 7] \cup [1, 3]$.

3. $[2, 5] \cap [3, 7]$.   **4.** $[3, 5] \cap (5, 8]$.

5. $(2, 5] \cup [3, 7)$.   **6.** $[4, 9) \cap [8, 10)$.

For each of the following, let $U = [-10, 10]$, an interval of real numbers. Draw the graph of each set and state the results, using the symbolism for intervals of real numbers.

7. $[-10, 3) \cup (5, 10]$.

8. $[-5, 2]'$; that is, the complement of the interval $[-5, 2]$.

9. $\{[-7, 2] \cap [3, 5]\}'$.

10. $[-10, 10]'$.

†**11.** $\{[-2, 5] \cup [3, 8]\} \cap \{[-5, 7] \cap [-3, 3]\}$.

†**12.** $\{(3, 7] \cap [-1, 2)\} \cup \{[-1, 2] \cap [-2, 1]\}$.

4-6 Sets in Mathematics

The concept of a set has often been referred to as one of the clarifying and unifying concepts of all of mathematics. As such it is being currently introduced into both elementary and secondary school courses in mathematics in an effort to help make clear many different aspects of the subject.

In this book we shall see the concept of a set used in a variety of different ways. We have already, in our discussion of mathematical systems, made reference to sets of elements as we explored various relationships between such elements under given operations. In the next chapter we turn our attention to geometry and again find the concept of a set quite useful in describing lines as sets of points, planes as sets of points on lines, and so forth. Later, in Chapter 6, the notion of a set helps in our discussion of probability.

When discussing the number systems in Chapter 7 we shall frequently refer to various sets of numbers. Then, in Chapter 8, we rely heavily on set notation as we describe solution sets for various statements of equality and inequality. It is for this reason, then, that we have paused long enough to provide the basic definitions of sets in this chapter. A study of these basic ideas will yield rewarding applications in any later study of mathematics.

AN INTRODUCTION TO GEOMETRY

Geometry has evolved from a concern for earth measure (geo-metry), through the use of line segments and other figures to represent physical magnitudes, to a study of properties of sets of geometric elements. The figures serve as the elements of geometry. Relations among these elements and proofs of their properties from given sets of postulates are considered in more advanced courses.

5-1 Points, Lines, and Planes

All geometric figures are usually considered to be sets of points. Although other basic elements are considered in abstract geometry, we shall restrict our consideration to points. This is not a serious restriction, since points may be *interpreted* in many ways. For example, we usually think of a point as a position on a line, on a plane, or in space. We may also think of a point on a number scale in terms of its coordinate. We may even think of cities as points on a map, with the air routes joining them considered as lines. This freedom to interpret points in a variety of ways provides a basis for more abstract geometries.

We have an intuitive idea of what is meant by a point but we have not and shall not *define* a point. In order to define a term, we need to distinguish it from other terms. In doing this, we must describe our term in words that are already known to us (that is, in simpler terms) in such a way that whenever the description is applicable, the term being defined is also appropriate.

The early Greeks described a point as "that which has no part." Today we recognize such a description as an aid to our interpretations but we do not consider it a definition. We object to it as a formal definition because simpler terms are not used and, indeed, are not available. Also, the referent for the word "that" in the description is not properly identified as one of a specified set of elements.

Lines also are left undefined. In any logical system there must be some undefined terms. In other words, it is not possible to define everything; we must start with something. In geometry we start with points and lines. Then we define other figures in terms of these.

Even though lines are undefined they do possess certain properties. Here are three of these properties:

1. *A line is a set of points.* Each point of the line is said to be *on* the line.

2. *Any two distinct points determine a unique line.* In other words, there is one and only one line AB through any two given points A and B. Thus a line may be named by any two of its points. If C and D are points on the line AB, then the line CD is the same as the line AB.

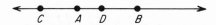

3. *Any point A on a line separates the line into three parts: the point A and two half-lines, one on each side of A.*

Each half-line is a set of points. The point A is not a point (member) of either half-line. The fact that the point A is at the end of each half-line is expressed by calling A the end-point of each half-line. Notice that the end-point of a half-line is not a point of the half-line, just as the center of a circle is not a point of the circle.

Three points A, B, C either lie on a line or do not lie on a line. Note that we think of (interpret) a "line" as a "straight line." If the points do not lie on the same straight line, then, since any two points determine a unique line, the three points determine three lines AB, BC, and AC as in the figure.

Each of the lines AB, BC, and AC is a set of points. Any two points on a line determine that line; for example, the points D and E on the line BC determine the line BC, and we say that BC and

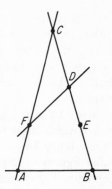

DE are two names for the same line. Any two points of the figure consisting of the lines *AB*, *BC*, and *AC* determine a line. If the points are not on the same one of these three lines, then the points determine a new line; for example, *D* and *F* determine a new line in the figure. Many new lines can be determined in this way. A few such lines are shown in the next figure. The set of all points on such lines is the set of points of the plane determined by the three points *A*, *B*, and *C*.

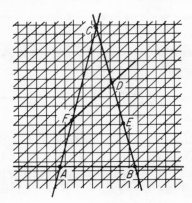

Planes are often accepted as undefined. However, all planes have certain basic properties. Here are five of these properties:

1. *A plane is a set of points.* Each point of the plane is said to be *on* the plane.

2. *Any three points that are not on the same line determine a unique plane.* In other words, there is one and only one plane through any three noncollinear points. For example, a piece of cardboard will balance firmly on the points of three thumbtacks; a three-legged stool is more stable than many four-legged chairs.

3. *If two distinct points of a line are on a plane, then every point of the line is on the plane.*

4. *Two distinct planes have either a line in common or no points in common.* In other words, any two distinct planes either intersect in a line or are parallel.

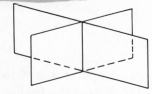 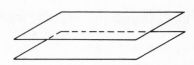

5. *Any line m on a plane separates the plane into three parts: the line m and two half-planes.* The points of the line m do not belong to either half-plane. However, the line m is often called the **edge** of both half-planes even though it is not a part of either.

Note that we may think of the points of the plane that are on the right of m as forming one half-plane and the points of the plane that are on the left of m as forming the other half-plane.

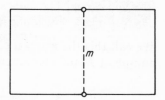

The elements of geometry are points, lines, and planes. The properties of a point's being on a line, a line's containing a point, a line's being on a plane, and a plane's containing a line are called *incidence relations.* We shall use these elements and relations as we define other geometric figures, that is, as we name other sets of points.

Exercises

Draw each of the following:

1. A line m, a point A on m, and two points B and C on the same half-line with end-point A.

2. A line m, a point R on m, and two points S and T on different half-lines with end-point R.

3. A plane with points A, B, C and a second plane with points A, B, D.

4. Five half-planes with a common edge m.

Explain your answer for each question:

5. A point P on a line MN separates the line into two half-lines. Is the union of these half-lines the same as the line MN?

6. In Exercise 5 what is the intersection of the two half-lines?

7. A line on a plane separates the plane into two half-planes just as a point separates a line. Is the union of these half-planes the same as the original plane?

8. In Exercise 7 what is the intersection of the two half-planes?

9. If you can find as many points as you wish on a line, how many points can you find on a plane?

10. In Exercise 9 how many lines can you find on a plane?

5-2 Rays, Line Segments, and Angles

Suppose that we are given a line m and two points A and B on m. There is one and only one line m on both A and B. We call this the line AB and write it as $\overleftrightarrow{AB}$. As in § 5-1 the point A separates the line m into two half-lines. Note that one of these half-lines contains the point B and one does not.

The set of points consisting of the points of a half-line and its end-point is called a **ray**. The end-point of the half-line is the **end-point** of the ray. There is one and only one ray with end-point A and containing the point B. We call this the ray AB and write it as $\overrightarrow{AB}$. There is also a ray BA with end-point B and containing A.

$\overleftrightarrow{AB}$		Line AB
$\overrightarrow{AB}$		Ray AB
$\overleftarrow{BA}$		Ray BA
$\overline{AB}$		Line segment AB

The **line segment** AB, written as $\overline{AB}$, consists of the points which $\overrightarrow{AB}$ and $\overrightarrow{BA}$ have in common. We may use the symbol $\cap$ for the intersection of two sets of elements (in this case, points) and write

$$\overline{AB} = \overrightarrow{AB} \cap \overrightarrow{BA}.$$

A line AB has no end-points and may be named by any two of its points. A ray AB has one end-point and may be named by that point A and any other point on the ray. A line segment AB has the two end-points A and B and is named by those two points. However, for a line segment those two points may be stated in either order; $\overline{AB} = \overline{BA}$. When a direction, such as from A to B, is assigned to the points of a line segment, we obtain a **vector**, $\overrightarrow{AB}$. The vector AB has both direction and length. The direction is from A to B; the length is the same as the length of the line segment AB.

$\overrightarrow{AB}$		Vector AB

Any point of a line segment AB that is not an end-point (that is, any point that is distinct from A and B) is called an **interior point of** $\overline{AB}$. If E is an interior point of AB, then E is **between** A and B. Thus the line segment AB consists of the end-points A and B and the points of the line AB that are between A and B. We use this concept to state another property of lines which we have been tacitly assuming:

   4. *On any line AB there is at least one point between A and B.* For example, think of a ruler with A at "1" and B at "5"; we certainly can find a point—such as the point located at "3" or "4" or "$1\frac{3}{4}$"—between A and B.

Any line AB is a set of points. If C is a point of the line such that A is between C and B, then the line is the union of the rays AB and AC. These two rays have a common end-point A and are both on the line AB. Any figure formed by two rays that have a common end-point is a **plane angle**. These rays may be on the same line but need not be on the same line. The angle in the figure may be designated as $\angle BAC$.

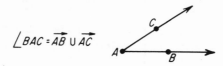

The rays AB and AC are called **sides** of $\angle BAC$. If the half-plane that contains C and has edge $\overleftrightarrow{AB}$ intersects the half-plane that contains B and has edge $\overleftrightarrow{AC}$, their intersection is called the **interior** of $\angle ABC$. Notice that it may or may not be possible to define the interior of an angle. In the figure the interior of $\angle RST$ has double shading; $\angle LMN$ does not have an interior since there does not exist a half-plane with edge $\overleftrightarrow{LM}$ and containing N; the interior of $\angle XYZ$ has double shading. From these definitions and figures persons who have previously studied geometry may observe that any angle that has an interior has a measurement between $0°$ and $180°$. For this reason some elementary books consider only angles whose measurements are greater than $0°$ and less than $180°$.

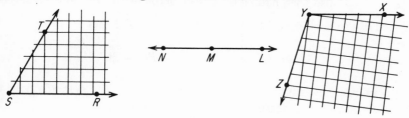

Plane angles may also be defined in terms of half-lines. Any point A of a line separates the line into two half-lines, and the point A is described as the common end-point of the half-lines even though it is not a point of either half-line. If B is a point of one half-line and C is a point of the other half-line, then the half-lines may be called AB and AC. The union of a point A and any two half-lines that have the point A as their common end-point is a plane angle. The union of each one of the half-lines with the vertex of the plane angle is a side of the plane angle.

Now consider these statements about lines and planes corresponding to the previous statements about points and lines. Any line CD of a plane

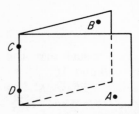

separates the plane into two half-planes and the line CD, which is described as the common **edge** of the half-planes even though it is not a line of either half-plane. If A is a point of one half-plane and B is a point of the other half-plane, then the half-planes may be called A-CD and B-CD. The union of a line CD and any two half-planes A-CD and B-CD that have the line CD as their common edge is a **dihedral angle** A-CD-B. The union of each one of the half-planes with the edge of the dihedral angle is a **face** of the dihedral angle.

The concept of **separation** (a point separates a line into two half-lines; a line separates a plane into two half-planes) may be extended to space. We have tacitly assumed that not all points are on the same plane. This is necessary if we are to have dihedral angles such that the two half-planes do not lie on the same plane. Under this assumption a plane divides space into two half-spaces of which it is the common **face**. Then the interior of a dihedral angle A-CD-B which has an interior may be defined as the intersection of the half-space with face ACD which contains B and the half-space with face BCD which contains A. As in the case of plane angles, persons who have previously studied geometry will recognize that a dihedral angle has an interior in the usual sense if and only if its measurement is greater than 0° and less than 180°.

Note that any line ABC may be considered as $\overrightarrow{BA} \cup \overrightarrow{BC}$ and thus satisfies the definition of a plane angle with vertex B. Similarly any plane containing a line m satisfies the definition of a dihedral angle with edge m. Note also that figures often can be named in any one of several ways. Thus in the figure for the examples $\overrightarrow{BF} = \overrightarrow{BA}$ and

$$\overleftrightarrow{AF} = \overleftrightarrow{AB} = \overleftrightarrow{AC} = \overleftrightarrow{FB} = \overleftrightarrow{FC} = \overleftrightarrow{BC}.$$

EXAMPLES. Describe the following sets of points (the symbols refer to the accompanying figure):

(1) $\overleftrightarrow{AB} \cap \overleftrightarrow{DE}$;   (2) $\overrightarrow{BC} \cup \overrightarrow{BD}$;   (3) $\angle CBD \cap \overrightarrow{ED}$;   (4) $\overline{AF} \cap \overrightarrow{BD}$.

Solutions: (1) B; the lines intersect in the single point B;   (2) $\angle CBD$;
(3) $\overrightarrow{BD}$;   (4) $\varnothing$.

Exercises

Describe the following sets of points. The symbols refer to the accompanying figure.

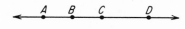

1. $\overline{AB} \cup \overline{BD}$.

2. $\overline{AB} \cap \overline{CD}$.

3. $\overline{AC} \cap \overline{BD}$.

4. $\overline{AB} \cap \overline{BC}$.

5. $\overline{AD} \cap \overline{BC}$.

6. $\overline{AD} \cup \overline{BC}$.

7. $\overleftrightarrow{AB} \cap \overline{BC}$.

8. $\overleftrightarrow{AB} \cap \overrightarrow{BC}$.

9. $\overrightarrow{BC} \cup \overrightarrow{CD}$.

10. $\overrightarrow{BC} \cap \overrightarrow{CD}$.

11. $\overrightarrow{BC} \cap \overrightarrow{BA}$.

12. $\overrightarrow{DC} \cup \overrightarrow{CA}$.

Describe the following sets of points, each referring to the accompanying figure.

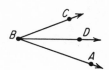

13. (Exterior $\angle ABC$) $\cap \overrightarrow{BD}$.

14. (Interior $\angle ABC$) $\cap \overrightarrow{BD}$.

15. (Interior $\angle ABC$) $\cap$ (exterior $\angle DBC$).

16. (Interior $\angle ABC$) $\cup$ (exterior $\angle ABC$) $\cup \angle ABC$.

17. (Exterior $\angle DBC$) $\cap \overrightarrow{AB}$.

18. (Exterior $\angle DBC$) $\cap \overline{AB}$.

Describe the following sets of points, each referring to the accompanying figure.

19. (Exterior $\angle BPC$) $\cap \overrightarrow{CP}$.

20. (Exterior $\angle BPA$) $\cap \overleftrightarrow{AP}$.

21. $\overrightarrow{PB} \cup \overrightarrow{PC}$.

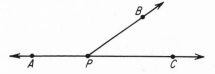

22. $\angle BPC \cap \angle BPA$.

23. $\angle BPC \cup \angle BPA$.

24. (Exterior $\angle BPC$) $\cap \overline{AC}$.

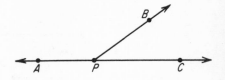

We now continue our study of geometric figures on a plane; that is, sets of points on a plane. Consider the four figures in the accompanying diagram, where each is a union of line segments. Notice that in each case

there seem to be three separate parts. A part may consist of one line segment or be the union of two or more line segments. However, you could pick out the three parts of each figure. You recognized that any two distinct parts were not "connected"; that you could not draw them both without removing the point of the pencil from the paper to move from one to the other. We now assume that the word "connected" is understood even though it has not been defined.

Each of the three figures in the next diagram is a union of line segments and each figure is connected. Each may be drawn by starting at one of the points A, B, and ending at the other.

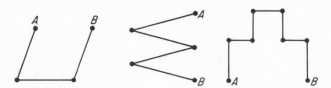

Each of the next five figures is a union of line segments, each is connected, each may be drawn as a continuous line by starting at one of the points R, S and ending at the other, and each differs from the figures A, B in the preceding set. See if you can identify that difference.

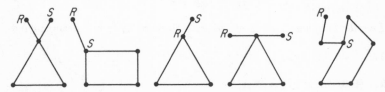

Any connected union of line segments is a broken line. Compare the three broken lines AB with the five broken lines RS. Each broken line AB may be drawn starting at A and ending at B without retracing any line segments or arriving at any point a second time. Each broken line RS may be drawn starting at R and ending at S without retracing any line segments, but for each broken line RS some point different from the starting point is used twice in the drawing. Briefly, we say that each broken line RS intersects itself. The word "simple" is used to distinguish between these two types of figures. A figure such as one of the broken lines AB which does not intersect itself is a **simple figure**. Figures such as triangles, squares, circles, and rectangles are also simple figures. The broken lines RS are not simple.

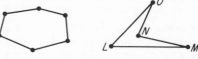

The broken lines AB and RS differ from each of the next two figures. Each of these figures is simple; each is connected; each is a union of line segments. Each differs from the previous figures in that when it is drawn one starts at a point and returns to that point. We say that such a figure is **closed**.

Figures may be either simple or not simple; they may also be either closed or not closed. For example, the figure $LMNO$ is simple and closed; the figure $PQRS$ is closed and not simple; the broken lines AB are simple and not closed; the broken lines RS are neither simple nor closed.

A simple closed broken line on a plane is called a **polygon**. The line segments are called **sides** of the polygon; the end-points of the line segments are called **vertices** of the polygon. Any polygon is either convex or concave.

Think of a point as dividing a line into two rays, of which it is the common end-point; think of a line as dividing a plane into two half-planes, of which it is the common edge. Then consider the half-planes determined by the lines along the sides of the polygon. The polygon is **convex** if and only if, in each of these cases, it lies entirely in or on the edge of a half-plane. For the convex polygon $ABCD$, we have:

Convex polygon   Concave polygon

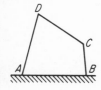

For the polygon $RSTU$, we have:

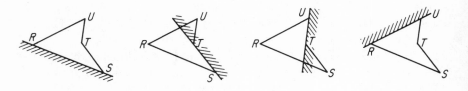

Note that when the sides ST and TU are used, the polygon does not lie entirely in or on the edge of one of the half-planes determined by the sides. Therefore, polygon $RSTU$ is not convex and thus is **concave**.

A polygon with three sides is a **triangle**. For example, triangle ABC consists of the points of $\overline{AB} \cup \overline{BC} \cup \overline{CA}$. The **interior** of triangle ABC consists of the points in the intersection of the interiors of the three angles, $\angle ABC$, $\angle BCA$, and $\angle CAB$. The **exterior** of triangle ABC consists of the points of the plane ABC that are neither points of the triangle nor points of the interior of the triangle.

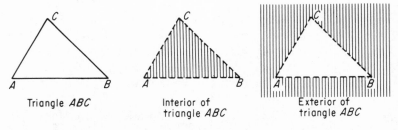

Triangle ABC Interior of triangle ABC Exterior of triangle ABC

In general, plane polygons are classified according to the number of sides. The common names are shown in this array:

Number of sides	Name of polygon
3	triangle
4	quadrilateral
5	pentagon
6	hexagon
7	heptagon
8	octagon
9	nonagon
10	decagon
12	dodecagon

Exercises

Sketch a union of line segments that is:

1. Connected.   **2.** Not connected.

Sketch a broken line that is:

3. Simple but not closed.

4. Closed but not simple.

5. Simple and closed.

6. Neither simple nor closed.

7. A convex polygon of five sides.

8. A concave polygon of six sides.

Describe the following sets of points, each referring to the accompanying figure:

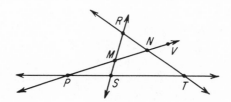

9. $\overrightarrow{MN} \cap \overrightarrow{TS}$.

10. $\overrightarrow{SR} \cap \overrightarrow{ST}$.

11. $\triangle RST \cap \overline{PM}$.

12. (Exterior $\triangle RST$) $\cap \overline{MN}$.

13. $\overrightarrow{TS} \cap \overline{PM}$.

14. $\overleftrightarrow{PV} \cap \triangle RST$.

15. (Interior $\triangle RST$) $\cap \overline{MN}$.

16. $\overline{RS} \cap \overline{ST}$.

17. $\overline{RM} \cup \overline{MN} \cup \overline{RN}$.

18. (Exterior $\triangle RST$) $\cap \overrightarrow{NM}$.

19. (Exterior $\triangle RST$) $\cap \overleftrightarrow{MN}$.

20. $\overrightarrow{PM} \cup \overrightarrow{PS}$.

21. $\overleftrightarrow{PV} \cap \triangle MRN$.

22. $\angle SRT \cap \angle RTS$.

23. (Interior $\triangle RST$) $\cap$ (interior $\triangle MRN$).

24. (Interior $\triangle RST$) $\cup$ (interior $\triangle MRN$).

25. (Interior $\angle VPT$) $\cap$ (interior $\triangle RST$).

26. (Interior $\angle SRT$) $\cap$ (interior $\angle RTS$).

27. (Interior $\angle RST$) $\cap$ (interior $\angle STR$) $\cap$ (interior $\angle TRS$).

28. (Interior $\triangle RMN$) $\cup$ (exterior $\triangle RMN$) $\cup \triangle RMN$.

5-4 Space Figures

Any two distinct points A and B determine $\overleftrightarrow{AB}$ and $\overline{AB}$. Any three distinct points that are not on the same line determine a unique triangle

ABC. The points A, B, C are the vertices of the triangle; then $\overline{AB}$, $\overline{BC}$, and $\overline{CA}$ are the sides of the triangle. The set of interior points of the triangle consists of the intersection of the interior points of the three angles ABC, BCA, and CAB.

In space we consider four points A, B, C, D which are not on the same plane. The four points A, B, C, D are the **vertices** of the space figure; then $\overline{AB}$, $\overline{AC}$, $\overline{AD}$, $\overline{BC}$, $\overline{BD}$, and $\overline{CD}$ are the six **edges**, and the triangles ABC, BCD, CDA, and ABD and their interiors are the four **faces** of the tetra-

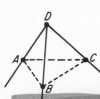

hedron. The **interior** of the tetrahedron $ABCD$ consists of the points of the intersection of four half-spaces. Each half-space has a plane containing a face of the tetrahedron as its face and includes the fourth vertex of the tetrahedron.

The three faces ABD, BCD, and ACD of the tetrahedron are in three planes having a single point D in common. The union of the plane angles ADB, BDC, and CDA and their interiors is called a **trihedral angle**. Notice that the points of the trihedral angle are on rays with end-point D

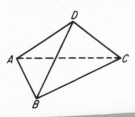

containing points of triangle ABC. Thus a trihedral angle may be determined by a triangle ABC and a point D that is not on the plane of the triangle. Then the trihedral angle is the union of the rays that contain points of triangle ABC and have end-point D. In general, a **polyhedral angle** is determined by a plane polygon and a point P that is not in the plane of the polygon; the polyhedral angle is the union of the rays that contain points of the polygon and have end-point D.

We have stated as properties of planes (§ 5-1) that if two planes have a point in common they have at least two points in common, and that if two points of a line are on a plane, then every point of the line is on the plane. Thus if two planes have a point P in common, they must have another point Q in common and, indeed, every point of the line PQ in common.

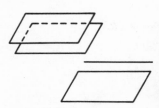

In ordinary geometry (often called Euclidean geometry) it is possible for two planes to fail to have a point in common. Two planes that do not have any point in common are said to be **parallel**. A line is parallel to a plane if it does not have any point in common with the plane.

Think of an ordinary classroom. On any given wall the line along the ceiling and the line along the floor do not appear to intersect, that is, do not have any point in common no matter how far they are extended. The line along the ceiling and one wall also does not appear to intersect the line of intersection of two other walls. Any distinction between these two situations must take into consideration the fact that in the first case the two lines were on the same wall (plane) whereas in the second case there could not be a single plane containing both lines. In general two lines that are on the same plane and do not have any point in common are also said to be **parallel**; two lines that are not on the same plane are called **skew** lines; two distinct lines that have a point in common are called **intersecting** lines; lines that have all their points in common may be visualized as two names for the same line and are called **coincident** lines.

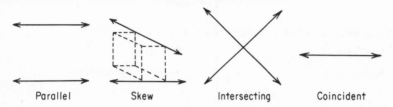

| | Parallel | Skew | Intersecting | Coincident |

Note that the arrows indicate that the lines may be extended indefinitely, that is, that the figure involves representations for lines rather than actual lines. These representations are on the printed page and thus on a plane. Thus the figure for skew lines must be visualized as a "picture" on a plane of skew lines in space.

The word "intersect" may also be used whenever two figures have at least one point in common. Two lines on the plane must either intersect or be parallel; any two parallel lines are on the same plane. Two parallel lines may be thought of as having **direction** in common. However, this direction is independent of the sense in which one travels along the line. For example, two

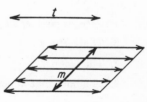

east-west lines have a single direction in common. Given two lines m and t, the union of all lines parallel to t and through points of m is the plane through m and parallel to t. We say that the plane may be **generated** by a line moving so that it is parallel to t and also intersects m.

In general, given a polygon and a line t that is not parallel to the plane of the polygon, the union of all lines parallel to t and through points of the polygon is called a **cylindrical surface**. Notice that cylindrical surfaces do not necessarily involve circles. Indeed, circles cannot be defined until

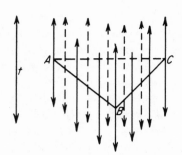

distances have been considered. Notice also that the cylindrical surfaces, like the lines that generate them, extend indefinitely.

Exercises

Consider the tetrahedron MNOP and identify its:

1. Vertices.   **2.** Edges.

3. Faces.   **4.** Trihedral angles.

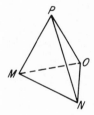

Consider the given space figure ABCD . . . H and identify:

5. The vertices.   **6.** The edges.

7. The faces.   **8.** The trihedral angles.

9. The lines that appear parallel to AB.

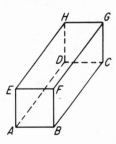

10. The lines that appear skew to AB.

11. The lines on the plane $ABCD$.

12. The lines parallel to the plane $ABCD$.

13. The lines that intersect but are not on the plane $ABCD$.

In Exercises 14 through 16 consider the given space figure $TWXYZ$ and identify its:

14. Vertices.

15. Edges.

16. Faces.

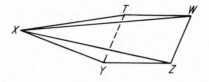

17. Make a table of the number E of edges, the number V of vertices, and the number F of faces for the three figures considered earlier in these exercises.

†18. Find a pattern (relationship) in the table for Exercise 17 such that if you are given any two of the numbers V, E, and F, you can find the third number. The desired pattern is the famous Euler formula.

In Exercises 19 through 25 sketch:

19. A trihedral angle.

20. A polyhedral angle with four faces.

21. A line m parallel to a line p and intersecting a line q.

22. A plane parallel to a line p and intersecting a line q.

23. Skew lines p and q.

24. A plane containing a line p where p and q are skew lines.

25. A cylindrical surface determined by a line m and a square $ABCD$.

†26. The "pictures" (sketches, drawings) of space figures on a sheet of paper never completely represent the figure and are often hard to visualize. Consider the accompanying pattern and make a model of a tetrahedron.

†27. As in Exercise 26 consider the pattern and make a model of a cube.

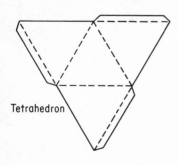

Tetrahedron

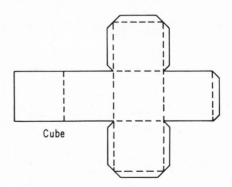

Cube

5-5 Plane Curves

Throughout this chapter we have considered points, lines, planes, rays, line segments, figures composed of line segments and rays, and regions of planes determined by line segments, rays, and half-planes. We now consider plane figures that may be approximated by broken lines and polygons; that is, we consider **plane curves**.

A **circle** is defined in elementary mathematics as a set of points—the set of all points on a plane that are at a given distance (called the **radius**) from a given point of the plane (called the **center**). The points of the circle form a curve; the length of this curve is called the **circumference** of the circle.

Any circle may be visualized as a polygon with many very short sides. If the sides of the polygon are all of the same length, then the more sides the polygon has, the more it appears to be like a circle. Consider the effect of increasing the number of sides of the polygons in the figure.

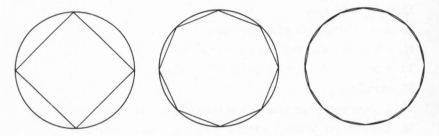

As the number of sides of these polygons "inscribed" in the circle is increased without bound, the polygon approaches (appears to be the same as) the circle. Each polygon is a simple closed broken line. The circle is not a simple closed broken line. However, the circle may be approximated as closely as we like by a simple closed broken line. Thus the circle is called a simple closed curve. The next figure gives some other examples of simple closed curves. Notice that a polygon is a special case of a simple closed curve.

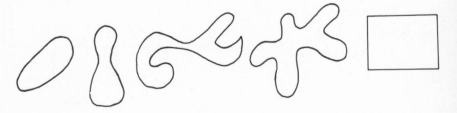

Any two simple closed curves have a common property. Can you find that property? Size, shape, angles, and straight lines are certainly not common properties here. What is left to be considered? Some readers may consider the common property that we are seeking trivial because of its simplicity. We prefer to believe that the really basic properties of mathematics are inherently simple. The property that we have in mind may be stated very easily: Any simple closed curve has an inside and an outside.

In advanced mathematics we say that *any simple closed curve in a plane divides the plane into two regions.* This is the **Jordan curve theorem.** The curve is the common boundary of the two regions, and one cannot cross from one region to the other without crossing the curve. The Jordan curve theorem is a very powerful theorem and yet a very simple one. Notice that it is independent of the size or shape of the curve.

How can such a simple theorem have any significance? It provides a basis for Euclid's assumption that any line segment joining the center of a circle to a point outside the circle must contain a point of the circle. In more advanced courses it provides a basis for the existence of a zero of a polynomial on any interval on which the polynomial changes sign. It provides a basis for Venn diagrams in any two-valued logic. For example, true statements may correspond to points inside or on the curve, false statements may correspond to points outside the curve. This simple theorem regarding the existence of an inside and an outside of any simple closed curve may also be used to answer questions raised by the next problem. This problem is a popular one, and many people have spent hours working on it.

Consider three houses (✕) in a row and three utilities (o) in a second row on a plane surface. The problem is to join each house to each utility by an arc on the plane in such a way that no two arcs cross or pass through houses or utilities except at their end-points. As in the figure on the left it is easy to designate paths from one house to each of the three utilities. One can also designate paths to each utility from the second house as in the second figure. Then one can designate two of the paths from the third house, but it is not possible on an ordinary plane to draw the path from the remaining house to the remaining utility. This assertion is based upon the fact that the simple closed curve indicated in the third figure divides the plane into two regions; the third house is inside the curve (shaded region), the remaining utility is outside the curve, and the two cannot be joined without crossing the curve.

 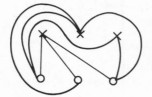 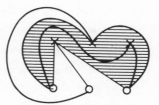

As in the case of broken lines, plane curves may be either simple or not simple and either closed or not closed. Each of the figures that follow is a plane curve that may be approximated by a closed broken line that is not simple. Each curve is a closed curve that is not simple.

The next figures may be approximated by simple broken lines that are not closed. They are called simple curves that are not closed. Notice that a line and a ray are special cases of simple curves that are not closed.

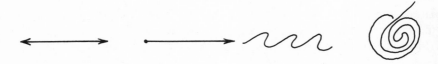

The next figures may be approximated by a broken line that is neither simple nor closed; each is called a curve that is neither simple nor closed.

Exercises

Sketch three different appearing curves that are:

1. Simple and closed.

2. Simple and not closed.

3. Closed and not simple.

4. Neither simple nor closed.

Sketch a broken line that closely approximates a given:

5. Simple closed curve.

6. Simple curve that is not closed.

7. Closed curve that is not simple.

8. Polygon.

5-6 Networks

Any set of line segments forms a **network**. If the network can be drawn tracing each line segment exactly once without removing the point of the pencil from the paper the network is **traversable**. For example, any connected simple network is traversable. If such a network is closed, any point may be selected as a starting point for the drawing and this point will also be the terminating point of the drawing. If the connected simple network is not closed, the drawing must start at one of the end points and terminate at the other.

The study of the traversability of networks probably stemmed from a problem concerning the bridges in the city of Königsberg. There was a river flowing through the city, two islands in the river, and seven bridges as in the figure. The people of Königsberg loved a Sunday stroll and 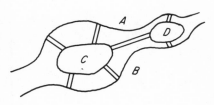 thought it would be nice to take a walk that would take them across each bridge exactly once. They found that no matter where they started or what route they tried, they could not cross each bridge exactly once. Gradually it was observed that the basic problem was concerned with paths between the two sides of the river A, B, and the two islands C, D as in the figure. With this representation of the problem by a network, it was no longer necessary to discuss the problem in terms of walking across the bridges. Instead one could discuss whether or not the network associated with the problem was traversable. The problem was solvable if and only if its network was traversable.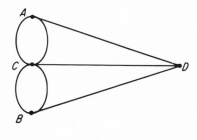

When is a network traversable? One can walk completely around any city block and it is not necessary to start at any particular point to do so. In general, one may traverse any simple closed broken line in a single trip. We next consider walking around two blocks and down the street separating them. This problem is a bit more interesting in that it is necessary to start at B or E. Furthermore, if one starts at B, one ends at E, and conversely. Note that it is permissible to pass through a vertex several times, but one may traverse a line segment only once. The peculiar property of the vertices B and E is based upon the fact that each of these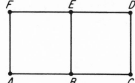

end-points is an end-point of three line segments, whereas each of the other vertices is an end-point of two line segments. A similar observation led a famous mathematician named Euler to devise a complete theory for traversable networks.

Euler classified the vertices of a network as odd or even. A vertex that is an end-point of an odd number of line segments is an odd vertex; a vertex that is an end-point of an even number of line segments is an even vertex. Since each line segment has two end-points, there must be an even number of odd vertices in any network. Any network that has only even vertices is traversable, and the trip may be started at any vertex. Furthermore, the trip will terminate at its starting point. If a network has exactly two odd vertices, it is traversable, but the trip must start at one of the odd vertices and will terminate at the other. If a network has more than two odd vertices, it is not traversable. In general, a network with $2k$ odd vertices may be traversed in k distinct trips. The network for the Königsberg bridge problem has four odd vertices and thus is not traversable in a single trip. Notice that the Königsberg bridge problem is independent of the size and shape of the river, bridges, or islands.

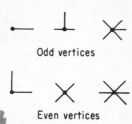

Odd vertices

Even vertices

Exercises

In Exercises 1 through 4 tell whether or not each network is traversable. If it is necessary to start at a particular vertex to traverse the network, identify the possible starting points.

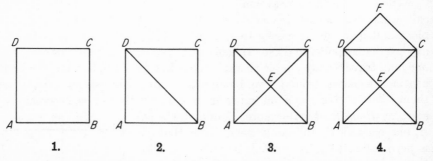

1.   2.   3.   4.

†5. Explain whether or not the network formed by the edges of a cube is traversable.

†6. Explain whether or not it is possible to draw a simple connected broken line cutting each line segment of the given figure exactly once.

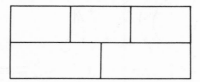

†7. Describe a modification that would make the Königsberg bridge problem possible.

†8. Describe a modification of the network for Exercise 6 such that the possibility of the desired construction is changed.

5-7 Topology

The study of points, lines, plane curves, and space figures is part of geometry. Actually there are several types of geometry. We shall mention only two types.

In Euclidean geometry line segments may be measured; angles may be measured; areas of triangles may be found. Two line segments of the same length are congruent; two angles of the same measure are congruent; two triangles of the same area are equal; two triangles of the same size (area) and shape (each angle of one triangle may be matched with and is equal to an angle of the other triangle) are congruent. You have probably studied this geometry of figures and their measurements before. Since it is a geometry involving measurements, it is called a **metric geometry**.

The study of simple closed curves, networks, and other plane curves that we have just considered did not involve measurement and is called a **nonmetric geometry**. Indeed, the topics that we considered were part of a particular geometry called **topology**.

We have selected topics that reflect the emphasis upon careful definitions and the use of sets of elements in both metric and nonmetric geometries. Several additional topics are considered in Chapter 10. Detailed study of geometry is regretfully left for future courses.

Let us continue our consideration of topology with a few comments on a surface that has several very unusual properties. This surface is one-sided. A fly can walk from any point on it to any other point without crossing an edge. Unlike a table top or a wall, it does not have a top and a bottom or a front and a back. This surface is called a **Möbius strip**, and it may be very easily constructed from a rectangular piece of paper such as a strip of gummed tape. Size is theoretically unimportant, but a strip an

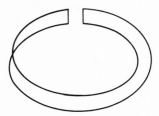 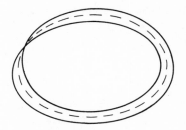

inch or two wide and about a foot long is easy to handle. We may construct a Möbius strip by twisting the strip of gummed tape just enough to stick the gummed edge of one end to the gummed edge of the other end. If we cut across this strip, we again get a single strip similar to the one we started with. But if we start with a rectangular strip and cut around the center of the Möbius strip (see the dotted line in the second figure), we do not get two strips. Rather, we get one strip with two twists in it.

On one occasion one-sided surfaces of this sort were used as place cards at a seven-year-old's birthday party. While waiting for dessert, the youngsters were encouraged to cut the strip down the middle while guessing what the result would be. They were suitably impressed when they found only one piece, and were anxious to cut it again. Once more they were impressed when they found two pieces linked together. Almost a year after the party, one of the boys asked about the piece of paper that was in only one piece after it was cut in two.

When confronted with unusual properties such as those of the Möbius strip, both children and adults may ask questions that the nearest teacher cannot answer and that most college mathematics professors cannot answer. This is good for all concerned, since it impresses upon them that there is more to mathematics than formal algebraic manipulations and classical geometric constructions.

Exercises

1. Construct a Möbius strip and cut around the center to obtain one strip with two twists in it.

2. Repeat Exercise 1 and then cut around the center again.

3. Construct a Möbius strip and cut along a path that is about one-third of the distance from one edge to the other.

4. Construct a Möbius strip, mark a point A on it, and draw an arc from A around the strip until you return to the point A.

AN INTRODUCTION TO PROBABILITY

We make frequent reference to probability in everyday language. For example we say, "It probably will rain," "The odds are in his favor," and make similar comments about many things.

Ever since the fifteenth century, mathematicians have been exploring the topic of probability. Interestingly enough, the subject is said to have had its foundation in the realm of gambling and to have arisen from a discussion of the distribution of stakes in an unfinished game. In this chapter we shall provide the basic groundwork for an understanding of the elements of probability.

6-1 Counting Problems

Many problems depend for their solution upon an enumeration of all possible outcomes. Thus, the simple task of counting becomes an important one in the study of probability. To illustrate various problems in this chapter, we shall invent a fictitious club consisting of a set, M, of members:

$$M = \{\text{Betty, Doris, Ellen, John, Tom}\}.$$

Let us form a committee that is to consist of one boy and one girl, each selected from the set M of club members. How many such committees are possible? One way to answer this question is by means of a tree diagram, which helps list each of the possibilities.

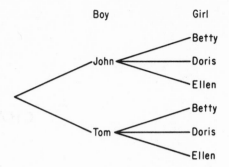

For each of the two possible choices of a boy, there are three possible choices of a girl. Thus the following six distinct possible committees can be formed and can be read from the tree diagram:

John–Betty,   Tom–Betty,
John–Doris,   Tom–Doris,
John–Ellen,   Tom–Ellen.

Suppose that we had selected a girl first. Then the tree diagram would be as shown in the next figure and there would still be six possibilities, the same six committees as before.

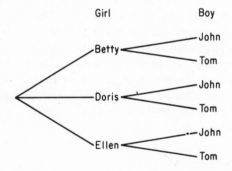

EXAMPLE 1. In how many different ways can two officers, a president and a vice-president, be elected from the set, M, of club members?

Solution: Let us select the officers in two stages. There are five possible choices for the office of president. Each of these five selections may be paired with any one of the remaining four members. Thus there are 20 possible choices in all, which can be read from the diagram shown on p. 103.

In general, if one task can be performed in m different ways and a second task can be performed in n different ways, then the first and second

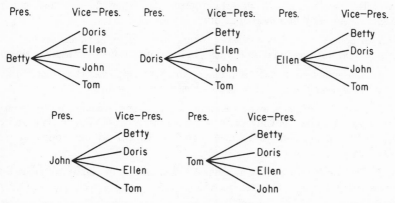

tasks together can be performed in $m \times n$ different ways. This general principle can be extended if there are additional tasks:

$$m \times n \times r \times \ldots \times t.$$

EXAMPLE 2. The club members M must send a delegate to a meeting tomorrow and also a delegate to a different meeting next week. In how many ways may these delegates be selected if any member of the club may serve as a delegate to each meeting?

Solution: There are five possible choices of a delegate to the first meeting. Since no restriction is made, we assume that the same member may attend each of the two meetings. Thus, there are five choices for the delegate to next week's meeting. In all, there are 5×5, that is, 25 choices. A tree diagram may be used to show this.

EXAMPLE 3. How many three-letter "words" may be formed from the set of vowels, $V = \{a, e, i, o, u\}$, if no letter may be used more than once? (A word in this sense is any arrangement of three letters, such as aeo, iou, etc.)

Solution: There are five choices for the first letter, four for the second, and three for the third. In all, there are $5 \times 4 \times 3$, that is, 60 possible "words." Notice that 125 words would be possible if repetitions of letters were permitted.

Exercises

1. How many different two-digit numbers may be formed from the set of digits $D = \{1, 2, 3, 4, 5\}$ if repetitions of digits are allowed? How many numbers of two different digits can be formed from the set D?

2. Find the number of five-letter "words" that may be formed from the set of vowels $V = \{a, e, i, o, u\}$ if: **(a)** no letter may be used more than once; **(b)** the same letter may be repeated as often as desired.

3. A college co-ed has 5 dresses, 3 hats, and 4 pairs of shoes. Assuming that she may wear any combination of these, in how many different ways can she dress?

4. A baseball team has six pitchers and four catchers. How many different batteries consisting of a pitcher and a catcher can they form?

5. Show, by means of a tree diagram, the number of different routes from New York to Los Angeles, via Chicago, if you can go from New York to Chicago by one train or one plane, and from Chicago to Los Angeles by one train, one plane, or one bus.

6. The Jonesboro Swim Club has 12 members. How many different sets of officers consisting of a president, a vice-president, and a secretary-treasurer can it form?

7. How many five-digit telephone numbers can be formed using the ten decimal digits if zero is not to be used as the first digit?

8. How many different two-digit even numbers can be formed from the set $I = \{1, 2, 3, \ldots, 9\}$?

9. Find the number of "words" of three different letters that may be formed from the set $V = \{a, e, i, o, u\}$ if: **(a)** the first letter must be i; **(b)** the first letter must be e and the last letter must be i.

10. How many license plates can be made using a letter from our alphabet followed by three decimal digits if the first digit must not be zero? How many are possible if the first digit must not be zero and no digit may be used more than once?

†11. Find the number of three-digit numbers that may be formed from the set $W = \{0, 1, 2, \ldots, 9\}$ if: **(a)** the number must be even; **(b)** the number must be divisible by 5; **(c)** no digit may be used more than once; **(d)** the number must be odd and less than 500.

†12. How many different subsets can be formed from the set of club members M, described in this section? Be sure to consider subsets of 0, 1, 2, 3, 4, and 5 members.

†13. In a certain so-called "combination" lock there are 50 different positions. To open the lock you move to a certain number in one direction, then to a different number in the opposite direction, and finally to a third number in the original direction. What is the total number of such "combinations"?

6-2 Permutations

Let us return to the set of club members, M, introduced in the previous section and consider again the election of two officers discussed in Example 1. We found that there were 20 possible sets of officers. Of course, we could have obtained this answer by asserting that there are five possible choices for the office of president, each of which can be matched with any one of four choices of a vice-president.

We say that there are 5×4, that is, 20 *permutations* of the set M, using two elements at a time. In each of the 20 cases the first person named would be president and the second person named would be vice-president; thus, the order in which two people are named is significant. A **permutation** of a set of elements is an arrangement of certain of these elements in a specified order. In the problem just discussed, the number of permutations of five things taken two at a time is 20. In symbols we write:

$$_5P_2 = 20.$$

($_5P_2$ is read: "The permutations of 5 things taken 2 at a time.")

In general, we wish to find a formula for $_nP_r$, that is, the permutations of n things taken r at a time. To do this we note that we can fill the first of the r positions in any one of n different ways. Then the second position can be filled in $n - 1$ different ways, and so on.

Position:	1	2	3	4	$\cdots$	r
	$\downarrow$	$\downarrow$	$\downarrow$	$\downarrow$		$\downarrow$
Number of choices:	n	$n - 1$	$n - 2$	$n - 3$	$\ldots n - (r - 1)$	
					(i.e., $n - r + 1$)	

The product of these r factors gives the number of different ways of arranging r elements selected from a set of n elements; that is, the permutation of n things taken r at a time.

$$_nP_r = (n)(n - 1)(n - 2) \ldots (n - r + 1),$$

where n and r are integers and $n \geq r$.

EXAMPLE 1. Find $_8P_4$.

Solution: Here $n = 8$, $r = 4$, and $n - r + 1 = 5$. Thus

$$_8P_4 = 8 \times 7 \times 6 \times 5 = 1,680.$$

Note that there are r—in this case 4—factors in the product.

EXAMPLE 2. How many different three-letter "words" can be formed from the 26 letters of the alphabet if each letter may be used at most once?

Solution: We wish to find the number of permutations of 26 things taken 3 at a time.

$$_{26}P_3 = 26 \times 25 \times 24 = 15,600.$$

A special case of the permutation formula occurs when we consider the permutations of n things taken n at a time. For example, let us see in how many different ways we may arrange the five members of set M in a row. Here we have the permutation of five things taken five at a time:

$$_5P_5 = 5 \times 4 \times 3 \times 2 \times 1.$$

In general, for n things n at a time, $n = n$, $r = n$, and $n - r + 1 = 1$;

$$_nP_n = (n)(n - 1)(n - 2) \ldots (3)(2)(1).$$

We use a special symbol, $n!$, read "n factorial," for this product of integers from 1 through n. The following examples should illustrate the use of the new symbol:

$$1! = 1; \qquad\qquad 5! = 5 \times 4 \times 3 \times 2 \times 1;$$
$$2! = 2 \times 1; \qquad\qquad 6! = 6 \times 5 \times 4 \times 3 \times 2 \times 1;$$
$$3! = 3 \times 2 \times 1; \qquad\qquad 7! = 7 \times 6 \times 5 \times 4 \times 3 \times 2 \times 1;$$
$$4! = 4 \times 3 \times 2 \times 1; \qquad\qquad \text{and so forth.}$$

Also, we *define* $0! = 1$ so that $(n - r)!$ may be used when $r = n$.

Using this factorial notation we are now able to provide a different, but equivalent, formula for $_nP_r$:

$$_nP_r = n(n - 1)(n - 2) \cdots (n - r + 1)$$
$$\times \frac{(n - r)(n - r - 1)(n - r - 2) \cdots (3)(2)(1)}{(n - r)(n - r - 1)(n - r - 2) \cdots (3)(2)(1)} = \frac{n!}{(n - r)!}$$

EXAMPLE 3. Evaluate $_7P_3$ in two different ways.

Solution:

(a) $_7P_3 = 7 \times 6 \times 5.$

(b) $_7P_3 = \dfrac{7!}{4!} = \dfrac{7 \times 6 \times 5 \times 4 \times 3 \times 2 \times 1}{4 \times 3 \times 2 \times 1} = 7 \times 6 \times 5.$

EXAMPLE 4. A certain class consists of 10 boys and 12 girls. They wish to elect officers in such a way that the president and treasurer are boys and the vice-president and secretary are girls. In how many ways can this be done?

Solution: The number of different ways of selecting the president and treasurer is $_{10}P_2$. The number of ways of selecting the vice-president and secretary is $_{12}P_2$. The total number of ways of choosing officers is

$$(_{10}P_2) \times (_{12}P_2) = (10 \times 9) \times (12 \times 11) = 11{,}880.$$

Exercises

1. Evaluate (a) $_8P_2$; (b) $_9P_3$.

2. Give a meaning to $_nP_0$.

3. Show that $_nP_r \times (n - r)! = n!$

4. Find n if $_nP_2 = 6$.

5. Find the number of different arrangements of the set of letters $V = \{a, e, i, o, u\}$ if they are taken **(a)** two at a time; **(b)** five at a time.

6. How many four-digit numbers can be formed using the digits 1, 2, 3, 4, 5 if no digit may be used more than once in a number? How many of these numbers will be even?

7. How many different signals can be formed by running up three flags on a flagpole, one above the other, if seven different flags are available?

8. How many different ways can a disc jockey arrange a musical program of six selections?

9. How many different ways can a manager of a nine-man baseball team arrange his batting order?

10. How many different license plates are possible if each one is to consist of two letters of the alphabet followed by three decimal digits, provided that the first digit may not be zero, and no repetitions of letters or numbers are permitted?

6-3 Combinations

In each of the problems that we solved concerning permutations, the order of the objects involved was important. For example, the number of ways of selecting a president and a vice-president from the set M was found to be $_5P_2$. Here order is important in that Betty as president and Doris as vice-president is a different set of officers than Doris as president and Betty as vice-president.

Now, suppose we wish to select a committee of two members from set M without attaching any meaning to the order in which the members are selected. Then the committee consisting of Betty and Doris is certainly the same as the one consisting of Doris and Betty. In this case, we see that order is not important and we call such an arrangement a **combination**. One way to determine the number of possible committees of two to be formed from the set M is by enumeration. We find that there are ten possible committees, as follows:

Betty–Doris,	Doris–John,
Betty–Ellen,	Doris–Tom,
Betty–John,	Ellen–John,
Betty–Tom,	Ellen–Tom,
Doris–Ellen,	John–Tom.

We summarize this discussion by saying that the number of combinations of five things, taken two at a time, is 10. In symbols we write

$$_5C_2 = 10.$$

In general, we wish to find a formula for $_nC_r$, that is, the combinations of n things taken r at a time. This is written in symbols in the form

$$_nC_r \quad \text{or} \quad \binom{n}{r}.$$

To find a formula for $_nC_r$ let us first consider a specific problem, that of selecting committees of three from the set M. There are 10 such possibilities and we list them below using the first initial of each name only:

B, D, E	B, J, T	$M = \{B, D, E, J, T\}$
B, D, J	D, E, J	$_5C_3 = 10.$
B, D, T	D, E, T	
B, E, J	D, J, T	
B, E, T	E, J, T	

Note that selecting committees of three is equivalent to selecting groups of two to be omitted. That is, omitting J and T is the same as selecting B, D, and E. Therefore, we find that $_5C_3 = {_5C_2} = 10$.

Inasmuch as we only wanted committees, and assigned no particular jobs to the members of each committee, we see that order is not important. However, suppose that each committee is now to elect a chairman, secretary, and historian. In how many ways can this be done within each committee? This is clearly a problem in which order is important, involving permutations. The number of such possible arrangements within each committee is $_3P_3$, that is, 3!. For example, the committee consisting of B, D, and E can rearrange themselves as chairman, secretary, and historian, respectively, as follows:

$$B, D, E; \quad B, E, D; \quad D, E, B; \quad D, B, E; \quad E, B, D; \quad E, D, B.$$

All six of these permutations constitute only one combination.

We know that $_5C_3 = 10$. If each of these combinations is multiplied by 3! we then will have the total number of permutations of five things taken three at a time:

$$_5C_3 \times 3! = {_5P_3} \quad \text{and} \quad {_5C_3} = \frac{_5P_3}{3!}.$$

In general, consider $_nC_r$. Each of these combinations, consisting of r elements each, may be used to form $r!$ permutations. Thus the number of combinations of n things taken r at a time is given by the formula

$$_nC_r \times r! = {_nP_r} \quad \text{and} \quad {_nC_r} = \frac{_nP_r}{r!}.$$

Since

$$_nP_r = (n)(n-1)(n-2) \cdots (n-r+1) = \frac{n!}{(n-r)!},$$

we also have the formula

$$_nC_r = \frac{(n)(n-1)(n-2) \cdots (n-r+1)}{r!} = \frac{n!}{r!(n-r)!},$$

EXAMPLE 1. Evaluate $_7C_2$ in two ways.

Solution:

(a) $_7C_2 = \dfrac{_7P_2}{2!} = \dfrac{7 \times 6}{2 \times 1} = 21.$

(b) $_7C_2 = \dfrac{7!}{2!5!} = \dfrac{7 \times 6 \times 5 \times 4 \times 3 \times 2 \times 1}{2 \times 1 \times 5 \times 4 \times 3 \times 2 \times 1} = 21.$

EXAMPLE 2. In how many different ways can a hand of five cards be dealt from a deck of 52 cards?

Solution: The order of the five cards is unimportant, so this is a problem involving combinations.

$$_{52}C_5 = \frac{52!}{5!47!} = \frac{52 \times 51 \times 50 \times 49 \times 48 \times (47!)}{5!} \frac{}{(47!)} = 2{,}598{,}960.$$

Exercises

1. Use a formula for $_nC_r$ to prove $_nC_r = {_nC_{n-r}}$.

2. Use a formula for $_nC_r$ to prove $_nC_n = 1$ and illustrate using the set M of club members.

3. Find the value of and give an interpretation of $_nC_0$.

4. Evaluate $_5C_0,\ _5C_1,\ _5C_2,\ _5C_3,\ _5C_4,\ _5C_5$.

5. Show that the sum of the combinations evaluated in Exercise 4 is 2^5. Try to relate your answer to the number of possible subsets that can be formed from a set of five elements.

6. Evaluate **(a)** $_8C_2$; **(b)** $_{10}C_8$.

7. A man has a penny, a nickel, a dime, a quarter, and a half-dollar in his pocket. In how many different ways can he give a tip if he wishes to use exactly two coins?

8. A class consists of 10 boys and 12 girls. How many different committees of four can be selected from the class if each committee is to consist of two boys and two girls?

9. In how many ways can a hand of 13 cards be selected from a bridge deck of 52 cards?

10. In how many ways can one choose three books to read from a set of seven books?

11. Explain why a so-called "combination" lock should really be called a permutation lock.

12. In how many different ways can a disc jockey select a program consisting of four records from a set of ten records?

13. Students taking a certain examination are required to answer four out of eight questions. In how many ways can a student select the four questions that he tries to answer?

14. How many different sums of money can be selected from a set of coins consisting of a penny, a nickel, a dime, a quarter and a half-dollar?

15. How many lines are determined by ten points if no three points are collinear?

16. Urn A contains five balls and urn B contains ten balls. In how many ways can ten balls be selected if three are to be drawn from urn A and seven from urn B?

17. An urn contains seven black and three white balls. In how many ways can four balls be selected from this urn? How many of these selections will include exactly three black balls?

†18. A class is to be divided into two committees. In how many different ways can some or all of eight of the students be assigned to one of the committees?

†19. In how many ways can eight students be divided into two equal groups of students?

†20. In how many different ways can eight students be divided into two groups of students?

6-4 Definition of Probability

When an ordinary coin is tossed, we know that there are two distinct and equally likely ways in which it may land, heads or tails. We say that the probability of getting a head is one out of two, or simply $\frac{1}{2}$.

In rolling one of a pair of ordinary dice, there are six equally likely ways in which the dice may land. We say that the probability of rolling a 5 on one toss of a die is one out of six, or $\frac{1}{6}$.

In each of these two examples, the events that may occur are said to be **mutually exclusive.** That is, one and only one of the events can occur at any given time. When a coin is tossed, there are two possible events (heads and tails); one and only one of these may occur. When a single die is rolled there are six events (1, 2, 3, 4, 5, 6); one and only one of these may occur. We may now define probability in general as follows:

If an event can occur in any one of n mutually exclusive and equally likely ways, and if m of these ways are considered favorable, then the **probability** $P(A)$ that a favorable event, A, will occur is given by the formula

$$P(A) = \frac{m}{n}.$$

The probability, $\frac{m}{n}$, satisfies the relation $0 \leq \frac{m}{n} \leq 1$ since m and n are integers and $m \leq n$. When success is inevitable, $m = n$ and the probability is 1; when an event cannot possibly succeed, $m = 0$ and the probability is 0. For example, the probability of getting either a head or a tail on a single toss of a coin is 1, assuming that the coin does not land on an edge. The probability of tossing a sum of 13 with a single toss of a pair of ordinary dice is 0. (Here, and in all future work, assume that normal dice are used unless otherwise instructed.)

The sum of the probability of an event's occurring and the probability of that same event's not occurring is 1.

$$\text{If} \quad P(A) = \frac{m}{n}, \quad \text{then} \quad P(\text{not } A) = 1 - \frac{m}{n}.$$

EXAMPLE 1. A single card is selected from a deck of 52 cards. What is the probability that it is a spade? What is the probability that it is not a spade?

Solution: Of the 52 cards, 13 are spades. Therefore, the probability of selecting a spade is $\frac{13}{52}$, that is, $\frac{1}{4}$. The probability that the card selected is not a spade is $1 - \frac{1}{4}$, that is, $\frac{3}{4}$.

EXAMPLE 2. A committee of two is to be selected from the set

$$M = \{\text{Betty, Doris, Ellen, John, Tom}\}$$

by drawing names out of a hat. What is the probability that both members of the committee will be girls?

Solution: This problem involves combinations, since the order in which the names are drawn is not important. The total number of ways in which two persons can be selected from a set of five is $_5C_2$. The number of ways in which two girls can be selected is $_3C_2$, since there are three girls in set M.

$$_3C_2 = \frac{3 \times 2}{2 \times 1} = 3; \qquad _5C_2 = \frac{5 \times 4}{2 \times 1} = 10.$$

The probability that both members selected are girls is

$$\frac{_3C_2}{_5C_2} = \frac{3}{10}.$$

Note that our knowledge of combinations made Example 2 easy to set up in symbols. We could also have solved the problem by actually listing all of the possibilities, although this process can become quite tedious. As in § 6-3 the set of all possible committees of two from the set M is

Betty–Doris	Doris–John
Betty–Ellen	Doris–Tom
Betty–John	Ellen–John
Betty–Tom	Ellen–Tom
Doris–Ellen	John–Tom

Of the ten possible committees, there are three (those circled) that consist of two girls. What is the probability of selecting a committee to consist of two boys?

Exercises

What is the probability:

1. Of tossing an even number on one throw of a single die?

2. Of tossing an even number or a number greater than 3 on a single toss of a die?

3. Of drawing an ace in a single draw from a deck of 52 bridge cards?

4. Of drawing a red card in a single draw from a deck of 52 bridge cards?

5. Of tossing a 10 on a single toss of a die?

6. The probability of obtaining all heads in a single toss of three coins is $\frac{1}{8}$. What is the probability that not all three coins are heads on such a toss?

7. A single die is tossed. Find the probability that **(a)** it is not a 5; **(b)** it is not a 7.

8. What is the probability that the next person you meet was not born on a Sunday?

9. A bag contains three red balls and seven white balls. **(a)** If one ball is drawn at random, what is the probability that it is white? **(b)** If two balls are drawn at random, what is the probability that they are both white?

10. Five cards are drawn at random from an ordinary bridge deck of 52 cards. Find the probability that **(a)** all five cards drawn are spades; **(b)** the four aces are drawn.

6-5 Sample Spaces

It is often convenient to solve problems of probability by making a list of all possible outcomes. Such a listing is called a **sample space**. Consider first the problem of tossing two coins. The sample space for this problem is given by the following set of all possible outcomes:

$$\{HH, HT, TH, TT\}.$$

We may also summarize these data by means of a chart:

First coin	Second coin
H	H
H	T
T	H
T	T

Another convenient way to list all of the logical possibilities is by means of a tree diagram, where the branches represent the possible choices.

The set of possible outcomes, $\{HH, HT, TH, TT\}$, may be read from the diagram. Note that there are four possible events: two heads occur in one event, one head and one tail occur in two events; no heads (that is, two tails) occur in one event. Thus we may list various probabilities regarding the tossing of two coins as follows:

Event	Probability
2 heads	$\frac{1}{4}$
1 head	$\frac{2}{4}$
0 heads	$\frac{1}{4}$

Since all possibilities have been considered, the sum of the probabilities should be 1; $\frac{1}{4} + \frac{2}{4} + \frac{1}{4} = 1$. This provides a check on our computation. The list of probabilities is sometimes called a **probability distribution**.

For the case of three coins, the following tree diagram and array may be made.

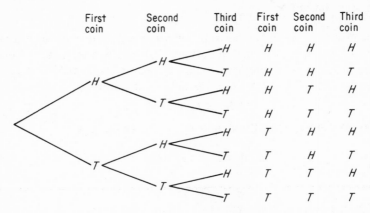

From the tree diagram, we may list the probabilities of specific numbers of heads by means of the following distribution.

In each case, both for two coins and for three coins, the sum of the probabilities is 1; that is, all possible events have been listed and these events are mutually exclusive. Note also that for two coins there were four possible outcomes, for three coins there were eight possible outcomes, and, in general, for n coins there would be 2^n possible outcomes.

Event	Probability
0 heads	$\frac{1}{8}$
1 head	$\frac{3}{8}$
2 heads	$\frac{3}{8}$
3 heads	$\frac{1}{8}$

Each of the preceding distributions is an example of a **binomial distribution**, since each is based upon the occurrence of one of *two* possibilities, in this case heads or tails.

EXAMPLE 1. A box contains two red and three white balls. Two balls are drawn in succession without replacement. List a sample space for this experiment.

Solution: To identify individual balls, we denote the red balls as R_1 and R_2; the white balls as W_1, W_2, W_3. Then the sample space is as follows:

$$R_1R_2, \quad R_2R_1, \quad W_1R_1, \quad W_2R_1, \quad W_3R_1,$$
$$R_1W_1, \quad R_2W_1, \quad W_1R_2, \quad W_2R_2, \quad W_3R_2,$$
$$R_1W_2, \quad R_2W_2, \quad W_1W_2, \quad W_2W_1, \quad W_3W_1,$$
$$R_1W_3, \quad R_2W_3, \quad W_1W_3, \quad W_2W_3, \quad W_3W_2.$$

EXAMPLE 2. Use a tree diagram to show the possible selections for Example 1.

Solution:

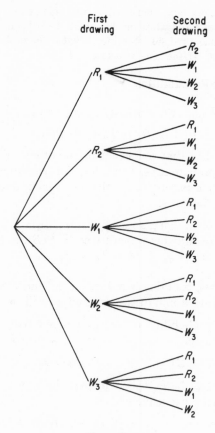

First
drawing

Second
drawing

Exercises

1. Use the sample space of Example 1 to find the probability that **(a)** both balls are red; **(b)** both balls are white; **(c)** the first ball is red; **(d)** the first ball is red and the second ball is white; **(e)** one ball is red and the other is white.

2. List the sample space for the outcomes when four coins are tossed.

3. List the sample space when a pair of dice is tossed. List each outcome as an ordered pair of numbers. For example, let (1, 3) denote a 1 on the first die and a 3 on the second die.

4. Draw a tree diagram and list the set of possible outcomes for a World Series contest between the Dodgers (*D*) and the Yankees (*Y*) where four victories out of seven games are required to win and where the Dodgers have won the first two games.

5. Use the sample space of Example 3 to find the probability that **(a)** each die produces the same number; **(b)** the sum obtained is 11; **(c)** the first die turns up with a number which is twice that of the second; **(d)** the sum obtained is not 7.

†6. Three cards are in a box. One is red on both sides, one is white on both sides, and one is red on one side and white on the other. A card is drawn at random and placed on a table. It has a red side showing. What is the probability that the side not showing is also red? [*Hint:* The answer is not $\frac{1}{2}$.]

6-6 Computation of Probabilities

If A and B represent two mutually exclusive events, then

$$P(A \text{ or } B) = P(A) + P(B).$$

That is, the probability that one event or the other will occur is the sum of the individual probabilities. Consider, for example, the probability of drawing an ace or a picture card (that is, a jack, queen, or king) from an ordinary deck of 52 cards.

The probability of drawing an ace, $P(A)$, is $\frac{4}{52}$.
The probability of drawing a picture card, $P(B)$, is $\frac{12}{52}$.
Then $P(A \quad \text{or} \quad B) = \frac{4}{52} + \frac{12}{52} = \frac{16}{52} = \frac{4}{13}$.

EXAMPLE 1. A bag contains 3 red, 2 black, and 5 yellow balls. Find the probability that a ball drawn at random will be red or black.

Solution: The probability of drawing a red ball, $P(R)$, is $\frac{3}{10}$. The probability of drawing a black ball, $P(B)$, is $\frac{2}{10}$. Then

$$P(R \text{ or } B) = P(R) + P(B) = \frac{5}{10} = \frac{1}{2}.$$

This process can be extended to find the probability of any finite number of mutually exclusive events.

$$P(A \text{ or } B \text{ or } C \text{ or } \cdots) = P(A) + P(B) + P(C) + \cdots$$

EXAMPLE 2. A single die is tossed. What is the probability that either an odd number or a number greater than 3 appears?

Solution: There are three odd numbers possible, (1, 3, 5), so that the probability of tossing an odd number is $\frac{3}{6}$. The probability of getting a number greater than 3 (that is, 4, 5, 6) is also $\frac{3}{6}$. Adding these probabilities gives $\frac{3}{6} + \frac{3}{6} = 1$. Something is obviously wrong since a probability of 1 implies certainty and we can see that an outcome of 2 is neither odd nor greater than 3. The difficulty lies in the fact that the events are *not* mutually exclusive; a number may be both odd and also greater than 3 at the same time. In particular, 5 is both odd and greater than 3 at the same time. Thus $P(5)$, that is, $\frac{1}{6}$, has been included twice and our answer should be $\frac{3}{6} + \frac{3}{6} - \frac{1}{6}$, that is, $\frac{5}{6}$.

In situations like that of Example 2 we need to subtract the probability that both events occur at the same time. Thus where A and B

are not mutually exclusive events, we have

$$P(A \text{ or } B) = P(A) + P(B) - P(A \text{ and } B).$$

Note that in Example 2, we had the following probabilities:

$P(A)$, the probability of an odd number is $\frac{3}{6}$.

$P(B)$, the probability of a number greater than 3 is $\frac{3}{6}$.

$P(A \text{ and } B)$, the probability that a number (in this case 5) is odd and greater than 3, is $\frac{1}{6}$.

$P(A \text{ or } B) = \frac{3}{6} + \frac{3}{6} - \frac{1}{6} = \frac{5}{6}.$

By an actual listing we can see that five of the six possible outcomes in Example 2 are either odd or greater than 3, namely 1, 3, 4, 5, and 6. The only "losing" number is 2. Thus the probability $P(A \text{ or } B)$ must be $\frac{5}{6}$.

These two situations $P(A \text{ or } B)$ and $P(A \text{ and } B)$ which we have considered can also be described by means of Venn diagrams (see § 4-4) where the points of the circular regions represent probabilities of events.

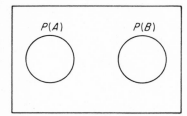
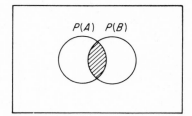

The first of the two accompanying figures shows mutually exclusive events:

$$P(A \text{ or } B) = P(A) + P(B).$$

The second shows events that are not mutually exclusive:

$$P(A \text{ or } B) = P(A) + P(B) - P(A \text{ and } B).$$

The shaded portion of the diagram represents $P(A \text{ and } B)$. We need to subtract this in that we have counted it twice in adding $P(A) + P(B)$.

Next we turn our attention to the probability that several events will occur, one after the other. Consider the probability of tossing a coin twice and obtaining heads on the first toss and tails on the second toss. From a sample space we see that the probability is $\frac{1}{4}$.

$$\{HH, \textcircled{HT}, TH, TT\}$$

Furthermore we see that the probability, $P(A)$, that the first coin is heads is $\frac{1}{2}$. The probability, $P(B)$, that the second coin is tails is $\frac{1}{2}$. Then $P(A \text{ and } B) = \frac{1}{2} \times \frac{1}{2} = \frac{1}{4}$. Note that these events are **independent**; that is, the outcome of the first toss does not affect the second toss.

In general, let the probability that an event A occurs be $P(A)$. Let the probability that an independent second event occurs, after A has occurred, be $P(B)$. Then

$$P(A \text{ and } B) = P(A) \times P(B).$$

This can be extended to any finite number of independent events.

$$P(A \text{ and } B \text{ and } C \text{ and } \cdots) = P(A) \times P(B) \times P(C) \times \cdots.$$

EXAMPLE 3. Urn A contains three white and five red balls. Urn B contains four white and three red balls. One ball is drawn from each urn. What is the probability that they are both red?

Solution: Let $P(A)$ be the probability of drawing a red ball from urn A and $P(B)$ be the probability of drawing a red ball from urn B. Then

$$P(A) = \tfrac{5}{8}, \quad P(B) = \tfrac{3}{7}, \quad P(A \text{ and } B) = \tfrac{5}{8} \cdot \tfrac{3}{7} = \tfrac{15}{56}.$$

EXAMPLE 4. Two cards are selected in succession, without replacement, from an ordinary bridge deck of 52 cards. What is the probability that they are both aces?

Solution: The probability that the first is an ace is $\tfrac{4}{52}$. Now the probability of success depends on the drawing of the first card. If it is an ace, then the probability that the second card is an ace is $\tfrac{3}{51}$. The probability that both cards are aces is $\tfrac{4}{52} \times \tfrac{3}{51}$, that is, $\tfrac{1}{221}$. This problem can also be solved by noting that $_{52}C_2$ is the total number of ways of selecting two cards from a deck of 52 cards. Also $_4C_2$ is the total number of ways of selecting two aces from the four aces in a deck. The required probability is then given as

$$\frac{_4C_2}{_{52}C_2} = \frac{\dfrac{4!}{2!2!}}{\dfrac{52!}{2!50!}} = \frac{4 \times 3}{52 \times 51} = \frac{1}{221}.$$

Exercises

1. A single card is drawn from an ordinary bridge deck of 52 cards. Find the probability that it is **(a)** an ace or a king; **(b)** a spade or a heart; **(c)** a spade or an ace; **(d)** a spade and an ace.

2. Two cards are drawn in succession from a deck of 52 cards without the first card's being replaced. Find the probability that **(a)** both cards are spades; **(b)** both cards are aces of spades; **(c)** the first card is a spade and the second card is a heart; **(d)** the first card is an ace and the second card is the king of hearts; **(e)** both cards are of the same suit.

3. Repeat Exercise 2 if the first card is replaced in the deck after the first drawing.

4. A coin is tossed five times. What is the probability that all five tosses are heads?

5. A coin is tossed five times. What is the probability that at least one head is obtained? [*Hint:* First find the probability of getting no heads.]

6. A coin is tossed and then a die is rolled. Find the probability of obtaining **(a)** a head and a 3; **(b)** a head and an even number; **(c)** a head or a 3; **(d)** a head or an even number.

7. A box contains three red, four white, and five green balls. Three balls are drawn in succession, without replacement. Find the probability that **(a)** all three are red; **(b)** the first is red, the second is white, and the third is green; **(c)** none are green; †**(d)** all three are of the same color.

8. Repeat Exercise 7 if each ball is replaced after it is drawn.

9. A die is tossed three times. Find the probability that **(a)** all three tosses produce a 6; **(b)** the first two tosses are even and the third is odd; **(c)** none of the tosses produces a 6; **(d)** at least one 6 is tossed; †**(e)** exactly one 6 is tossed.

†**10.** Five cards are dealt from an ordinary bridge deck of 52 cards. Find the probability that the hand consists of three aces and two kings.

6-7 Odds and Mathematical Expectation

One often reads statements in the sports section of the daily newspaper concerning "odds" in favor of, or against, a particular team or individual's winning or losing some encounter. For example, we may read that the odds in favor of the Yankees' winning the pennant are "4 to 1." In this section we shall attempt to discover just what such statements really mean.

Consider the problem of finding the odds against obtaining a 3 in one toss of a die. Since the probability of obtaining a 3 is known to be $\frac{1}{6}$, most people would say that the odds are therefore 6 to 1 against rolling a 3. This is not correct—because out of every six tosses of the die, in the long run, one expects to toss one 3. The other five tosses are not expected to be 3's. Therefore the correct odds against rolling a 3 in one toss of a die are 5 to 1. The odds in favor of tossing a 3 are 1 to 5. Formally we define odds as follows:

> The **odds in favor** of an event are defined as the ratio of the probability that an event will occur to the probability that the event will not occur. The reciprocal of this ratio gives the **odds against** the occurrence of the event.

EXAMPLE 1. Find the odds in favor of drawing a spade from an ordinary deck of 52 cards.

Solution: Since there are 13 spades in a deck of cards, the probability of drawing a spade is $\frac{13}{52} = \frac{1}{4}$. The probability of failing to draw a spade is $\frac{3}{4}$. The odds in favor of obtaining a spade are $\frac{1}{4} \div \frac{3}{4}$, that is, $\frac{1}{3}$.

The odds in favor of drawing a spade are stated as $\frac{1}{3}$. They may also be stated as "1 to 3" or as "1:3." Similarly the odds against drawing a spade are $\frac{3}{1}$, which may be written as "3 to 1" or "3:1."

Mathematical expectation is closely related to odds and is defined as the product of the probability that an event will occur and the amount to be received upon such occurrence. Suppose that you are to receive $2.00 each time you obtain two heads on a single toss of two coins. You do not receive anything for any other outcome. Then your mathematical expectation will be one-fourth of $2.00; that is, $0.50. This means that you should be willing to pay $0.50 each time you toss the coins if the game is to be a fair one. In the long run, both you and the person who is running the game would break even. For example, if you played the game four times it would cost you 4 × $0.50, that is, $2.00. You expect to win, in the long run, once out of every four games played. Assuming that you do so, you will win $2.00 once every four times and thus be even.

If an event has several possible outcomes that occur with probabilities p_1, p_2, p_3, and so forth, and for each of these outcomes one may expect the amounts m_1, m_2, m_3, and so on, then the mathematical expectation, E, may be defined as:

$$E = m_1 p_1 + m_2 p_2 + m_3 p_3 + \cdots$$

EXAMPLE 2. Suppose that you play a game wherein you are to toss a coin twice and are to receive 10 cents if two heads are obtained, 5 cents if one head is obtained, and nothing if both tosses produce tails. What is your expected value in this game?

Solution: The probabilities of obtaining two, one, and no heads, respectively, are $\frac{1}{4}$, $\frac{1}{2}$, and $\frac{1}{4}$. Therefore, the expected value, E, in cents, is found to be

$$E = (10)(\tfrac{1}{4}) + (5)(\tfrac{1}{2}) + (0)(\tfrac{1}{4}) = 5.$$

This solution may be interpreted in several ways. For one thing, it is the price you should be willing to pay for the privilege of playing this game. It may also be interpreted as the average amount of winnings per game that one may expect when one is playing a large number of games.

Exercises

1. What are the odds in favor of obtaining three heads in a single toss of three coins?

2. What are the odds against drawing an ace in a single draw from a deck of cards?

3. What are the odds in favor of rolling a 7 or an 11 in a single toss of a pair of dice?

4. One hundred tickets are sold for a lottery. The grand prize is $1,000. What is a fair price to pay for a ticket?

5. What is your mathematical expectation in a game in which you will receive $10 if you toss a "double" (the same number on both dice) on a single toss of a pair of dice?

6. A box contains three dimes and two quarters. You are to reach in and select one coin, which you may then keep. Assuming that you are not able to determine which coin is which by its size, what would be a fair price for the privilege of playing this game?

7. There are three identical boxes on a table. One contains a five-dollar bill, one contains a one-dollar bill, and the third is empty. A man is permitted to select one of these boxes and to keep its contents. What is his expectation?

8. Three coins are tossed. What is the expected number of heads?

9. Two bills are to be drawn from a purse which contains three five-dollar bills and two ten-dollar bills. What is the mathematical expectation for this drawing?

10. Three cards are dealt from a deck of 52 cards. What are the odds against their all being of the same suit?

6-8 Pascal's Triangle

The final problem that we shall consider in this chapter is that of finding the number of different subsets of various sizes that can be formed from a given set. To illustrate this we return to our original set, M:

$$M = \{\text{Betty, Doris, Ellen, John, Tom}\}.$$

We wish to know the number of different committees that can be formed consisting of 0, 1, 2, 3, 4, and 5 members. Each of these can be found:

$$_5C_0 = 1; \quad _5C_1 = 5; \quad _5C_2 = 10; \quad _5C_3 = 10; \quad _5C_4 = 5; \quad _5C_5 = 1.$$

Recall that the notation $_nC_r$ may also be written in the form $\binom{n}{r}$. The preceding results may then be written in the form:

$$\binom{5}{0} = 1; \quad \binom{5}{1} = 5; \quad \binom{5}{2} = 10;$$

$$\binom{5}{3} = 10; \quad \binom{5}{4} = 5; \quad \binom{5}{5} = 1.$$

We shall use the form $\binom{n}{r}$ to simplify the arrays in this section. In any case the total number of subsets of a set of five elements is $1 + 5 + 10 + 10 + 5 + 1$; that is, 32.

In like manner, if our original set had consisted of only four members, the number of different committees of 0, 1, 2, 3, and 4 members each would be found as:

$$\binom{4}{0} = 1; \quad \binom{4}{1} = 4; \quad \binom{4}{2} = 6; \quad \binom{4}{3} = 4; \quad \binom{4}{4} = 1.$$

Notice that $1 + 4 + 6 + 4 + 1 = 16$.

There is a convenient way to summarize these data for sets of n elements where $n = 1, 2, 3, \ldots :$

$$n = 1: \qquad \binom{1}{0} \quad \binom{1}{1}$$

$$n = 2: \qquad \binom{2}{0} \quad \binom{2}{1} \quad \binom{2}{2}$$

$$n = 3: \qquad \binom{3}{0} \quad \binom{3}{1} \quad \binom{3}{2} \quad \binom{3}{3}$$

$$n = 4: \qquad \binom{4}{0} \quad \binom{4}{1} \quad \binom{4}{2} \quad \binom{4}{3} \quad \binom{4}{4}$$

$$n = 5: \quad \binom{5}{0} \quad \binom{5}{1} \quad \binom{5}{2} \quad \binom{5}{3} \quad \binom{5}{4} \quad \binom{5}{5}$$

If we replace each symbol by its equivalent number we may write the following array, known as **Pascal's triangle**. Generally ascribed to the French mathematician Blaise Pascal (1623–1662), this array of numbers is said to have been known to the Chinese in the early fourteenth century.

$n = 1:$				1		1			
$n = 2:$			1		2		1		
$n = 3:$		1		3		3		1	
$n = 4:$	1		4		6		4		1
$n = 5:$	1	5		10		10		5	1

We read each row of this array by noting that the first entry in the nth row is $\binom{n}{0}$, the second is $\binom{n}{1}$, the third is $\binom{n}{2}$, and so on until the last entry which is $\binom{n}{n}$. Since $\binom{n}{0} = \binom{n}{n} = 1$, each row begins and ends with 1.

There is a simple way to continue the array with very little computation. In each row the first number is 1 and the last number is 1. Each of the other numbers may be obtained as the sum of the two numbers appearing in the preceding row to the right and left of the position to be filled. Thus, to obtain the sixth row, begin with 1. Then fill the next position by adding 1 and 5 from the fifth row. Then add 5 and 10 to obtain 15, add 10 and 10 to obtain 20, and so forth as in this diagram:

$n = 5$:   1   5   10   10   5   1

$n = 6$: 1   6   15   20   15   6   1

Let's see if we can find out why this pattern works as it does. To do so, consider the rows for $n = 4$ and $n = 5$:

$n = 4$:   1   4   6   4   1

$n = 5$: 1   5   10   10   5   1

We will consider the fourth entry in row 5 and give an example of why it is equal to the sum of the third and fourth entries in row 4. That is, we shall show that

$$\binom{5}{3} = \binom{4}{2} + \binom{4}{3}.$$

Consider our original set M and the problem of selecting different committees of three. Each of these committees either will or will not include Betty. First, we shall assume Betty *is* to be included. Then the other two members of the committee will be selected from the remaining four members of M in $\binom{4}{2}$ different ways. If Betty is *not* to be included on the committee, then the committee of three will be selected from the other four members of M in $\binom{4}{3}$ different ways. Together, $\binom{4}{2} + \binom{4}{3}$, we have the total number of ways in which a committee of three can be selected from the set M. But this is given as $\binom{5}{3}$, which illustrates the relationship that we set out to demonstrate. This relationship and, in general,

$$\binom{n}{r} = \binom{n-1}{r-1} + \binom{n-1}{r}$$

can be formally proved by using the formula for $_nC_r$ (Exercise 8).

Pascal's triangle may be used mechanically to compute probabilities as follows:

The elements of the second row are the numerators for the probabilities when two coins are tossed; the elements of the third row are the numerators when three coins are tossed; and so on. The denominator in each case is found as the sum of the elements in the row used. For example, when three coins are tossed, we examine the third row (1, 3, 3, 1). The sum is 8. The probabilities of 0, 1, 2, and 3 heads are then given as $\frac{1}{8}$, $\frac{3}{8}$, $\frac{3}{8}$, $\frac{1}{8}$, as in § 6-5.

Note that the sum of the entries in the second row is 4, the sum in the third row is 2^3 or 8, the sum in the fourth row is 2^4 or 16, and, in general, the sum in the nth row will be 2^n.

As another example, we may obtain the probability of 0, 1, 2, 3, or 4 heads, when four coins are tossed, from the fourth row of Pascal's triangle. The numerators are the entries 1, 4, 6, 4, 1; the denominator is 2^4 or 16 (that is, $1 + 4 + 6 + 4 + 1$). Thus, we have

Event	Probability
0 heads	$\frac{1}{16}$
1 head	$\frac{4}{16}$
2 heads	$\frac{6}{16}$
3 heads	$\frac{4}{16}$
4 heads	$\frac{1}{16}$

[*Note:* The preceding analysis could also have been made for the probabilities of obtaining specific numbers of tails.]

Exercises

1. Construct Pascal's triangle for $n = 1, 2, 3, \ldots, 10$.

2. List the entries in the eleventh row of Pascal's triangle using the notation
$$\binom{n}{r}.$$

3. Make a table of probabilities for all the possible outcomes of heads when five coins are tossed.

4. Four coins are tossed. What is the probability of obtaining *at least* 2 heads? Note that this is the sum of the probabilities of obtaining 2, 3, and 4 heads.

5. What is the probability of obtaining at least 2 heads in a single toss of 10 coins?

6. Five coins are tossed. What is the probability of obtaining *more than* 3 heads?

7. What is the probability of obtaining all heads on a single toss of 10 coins? On 10 tosses of a single coin?

†**8.** Use the definition $\binom{n}{r} = \dfrac{n!}{r!(n-r)!}$, and prove that

$$\binom{n}{r} = \binom{n-1}{r-1} + \binom{n-1}{r}.$$

†**9.** Pascal's triangle may be used to determine the coefficients in the binomial expansion of $(a+b)^n$. For example,

$$(a+b)^4 = \underline{1}a^4 + \underline{4}a^3b + \underline{6}a^2b^2 + \underline{4}ab^3 + \underline{1}b^4.$$

Note the pattern exhibited by the variables a and b, and use the results of Exercise 1 to write the expansion of $(a+b)^6$.

†**10.** Repeat Exercise 9 for $(a+b)^7$.

SETS OF NUMBERS

Sets of elements were considered in Chapter 4. A number is associated with a set of elements whenever the elements of a set are counted. The set $\{1, 2, 3, \ldots\}$ of numbers used in counting is called the set of counting numbers. In this chapter we assume that the counting numbers are familiar to the reader. Then we shall consider properties of the counting numbers and extensions of the set of counting numbers to obtain other sets of numbers.

A difference of two counting numbers may or may not represent a counting number; $5 - 3 = 2$ but $3 - 5$ does not represent a counting number. Accordingly, we extend the set of numbers under consideration to include all integers (positive, negative, and zero) so that subtraction will always be possible.

A quotient of two counting numbers may or may not represent a counting number; $6 \div 2 = 3$ but $2 \div 6$ does not represent a counting number. Accordingly, we extend the set of numbers under consideration to include the rational numbers so that division, except by zero, will always be possible.

Finally, we include all real numbers so that all points on a line in our ordinary geometry will have coordinates. Further extensions of the set of numbers are possible but are not needed for the purposes considered here. In each case we shall examine some of the properties of the particular set of numbers under consideration.

7-1 Numbers and Sets

If you have a set of books, you can count them and use a number to tell how many books there are in the set. If you have a set of bookmarks, you can count them and use a number to tell how many bookmarks there are in the set. If your purpose was to be sure that you had exactly one

bookmark for each of your books, you could have done this without counting either the books or the bookmarks. Instead you could have placed one bookmark in each book. If this one-to-one matching of books and bookmarks could be continued until all books and bookmarks were used, you would know that you had the same number of books in the set of books as you had bookmarks in the set of bookmarks. We would then say that there is a one-to-one correspondence between the books and the bookmarks.

You may use the concept of a one-to-one correspondence to show whether or not any two sets of elements have the same number of members. You also use this concept of a one-to-one correspondence when you count the elements of a set. To count, you use the set of counting numbers

$$\{1, 2, 3, 4, 5, 6, \ldots\}.$$

As in § 4-5, the dots indicate that the pattern continues indefinitely. If you were to count the books in the set shown in the previous figure, you would use the set of numbers $\{1, 2, 3, 4, 5\}$. You would form a one-to-one correspondence of the books with the numbers. If you were to count the bookmarks, you would use the same set of numbers. *Two sets that may be placed in one-to-one correspondence with the same set of numbers may be placed in one-to-one correspondence with each other and thus have the same number of elements.*

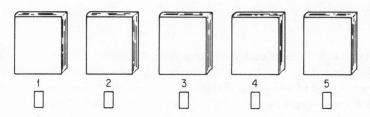

Any set A of elements that may be placed in one-to-one correspondence with the set of elements $\{1, 2, 3, 4, 5\}$ is said to have 5 elements; we write $n(A) = 5$ to show that the number of elements in the set A is 5. Any set B of elements that may be placed in one-to-one correspondence with the set of elements $\{1, 2, 3, 4, \ldots, k - 1, k\}$ is said to have k elements; $n(B) = k$. Notice this use of the set of counting numbers and one-to-one correspondences to determine how many elements there are in a set; that is, to determine the **cardinal number** of a set. When the counting numbers are taken in order, the last number used in the one-to-one correspondence is the cardinal number of the set.

Counting numbers may also be used to assign an order to the elements of a set. For example, you expect page 15 of this book to follow page 14. Numbers used to assign an order to the elements of a set are called **ordinal numbers**.

Properties of sets may be used to identify properties of numbers. For example, let M stand for a set of mathematics books and P stand for a set of physics books. We assume that $M \cap P = \varnothing$, that is, no book is both a mathematics book and a physics book. Then $M \cup P$ and $P \cup M$ both represent the set of mathematics and physics books; $M \cup P = P \cup M$. Accordingly,

$$n(M) + n(P) = n(M \cup P) = n(P \cup M) = n(P) + n(M).$$

This gives us a basis for a formal statement of the property

$$x + y = y + x$$

for the addition of counting numbers. This property is called the **commutative property for addition**. The sum of two numbers does not depend upon the order in which the numbers are added: $2 + 7 = 7 + 2$, $3 + 100 = 100 + 3$, and so forth.

The empty set, $\varnothing$, has the property

$$\varnothing \cup A = A$$

for any set A. We introduce the number zero, $0 = n(\varnothing)$, as the cardinal number of the empty set. Then

$$n(\varnothing) + n(A) = n(\varnothing \cup A) = n(A \cup \varnothing) = n(A)$$

and if $n(A) = a$, we have

$$0 + a = a + 0 = a.$$

We say that 0 is the **identity element for addition**.

We have used one-to-one correspondence to determine the cardinal number of a set of numbers. Specifically, we asserted that the last counting number used would be the cardinal number of the set. However, is there always a "last" counting number used? Consider each of the following sets:

$$A = \{1, 2, 3, 4, 5, \ldots, n, \ldots\},$$
$$B = \{2, 4, 6, 8, 10, \ldots, 2n, \ldots\},$$
$$C = \{1, 3, 5, 7, 9, \ldots, 2n - 1, \ldots\},$$
$$D = \{2, 2^2, 2^3, 2^4, 2^5, \ldots, 2^n, \ldots\},$$

$$E = \{1, \frac{1}{2}, \frac{1}{3}, \frac{1}{4}, \frac{1}{5}, \ldots, \frac{1}{n}, \ldots\},$$

$$F = \{10, 10^2, 10^3, 10^4, \ldots, 10^n, \ldots\}.$$

In each case the set fails to have a last element; consequently, the set does not have a counting number as its cardinal number. Note that each element of B is also an element of A, $B \subseteq A$. The set B is a proper subset of A since there are elements of A that are not elements of B. However, there is a one-to-one correspondence (n to $2n$) between the elements of A and the elements of B. Thus the set A is equivalent to one of its proper subsets.

$$
\begin{array}{cccccccc}
A: & \{1, & 2, & 3, & 4, & \ldots, & n, & \ldots\} \\
   & \updownarrow & \updownarrow & \updownarrow & \updownarrow & & \updownarrow & \\
B: & \{2, & 4, & 6, & 8, & \ldots, & 2n, & \ldots\}
\end{array}
$$

A set that is equivalent to one of its proper subsets is an **infinite set**. Any infinite set fails to have a last element and fails to have a counting number as its cardinal number. Any set that has a counting number as its cardinal number is called a **finite set**.

The cardinal number of an infinite set is called a **transfinite cardinal number**. However, as in the case of the books and bookmarks, we do not need to find the cardinal numbers of two sets in order to show that they have the same number of elements. We need only demonstrate that a one-to-one correspondence exists between the sets. The sets A and B have the same number of elements, $n(A) = n(B)$, because there is a one-to-one correspondence of n to $2n$ between the elements of the sets. In other words, there are just as many even counting numbers as there are counting numbers.

Each of the sets A, B, C, D, E, and F may be placed in one-to-one correspondence with the set A. Each of these sets is an infinite set and each has the same transfinite cardinal number as the set of counting numbers.

The properties of infinite sets confused mathematicians for centuries. Indeed, it is only within the last century that infinite sets have been reasonably well understood. The symbol $\aleph_0$ (read "aleph null") has been introduced in § 1-2 as the transfinite cardinal number of the set of counting numbers. We now list a few of the unusual arithmetic properties of this number and illustrations of these properties based upon the following sets:

$$A = \{1, 2, 3, 4, \ldots, n, \ldots\};$$
$$B = \{2, 4, 6, 8, \ldots, 2n, \ldots\};$$
$$C = \{1, 3, 5, 7, \ldots, 2n - 1, \ldots\}.$$

1. $\aleph_0 + 1 = \aleph_0$. The set A has the transfinite cardinal number $\aleph_0$; the set A with one element 0 added has cardinal number $\aleph_0 + 1$. The equivalence of these two sets may be shown as follows:

$$\{0, \quad 1, \quad 2, \quad 3, \quad 4, \quad \ldots, \quad n, \quad \ldots\};$$
$$\updownarrow \quad \updownarrow \quad \updownarrow \quad \updownarrow \quad \updownarrow \quad \quad \quad \updownarrow$$
$$\{1, \quad 2, \quad 3, \quad 4, \quad 5, \quad \ldots, \quad n + 1, \quad \ldots\}.$$

2. $\aleph_0 - 5 = \aleph_0$. The set A has the transfinite cardinal number $\aleph_0$; the set A with the numbers 1, 2, 3, 4, 5 removed has the cardinal number $\aleph_0 - 5$. The equivalence of the two sets may be shown as follows:

$$\{6, \quad 7, \quad 8, \quad 9, \quad 10, \quad \ldots, \quad n + 5, \quad \ldots\};$$
$$\updownarrow \quad \updownarrow \quad \updownarrow \quad \updownarrow \quad \updownarrow \quad \quad \quad \updownarrow$$
$$\{1, \quad 2, \quad 3, \quad 4, \quad 5, \quad \ldots, \quad n, \quad \ldots\}.$$

3. $\aleph_0 + \aleph_0 = \aleph_0$. The sets B and C each have the transfinite cardinal number $\aleph_0$; the union of these sets has the cardinal number $\aleph_0 + \aleph_0$ since $B \cap C = \varnothing$. However, $B \cup C = A$, and the set A has cardinal number $\aleph_0$.

Exercises

Find the cardinal number of each of the sets in Exercises 1 through 8:

1. $\{\triangle, >, =, \square\}$.   **2.** $\{3, 5, 7\}$.

3. $\{x\}$.   **4.** $\{11, 12, \ldots, 18\}$.

5. $\{5\}$.   **6.** $\varnothing$.

7. $\{\varnothing\}$.   **8.** $\{\varnothing, \{\varnothing\}\}$.

9. Give a set with cardinal number 15.

10. Give a set with cardinal number 87.

11. Give a set that may be placed in one-to-one correspondence with the set of positive integers.

†**12.** Use sets to show that for cardinal numbers, $2 + 3 = 3 + 2$.

†**13.** Use sets to show that $\aleph_0 + 2 = \aleph_0$.

†**14.** Use sets to show that $\aleph_0 - 3 = \aleph_0$.

7-2 Prime Numbers

The counting number 6 is divisible by 2 since there is a counting number 3 such that $6 = 2 \times 3$; the counting number 7 is not divisible by 2 since there exists no counting number b such that $7 = 2 \times b$. In general, a counting number n is **divisible by** a counting number t if and only if there is a counting number k such that $n = t \times k$. If n is divisible by t, then n is a **multiple of** t and t is a **factor of** n. For example, 6 is a multiple of 2 and 2 is a factor of 6.

The counting numbers are often considered in terms of the numbers by which they are divisible. The set

$$A = \{2, 4, 6, 8, 10, 12, \ldots\}$$

consists of the numbers that are divisible by 2—that is, the numbers expressible in the form $2k$, where k stands for a counting number. The set

$$B = \{3, 6, 9, 12, 15, 18, \ldots\}$$

consists of the numbers divisible by 3; the set

$$C = \{4, 8, 12, 16, 20, 24, \ldots\}$$

consists of the numbers divisible by 4; the set

$$D = \{5, 10, 15, 20, 25, 30, \ldots\}$$

consists of the numbers divisible by 5; the set

$$E = \{6, 12, 18, 24, 30, 36, \ldots\}$$

consists of the numbers divisible by 6; and so forth.

Notice that $C \subset A$; in other words, any number that is divisible by 4 is also divisible by 2. Notice also that $A \cap B = E$; in other words, the set of numbers that are divisible by both 2 and 3 is the set of numbers that are divisible by 6.

The number 1 divides every counting number since $k = 1 \times k$ for every counting number k. Accordingly, the number 1 is called a **unit**. Since the set A does not include all counting numbers, divisibility by 2 is a special property of the elements of the set A. The counting numbers that are divisible by 2 are called **even numbers**. Zero is an even number since $2 \times 0 = 0$. The counting numbers that are not divisible by two are called **odd numbers**. We shall consider properties of even and odd numbers in § 7-7.

The number 2 is a member of the set A and is not a member of any other set; that is, 2 is not divisible by any counting number except itself and 1. Any counting number greater than 1 that is divisible only by itself and 1 is called a **prime number**. Thus 2 is prime, 3 is prime, 4 is not prime since 4 is divisible by 2 (that is, 4 is a member of the set A as well as the set C), 5 is prime, and 6 is not prime since 6 is divisible by both 2 and 3. The counting numbers that are greater than 1 and are not prime are called **composite numbers**.

We could extend the list of sets A, B, C, D, E, F to identify other prime numbers; that is, elements that belong to one and only one of these sets. However, the method used to select these sets may be applied to the entire set of counting numbers. We shall illustrate this for the set $\{1, 2, \ldots, 70\}$. The number 1 is excluded since it is a unit. The number 2 is prime, and the other numbers of the set A must be excluded since they are divisible by 2. We do this by excluding every second number after 2. The number 3 is prime and we exclude the other members of the

```
 ①    2    3   >4    5   >6    7   >8   >9  +0

11  +2   13  +4  +5  +6   17  +8   19  20

2+  22   23  24  25  26  27  28   29  30

31  32   33  34  35  36   37  38  39  40

41  42   43  44  45  46   47  48  49  50

5+  52   53  54  55  56  57  58   59  60

61  62   63  64  65  66   67  68  69  70
```

set B, that is every third number after 3. The number 4 has already been excluded and thus is composite. The number 5 is prime and we exclude each fifth number after 5. The next prime number is 7 and we exclude each seventh number after 7. Note that only 49 has not already been excluded. The next prime is 11; since all multiples of 11 in this set have already been excluded, the remaining numbers that have not been excluded are prime numbers.

Notice that 49 is the first number that is divisible by 7 that is not also divisible by a prime number less than 7; in other words, each composite number less than 49 (that is, 7^2) has at least one of its factors less than 7. Similarly we might have observed that each composite number less than 5^2 has at least one factor less than 5. In general, *each composite number less than the square of a prime number p has a prime number less than p as a factor.*

We use this property to tell us when we have excluded all composite numbers from a set. In the set of numbers $\{1, 2, \ldots, 70\}$ we have considered the primes 2, 3, 5, and 7. The next prime is 11. Thus by our method we would have already excluded all composite numbers up to but not including 11^2, that is, 121. In particular, we have identified the set

$$\{2, 3, 5, 7, 11, 13, 17, 19, 23, 29, 31, 37, 41, 43, 47, 53, 59, 61, 67\}$$

of prime numbers less than or equal to 70. This method of finding prime numbers is called the **sieve of Eratosthenes**. It may be used to find the prime numbers less than or equal to n for any counting number n.

Exercises

Let B = the set of numbers divisible by 3, D = the set of numbers divisible by 5, and H = the set of numbers divisible by 15. Restate each of the statements in Exercises 1 through 3 in terms of divisibility.

1. $H \subset B$.   **2.** $H \subset D$.   **3.** $B \cap D = H$.

4. Use a sieve of Eratosthenes to find the prime numbers less than or equal to 200.

5. Here is a famous theorem that has not yet been proved: Every even number greater than 2 is expressible as the sum of two prime numbers. (This theorem is often called **Goldbach's conjecture**.) Express each even number from 4 to 40 inclusive as a sum of two prime numbers.

6. Here is another famous theorem. Two prime numbers such as 17 and 19 that differ by 2 are called *twin primes*. It is believed but has not yet been proved that there are infinitely many twin primes. Find a pair of twin primes that are between **(a)** 25 and 35; **(b)** 55 and 65; **(c)** 95 and 105.

†7. What is the largest prime that you need to consider to be sure that you have excluded all composite numbers less than or equal to **(a)** 200; **(b)** 500; **(c)** 1,000?

†8. Explain why $\{3, 5, 7\}$ is the only set of three consecutive odd numbers that are all prime numbers.

7-3 Prime Factorization

We have seen that every counting number greater than 1 is either a prime number or a composite number. In this section we shall find that every counting number greater than 1 can be expressed in terms of its prime factors in essentially only one way.

Consider the various ways of factoring 24:

$$24 = 1 \times 24;$$
$$24 = 2 \times 12;$$
$$24 = 3 \times 8;$$
$$24 = 4 \times 6;$$
$$24 = 2 \times 2 \times 6;$$
$$24 = 2 \times 3 \times 4;$$
$$24 = 2 \times 2 \times 2 \times 3 = 2^3 \times 3.$$

The last factorization in terms of the prime numbers 2 and 3 could be written as $2 \times 3 \times 2^2$ and in other ways. However, these ways are equivalent since the order of the factors does not affect the product. Thus 24 can be expressed in terms of its prime factors in one and only one way.

One of the easiest ways to find the prime factors of a number is to consider the prime numbers

$$2, 3, 5, 7, 11, 13, 17, 19, 23, 29, 31, \ldots$$

in order and use each one as a factor as many times as possible. Then for 24 we would have

$$24 = 2 \times 12$$
$$= 2 \times 2 \times 6$$
$$= 2 \times 2 \times 2 \times 3.$$

Some people prefer to write these steps using division:

$$2 \underline{|\,24}$$
$$2 \underline{|\,12}$$
$$2 \underline{|\,6}$$
$$3$$

Since 3 is a prime number, no further steps are needed and $24 = 2^3 \times 3$.

EXAMPLE 1. Express 3,850 in terms of its prime factors.

Solution:

$$2 \underline{|\,3{,}850}$$
$$5 \underline{|\,1{,}925}$$
$$5 \underline{|\,385} \qquad 3{,}850 = 2 \times 5^2 \times 7 \times 11.$$
$$7 \underline{|\,77}$$
$$11$$

In general, if a counting number n is greater than 1, then n has a prime number p_1 as a factor. Suppose

$$n = p_1 n_1.$$

Then if n is a prime number, $n = p_1$ and $n_1 = 1$. If n is not a prime number, then n_1 is a counting number greater than 1. In this case n_1 is either a prime number or a composite number. Suppose

$$n_1 = p_2 n_2 \quad \text{and thus} \quad n = p_1 p_2 n_2,$$

where p_2 is a prime number. As before, if $n_2 \neq 1$, then

$$n_2 = p_3 n_3 \quad \text{and thus} \quad n = p_1 p_2 p_3 n_3,$$

where p_3 is a prime number, and so forth. We may continue this process until some $n_k = 1$, since there are only a finite number of counting numbers less than n and

$$n > n_1 > n_2 > n_3 > \cdots > n_k = 1.$$

Then we have an expression for n as a product of prime numbers:

$$n = p_1 p_2 p_3 \cdots p_k.$$

We call this the prime factorization of n; that is, the factorization of n into its prime factors. Except for the order of the factors, the prime factorization of any counting number greater than 1 is unique; that is, *any counting number greater than 1 may be expressed as a product of prime numbers in one and only one way.* As in the examples, we usually write the prime factorization as a product of powers of prime numbers.

EXAMPLE 2. Find the prime factorization of 5,280.

Solution:

$$
\begin{array}{r|l}
2 & 5{,}280 \\ \hline
2 & 2{,}640 \\ \hline
2 & 1{,}320 \\ \hline
2 & 660 \\
2 & 330 \\
3 & 165 \\
5 & 55 \\ \hline
& 11
\end{array}
\qquad 5{,}280 = 2^5 \times 3 \times 5 \times 11.
$$

Greatest common divisor

The set of divisors of 12 is

$$\{1, 2, 3, 4, 6, 12\};$$

the set of divisors of 18 is

$$\{1, 2, 3, 6, 9, 18\};$$

the set of common divisors of 12 and 18 is

$$\{1, 2, 3, 6\}.$$

Notice that the "greatest" of these common divisors 6 is divisible by each of the common divisors. In general, the common divisor of two numbers that is divisible by each of the common divisors is called the **greatest common divisor** (G.C.D.) of the two numbers.

We may use the prime factorization of two counting numbers to find their greatest common divisor. We express each number by its prime factorization; consider the prime numbers that are factors of both of the given numbers; and take the product of those prime numbers with each raised to the highest power that is a factor of both of the given numbers. For $12 = 2^2 \times 3$ and $18 = 2 \times 3^2$ we have G.C.D. $= 2 \times 3$; that is, 6.

EXAMPLE 3. Find the greatest common divisor of 60 and 5,280.

Solution:

$$\begin{array}{c|c} 2 & 60 \\ 2 & \overline{30} \\ 3 & \overline{15} \\ \hline & 5 \end{array} \qquad 60 = 2^2 \times 3 \times 5.$$

As in Example 2 we have $5{,}280 = 2^5 \times 3 \times 5 \times 11$. Then the highest power of 2 that is a common factor of 60 and 5,280 is 2^2; 3 is a common factor; 5 is a common factor; 11 is not a common factor. The greatest common divisor of 60 and 5,280 is $2^2 \times 3 \times 5$; that is, 60.

EXAMPLE 4. Find the greatest common divisor of 3,850 and 5,280.

Solution: As in Examples 1 and 2

$$3{,}850 = 2 \times 5^2 \times 7 \times 11;$$
$$5{,}280 = 2^5 \times 3 \times 5 \times 11.$$

The greatest common divisor of 3,850 and 5,280 is $2 \times 5 \times 11$; that is, 110.

We may use the greatest common divisor when we reduce (simplify) a fraction. For example,

$$\frac{60}{4{,}880} = \frac{(2^2 \times 5) \times 3}{(2^2 \times 5) \times (2^2 \times 61)} = \frac{3}{2^2 \times 61} = \frac{3}{244}.$$

Since 3 is the only prime factor of the numerator and 3 is not a factor of the denominator, the fraction $\frac{3}{244}$ is in **lowest terms**. The numerator and the denominator do not have any common prime factors and are said to be **relatively prime**.

EXAMPLE 5. Reduce the fraction $\frac{60}{168}$ to lowest terms.

Solution:
$$60 = 2^2 \times 3 \times 5,$$
$$168 = 2^3 \times 3 \times 7.$$

The greatest common divisor is $2^2 \times 3$.

$$\frac{60}{168} = \frac{(2^2 \times 3) \times 5}{(2^2 \times 3) \times 2 \times 7} = \frac{5}{14}.$$

Lowest common multiple ✔

The set of multiples of 12 is

$$\{12, 24, 36, 48, 60, 72, 84, 96, 108, 120, \ldots\};$$

the set of multiples of 18 is

$$\{18, 36, 54, 72, 90, 108, 126, \ldots\};$$

the set of common multiples of 12 and 18 is

$$\{36, 72, 108, \ldots\}.$$

Notice that the "lowest" of these common multiples, 36, is a divisor of each of the common multiples. In general, the common multiple of two numbers that is a divisor of each of the common multiples is called the **lowest common multiple** (L.C.M.) of the two numbers.

We may use the prime factorization of two numbers to find their lowest common multiple. We express each number by its prime factorization; consider the prime factors that are factors of either of the given numbers; and take the product of these prime numbers with each raised to the highest power that occurs in either of the prime factorizations. For $12 = 2^2 \times 3$ and $18 = 2 \times 3^2$, we have L.C.M. $= 2^2 \times 3^2$; that is, 36.

EXAMPLE 6. Find the lowest common multiple of 3,850 and 5,280.

Solution: As in Examples 1 and 2

$$3,850 = 2 \times 5^2 \times 7 \times 11;$$
$$5,280 = 2^5 \times 3 \times 5 \times 11.$$

The lowest common multiple of 3,850 and 5,280 is $2^5 \times 3 \times 5^2 \times 7 \times 11$; that is, 184,800.

We use the lowest common multiple of the denominators of two fractions when we add or subtract fractions. For example, the lowest common multiple of 12 and 18 is 36;

$$\frac{7}{12} + \frac{5}{18} = \frac{21}{36} + \frac{10}{36} = \frac{31}{36}.$$

The answer is in reduced form since 31 and 36 are relatively prime.

EXAMPLE 7. Simplify: $\dfrac{37}{5,280} - \dfrac{19}{3,850}.$

Solution: We use the lowest common multiple as found in Example 6.

$$\frac{37}{5,280} - \frac{19}{3,850} = \frac{37}{2^5 \times 3 \times 5 \times 11} - \frac{19}{2 \times 5^2 \times 7 \times 11}$$

$$= \frac{37 \times 5 \times 7}{2^5 \times 3 \times 5^2 \times 7 \times 11} - \frac{19 \times 2^4 \times 3}{2^5 \times 3 \times 5^2 \times 7 \times 11}$$

$$= \frac{1,295 - 962}{2^5 \times 3 \times 5^2 \times 7 \times 11} = \frac{383}{184,800}.$$

The instruction "simplify" is used as in Example 7 to mean "perform the indicated operations and express the answer in simplest form." In the case of fractions "express in simplest form" means "reduce to lowest terms."

Exercises

Find the prime factorization of each counting number:

1. 68.   **2.** 76.   **3.** 123.   **4.** 215.

5. 1,425.   **6.** 738.   **7.** 819.   **8.** 341.

Find the greatest common divisor of:

9. 68 and 76.   **10.** 123 and 215.   **11.** 76 and 1,425.

12. 123 and 1,425.   **13.** 215 and 1,425.   **14.** 68 and 738.

Find the lowest common multiple of:

15. 68 and 76.   **16.** 123 and 215.   **17.** 76 and 1,425.

18. 123 and 1,425.   **19.** 215 and 1,425.   **20.** 68 and 738.

Simplify:

21. $\dfrac{123}{215}$.   **22.** $\dfrac{76}{1,425}$.   **23.** $\dfrac{11}{12} - \dfrac{9}{18}$.

24. $\dfrac{5}{68} + \dfrac{11}{76}$.   **25.** $\dfrac{7}{123} - \dfrac{2}{215}$.   **26.** $\dfrac{41}{215} + \dfrac{19}{1,425}$.

7-4 Order Relations

The set of numbers $\{1, 3, 5\}$ is *equivalent* to the set of numbers $\{3, 1, 5\}$ since two sets are equivalent if they have the same members. However, we think of the elements of the set $\{1, 3, 5\}$ as being listed in their natural order whereas the elements of the set $\{3, 1, 5\}$ are not listed in their natural order. The purpose of this section is to extend our intuitive concept of the order of counting numbers.

The counting numbers are normally listed as

$$\{1, 2, 3, 4, 5, 6, 7, \ldots\}$$

and this ordering of them is considered to be their **natural order**. Let a and b represent counting numbers. We define a to be less than b (that is, $a < b$) if and only if there is a counting number c such that $a + c = b$. In other words, $a < b$ if and only if a precedes b when the counting numbers are considered in their natural order. Then $2 < 5$ since $2 + 3 = 5$; $6 < 7$ since $6 + 1 = 7$.

We define $b > a$ if and only if $a < b$. Then $5 > 2$ since $2 < 5$; $7 > 6$ since $6 < 7$.

The following relations between counting numbers have been or may be defined for counting numbers:

$a = b$ if and only if a and b stand for the same number;

$a \neq b$ (read "a is not equal to b") if and only if a and b stand for different numbers;

$a < b$ (read "a is less than b") if and only if there exists a counting number c such that $a + c = b$;

$a \not< b$ (read "a is not less than b") if and only if there does not exist a counting number c such that $a + c = b$;

$b > a$ (read "b is greater than a") if and only if $a < b$;

$b \not> a$ (read "b is not greater than a") if and only if $a \not< b$;

$b \leq a$ (read "b is less than or equal to a") if and only if $b \not> a$; and

$a \geq b$ (read "a is greater than or equal to b") if and only if $b \leq a$.

The last two relations are based upon a very important **trichotomy** principle of the counting numbers: *if a and b stand for counting numbers, then exactly one of the relations*

$$a < b, \qquad a = b, \qquad a > b$$

must hold. In other words, in the natural ordering of the counting numbers a precedes b, a and b stand for the same number, or b precedes a. Then if $a \neq b$ either $a < b$ or $b < a$. This is often called the **comparison property** of the numbers.

Here are a few examples of correct statements according to the natural order of the numbers: $2 < 5$, $3 \leq 7$, $4 \leq 4$, $7 \geq 6$, $7 \geq 7$, $6 \neq 7$.

Exercises

In Exercises 1 through 12 consider the natural order of the counting numbers and insert the proper symbol ($<$, $=$, or $>$):

1. $3 \underline{\leq} 6$.

2. $11 \underline{\qquad} 17$.

3. $7 \underline{\leq} 11$.

4. $7 \underline{\qquad} 3$.

5. $3 + 4 \underline{\geq} 5$.

6. $3 + 4 \underline{\qquad} 7$.

7. $3 - 2 \underline{\leq} 5 - 3$.

8. $7 + 5 \underline{\qquad} 5 + 7$.

9. $5 \times 6 \underline{=} 6 \times 5$.

10. $120 \div 30 \underline{\qquad} 120 \div 40$.

11. $720 \div 180 \underline{\leq} 720 \div 120$.

12. $17 \times 31 \underline{\qquad} 17 \times 29$.

13. Repeat Exercises 1 through 12 using the symbols $=$ and $\neq$.

14. Repeat Exercises 1 through 12 using the symbols $<$ and $\geq$.

15. Repeat Exercises 1 through 12 using the symbols $>$ and $\leq$.

List the counting numbers $n \leq 10$ such that:

16. $n + 2 \geq 5$.

17. $n + 1 < 7$.

18. $2n > 11$.

19. $3n < 13$.

20. $7 < n - 2$.

21. $2n - 5 \geq 7$.

22. $3 + 2n \leq 17$.

23. $n^2 > 5 + n$.

24. $n + 2 \leq 3n$.

†**25.** $n + 5 \leq 9 - n$.

7-5 Integers

Each of the counting numbers may be used as the cardinal number of a set as in § 7-1. The number 0 was defined as the cardinal number of the empty set. The set of numbers

$$\{0, 1, 2, 3, 4, 5, \ldots\}$$

is the set of **finite cardinal numbers** and is often called simply the set of **whole numbers**.

The number 0 has the properties

$$0 + a = a = a + 0 \quad \text{and} \quad 0 \times a = 0 = a \times 0$$

for every whole number a. Also

$$0 < b$$

for every counting number b since $0 + b = b$. Furthermore $bd = 0$ if and only if $b = 0$ and/or $d = 0$; that is, $bd \neq 0$ if $b \neq 0$ and $d \neq 0$.

Each whole number may be associated with a set of elements such that the sum of the numbers is associated with the union of the two sets. Thus the sum of any two whole numbers is a whole number. Also the product of any two whole numbers is a whole number. Differences of whole numbers may or may not be whole numbers; for example, $5 - 3 = 2$ but $3 - 5$ does not stand for a whole number. Also, quotients of whole numbers may or may not stand for whole numbers; for example, $6 \div 2 = 3$ but $5 \div 2$ does not stand for a whole number. In this section we extend the set of numbers under consideration so that all differences of whole numbers are numbers; that is, subtraction is always possible. In § 7-6 we further extend the set of numbers under consideration so that division except by zero is always possible; division by zero is excluded.

If $b + d = x$, we call x the **sum** of b and d. If $b + x = d$, we call x the **difference** $d - b$. If $b = d$, then $b + 0 = d$ and the difference $d - b = 0$. If $b \neq d$, then as in § 7-4 either

$$b < d, \quad b + c = d \quad \text{and} \quad d - b = c$$

or

$$b > d, \quad d < b, \quad d + e = b \quad \text{and} \quad b - d = e.$$

Thus at least one of the differences $d - b, b - d$ is a whole number for any two whole numbers b and d. In order to have all differences as numbers, we introduce for each whole number c a new type of number $-c$ (called a **negative number** and read as "negative c") such that if $d > b$ and $d - b = c$, then $b - d = -c$.

Now subtraction is always possible:

if $b = d$, we have

$$b - d = d - b = 0;$$

if $b < d$, $b + c = d$ and we have

$$d - b = c \quad \text{and} \quad b - d = -c;$$

if $b > d$, $b = d + e$ and we have

$$b - d = e \quad \text{and} \quad d - b = -e.$$

The set consisting of the counting numbers b, their negatives, and the number 0 is called the set of **integers**:

$$\{\ldots, -5, -4, -3, -2, -1, 0, 1, 2, 3, 4, 5, \ldots\}.$$

The numbers of the set

$$\{1, 2, 3, 4, 5, \ldots\}$$

are called **positive integers** and the numbers of the set

$$\{-1, -2, -3, -4, -5, \ldots\}$$

are called **negative integers**. Notice that zero is an integer but is neither positive nor negative. The integers may be represented on a number line as follows (§ 7-8):

We assume that $0 + a = a = a + 0$ and $0 \times a = 0 = a \times 0$ for every integer a. Then

$$a - 0 = a \quad \text{and} \quad 0 - a = -a.$$

In general, addition, subtraction, and multiplication of integers are defined so that they are consistent with the operations upon counting numbers. In more advanced courses it can be proved that

$$2 + (-2) = 0; \quad (-2) + 2 = 0;$$
$$7 + (-7) = 0; \quad (-7) + 7 = 0;$$

and so forth. In general, since

$$b + (-b) = 0 \quad \text{and} \quad (-b) + b = 0$$

for any integer b, we call each of the numbers b and $-b$ **the negative of** the other. Thus -2 is the negative of 2 and also 2 is the negative of -2. The negative of a positive number is a negative number; the negative of a negative number is a positive number; the negative of 0 is 0. In general, the negative of a number is its inverse with respect to addition.

The properties of negative numbers may be used in subtraction problems:

$$5 - 2 = 5 + (-2); \quad 7 - 4 = 7 + (-4); \quad 6 - (-4) = 6 + 4;$$

in general, for any integers b and d

$$b - d = b + (-d).$$

This relationship may be taken as the definition of subtraction. It enables us to replace any subtraction problem by an equivalent addition problem. To subtract a number, add its negative; that is, in the language of the old rule, "to subtract a number, change its sign and add."

Notice that under the usual properties of addition and multiplication:

$$5 + (-5) = 0;$$
$$2 \times [5 + (-5)] = 2 \times 0 = 0;$$
$$(2 \times 5) + [2 \times (-5)] = 0 \qquad \text{(by the distributive property).}$$

Since the sum of 2×5 and $2 \times (-5)$ is zero, each must be the negative of the other. Then since $2 \times 5 = 10$, we have $2 \times (-5) = -10$. Also since $2 \times (-5) = (-5) \times 2$, we have $(-5) \times 2 = -10$. In general, for any positive integers b and c:

$$b + (-b) = 0;$$
$$c \times [b + (-b)] = c \times 0 = 0;$$
$$(c \times b) + [c \times (-b)] = 0;$$

whence $c \times b$ and $c \times (-b)$ are each the negative of the other; $c \times b = cb$ and $c \times (-b) = -cb$. Since $cb = bc$ and $c \times (-b) = (-b) \times c$, we have $(-b) \times c = -bc$. Thus the product of a positive integer and a negative integer is a negative integer.

Similarly, notice that under the usual properties of addition and multiplication:

$$5 + (-5) = 0;$$
$$(-2) \times [5 + (-5)] = (-2) \times 0 = 0;$$
$$[(-2) \times 5] + [(-2) \times (-5)] = 0 \qquad \text{(by the distributive property).}$$

Since the sum of $(-2) \times 5$ and $(-2) \times (-5)$ is zero, each must be the negative of the other. Then, since $(-2) \times 5 = -10$, we have $(-2) \times (-5) = 10$. In general, for any positive integers b and c:

$$b + (-b) = 0;$$
$$(-c) \times [b + (-b)] = (-c) \times 0 = 0;$$
$$[(-c) \times b] + [(-c) \times (-b)] = 0;$$

whence $(-c) \times b$ and $(-c) \times (-b)$ are each the negative of the other. Then, since $(-c) \times b = -cb$, we have $(-c) \times (-b) = cb$. Thus the product of two negative integers is a positive integer. Briefly, the operations on integers are defined to keep as many as possible of the properties that the operations had for counting numbers. In more advanced courses it is proved that the integers form a *commutative group* (see § 3-2) under addition since the set

(a) is *closed* with respect to addition (the sum of any two integers is an integer),

(b) is *commutative* with respect to addition ($p + q = q + p$ for any two integers p and q),

(c) is *associative* with respect to addition $[p + (q + r) = (p + q) + r$ for any three integers p, q, and $r]$,

(d) contains an *identity element*, 0, with respect to addition, and

(e) contains an *inverse* (called the negative) for each of its elements with respect to addition.

The set of integers is also closed, commutative, and associative with respect to multiplication; and contains an identity element 1 with respect to multiplication. The set of integers does not contain inverses for each of its elements with respect to multiplication. However, the *distributive property* of multiplication with respect to addition does hold:

$$p(q + r) = pq + pr.$$

EXAMPLE. Express $5 - (3 - 4)$ as an integer.

Solution: $5 - (3 - 4) = 5 - (-1) = 5 + 1 = 6.$

Exercises

1. What is the intersection of the set of positive integers and the set of negative integers?

2. Is the union of the set of positive integers and the set of negative integers equal to the set of integers? Explain your answer.

3. Find the negative of:

(a) 2;   **(b)** -5;   **(c)** 8;   **(d)** -7.

4. Find the inverse with respect to addition of:

(a) 3;   **(b)** -4;   **(c)** 17;   **(d)** -25.

5. Given that $a > b > 0$, compare $-a$ and $-b$.

Express as an integer:

6. $(5 - 2) + (2 - 1)$.   **7.** $(3 - 1) + (4 - 2)$.

8. $(0 - 3) \times (0 - 2)$.   **9.** $(1 - 5) \times (6 - 7)$.

10. $(7 - 4) + (11 - 7)$.   **11.** $(7 - 4) \times (11 - 7)$.

12. $(1 - 6) + (13 - 5)$.   **13.** $(19 - 11) + (7 - 3)$.

14. $(1 - 6) \times (13 - 5)$.   **15.** $(19 - 11) \times (7 - 3)$.

16. $(2 - 6) - (4 - 1)$.   **17.** $(7 - 2) - (3 - 11)$.

7-6 Rational Numbers ✓

The integers were introduced as differences of cardinal numbers. We now introduce the rational numbers as quotients of integers. In other words, we extend our concept of number to include $\frac{3}{2}, \frac{7}{8}, \frac{112}{5}$, and, in general, $\frac{a}{b}$, where a stands for any integer and b stands for any integer different from zero.

As in the case of the integers we must define the conditions under which two of the new symbols stand for the same number. Notice that $\frac{6}{12} = \frac{1}{2} = \frac{5}{10}$; also $\frac{6}{3} = \frac{18}{9} = \frac{2}{1}$. In general, we define

$$\frac{a}{b} = \frac{c}{d} \quad \text{if and only if} \quad ad = bc.$$

The equality $ad = bc$ involves only products of integers and thus only integers.

This definition gives rise to a very useful rule

$$\frac{a}{b} = \frac{ak}{bk} \qquad \text{for any integer } k \neq 0,$$

since $a(bk) = b(ak)$, even though we have not explicitly developed this property of integers. This rule enables us to find as many ways of writing a rational number as we like. For example,

$$\frac{2}{3} = \frac{4}{6} = \frac{6}{9} = \frac{8}{12} = \frac{10}{15} = \cdots.$$

The rule also allows us to "reduce" quotients by finding factors k as in these examples:

$$\frac{12}{30} = \frac{2 \times 6}{5 \times 6} = \frac{2}{5};$$

$$\frac{72}{18} = \frac{36}{9} = \frac{4}{1};$$

$$\frac{16}{80} = \frac{1}{5}.$$

Each quotient $\frac{a}{b}$ has two parts: the **numerator** a and the **denominator** b. In one sense the denominator names the fractional part under consideration and the numerator tells the number of those units. For example, $\frac{3}{4}$ may be thought of as three-fourths $\left(\text{i.e., as } 3 \times \frac{1}{4}\right)$ of a complete unit.

The rule $\frac{a}{b} = \frac{ak}{bk}$ means that the numerator a and the denominator b of any quotient $\frac{a}{b}$ may both be multiplied by the same integer k for any $k \neq 0$

without changing the **value** of the quotient, i.e., without changing the rational number that the quotient represents. When considered in the form $\frac{ak}{bk} = \frac{a}{b}$, the rule implies that the numerator and denominator may both be divided by any integer k that divides them both without changing the value of the quotient. We use this rule to pick the most useful representation of any set of quotients representing the same rational number. We select $\frac{1}{2}$ as the representative of the set

$$\left\{ \frac{1}{2}, \frac{2}{4}, \frac{3}{6}, \frac{4}{8}, \frac{5}{10}, \cdots \right\};$$

we select $\frac{3}{1}$ as the representative of the set

$$\left\{ \frac{3}{1}, \frac{6}{2}, \frac{9}{3}, \frac{12}{4}, \frac{15}{5}, \cdots \right\}.$$

Whenever it is possible to select a representative with either its numerator or its denominator 1 we do so. When it is not possible to find a representative having 1 as one of its elements we select the representative for which there are no positive integers k greater than 1 that divide both the numerator and denominator. For example, we select $\frac{2}{3}$ as the representative of the set

$$\left\{ \frac{2}{3}, \frac{4}{6}, \frac{6}{9}, \frac{8}{12}, \frac{10}{15}, \cdots \right\}.$$

The set of **rational numbers** consists of the set of quotients of integers $\frac{a}{b}$ where $b \neq 0$. We have specified the conditions under which two quotients stand for the same number, i.e., are equal. Some people define all rational numbers to be "fractions." We shall associate rational numbers that can be expressed in the form $\frac{a}{1}$ with the integers a and call these rational numbers "integers." Then the rational numbers that are not integers are called **fractions.** For example, we write, $\frac{12}{3} = \frac{4}{1} = 4$ and call $\frac{12}{3}$ an integer since it is another expression for 4. However, $\frac{18}{12} = \frac{3}{2}$ and cannot be written in the form $\frac{a}{1}$ for any integer a; therefore $\frac{18}{12}$ is a fraction. The set of rational numbers includes the integers and the fractions.

The sum of any two rational numbers is defined to be a rational number:

$$\frac{a}{b} + \frac{c}{d} = \frac{ad + bc}{bd}.$$

For example, $\frac{1}{3} + \frac{1}{2} = \frac{2+3}{6} = \frac{5}{6}$. This is consistent with the procedure

$$\frac{1}{3} = \frac{2}{6}, \quad \frac{1}{2} = \frac{3}{6}, \quad \frac{1}{3} + \frac{1}{2} = \frac{2}{6} + \frac{3}{6} = \frac{5}{6},$$

which we often justify by using the distributive property of multiplication with respect to addition (see § 3-3):

$$\frac{1}{3} + \frac{1}{2} = \frac{1 \times 2}{3 \times 2} + \frac{1 \times 3}{2 \times 3} = \frac{2}{6} + \frac{3}{6} = \frac{1}{6}(2+3) = \frac{2+3}{6};$$

$$\frac{a}{b} + \frac{c}{d} = \frac{ad}{bd} + \frac{bc}{bd} = \frac{1}{bd}(ad + bc) = \frac{ad+bc}{bd}.$$

The negative of a rational number $\frac{2}{3}$ may be expressed in any one of the following ways:

$$-\frac{2}{3}, \quad \frac{-2}{3} \quad \text{and} \quad \frac{2}{-3}.$$

The form $\frac{-a}{b}$ is usually the most convenient. Notice that by the definition of the sum of two rational numbers

$$\frac{2}{3} + \frac{-2}{3} = \frac{2(3) + 3(-2)}{3 \times 3} = \frac{6 + (-6)}{9} = \frac{0}{9} = 0$$

and, in general,

$$\frac{a}{b} + \frac{-a}{b} = \frac{ab + b(-a)}{b^2} = \frac{ab + (-ab)}{b^2} = \frac{0}{b^2} = 0.$$

Then, as in the case of integers, we may define subtraction in terms of an equivalent addition;

$$\frac{a}{b} - \frac{c}{d} = \frac{a}{b} + \frac{-c}{d}.$$

The product of any two rational numbers is defined to be a rational number:

$$\frac{a}{b} \times \frac{c}{d} = \frac{ac}{bd}.$$

Note that $bd \neq 0$ since $b \neq 0$ and $d \neq 0$. Consider these examples:

$$\frac{2}{3} \times \frac{5}{6} = \frac{10}{18} = \frac{5}{9}; \quad \frac{4}{5} \times \frac{25}{2} = \frac{100}{10} = \frac{10}{1} = 10.$$

Just as the integers gave rise to integers when added, multiplied, or subtracted, so all sums, products, and differences of rational numbers are rational numbers. However, in the set of rational numbers we also obtain a rational number when we divide by any number different from zero. We define the **reciprocal** of any rational number $\frac{a}{b}$ different from zero to be the

rational number $\frac{b}{a}$. Notice that

$$\frac{a}{b} \times \frac{b}{a} = \frac{ab}{ba} = 1;$$

that is, the reciprocal of a number is its inverse with respect to multiplication. Then we define **division** in terms of an equivalent multiplication; for

any $\frac{c}{d} \neq 0$,

$$\frac{a}{b} \div \frac{c}{d} = \frac{a}{b} \times \frac{d}{c}.$$

In other words, to divide by a number different from zero we multiply by its reciprocal. This is a formal statement of the common procedure described by "invert and multiply." This procedure may also be justified as follows:

$$\frac{\frac{a}{b}}{\frac{c}{d}} = \frac{\frac{a}{b} \times \frac{d}{c}}{\frac{c}{d} \times \frac{d}{c}} = \frac{\frac{a}{b} \times \frac{d}{c}}{1} = \frac{a}{b} \times \frac{d}{c}.$$

Order relations for the rational numbers are defined in terms of the order relations for integers. First each rational number is expressed so that its denominator is positive; then $0 < b$, $0 < d$, and

$$\frac{a}{b} < \frac{c}{d} \quad \text{if and only if} \quad ad < bc.$$

Notice that under this definition

$$\frac{2}{1} < \frac{3}{1}, \qquad \frac{-4}{1} < \frac{-3}{1}, \qquad \frac{2}{3} < \frac{7}{8}.$$

In general, the order relations for the integers are the same as before, and the concept of order has been extended to include all rational numbers.

The rational numbers are closed, associative, and commutative with respect to both addition and multiplication. The identity elements, 0 for addition and 1 for multiplication, are both rational numbers. The negative (inverse with respect to addition) of any rational number is a rational number; the reciprocal (inverse with respect to multiplication) of any rational number different from zero is a rational number. Also the distributive property of multiplication with respect to addition holds for rational numbers.

A few other properties of rational numbers are considered in the exercises.

Exercises

1. Is every integer a rational number?

2. Is every rational number an integer?

3. What is the inverse under multiplication of

(a) 3;   (b) -2;   (c) $\dfrac{5}{3}$;   (d) $\dfrac{-1}{2}$.

4. Given that $a > b > 0$, compare $\dfrac{1}{a}$ and $\dfrac{1}{b}$.

5. Given that $a < b < 0$, compare $\dfrac{1}{a}$ and $\dfrac{1}{b}$.

Give three quotients representing each rational number:

6. $\dfrac{1}{2}$.   7. $\dfrac{3}{4}$.   8. $\dfrac{6}{18}$.

9. $\dfrac{-2}{5}$.   10. $\dfrac{125}{25}$.   11. $\dfrac{-12}{64}$.

Find the most useful representative of the set of rational numbers represented by each expression:

12. $\dfrac{2}{3} + \dfrac{1}{2}$.   13. $\dfrac{5}{6} + \dfrac{3}{4}$.   14. $\dfrac{6}{18} \times \dfrac{10}{7}$.

15. $\dfrac{12}{15} \times \dfrac{28}{10}$.   16. $\dfrac{2}{3} \div \dfrac{4}{5}$.   17. $\dfrac{7}{8} \div \dfrac{3}{4}$.

18. $\dfrac{5}{12} \div \dfrac{10}{18}$.   19. $\dfrac{17}{34} \div \dfrac{25}{10}$.   20. $\dfrac{5}{6} - \dfrac{1}{3}$.

21. $\dfrac{2}{5} - \dfrac{1}{4}$.   22. $\dfrac{15}{8} - \dfrac{3}{4}$.   23. $\dfrac{11}{9} - \dfrac{7}{5}$.

Give an example illustrating each statement:

24. The sum of two fractions may be an integer.

25. The product of two fractions may be an integer.

26. The quotient of two fractions may be an integer

Prove the following:

†27. Any difference of rational numbers is a rational number.

†**28.** Any quotient of rational numbers $\frac{a}{b} \div \frac{c}{d}$, where $\frac{c}{d} \neq 0$, is a rational number.

†**29.** Any rational number may be expressed in the form $\frac{a}{b}$, where $0 < b$.

7-7 Odd Integers and Even Integers

An integer is **even** if it is a multiple of 2; that is, if it may be expressed as $2k$, where k stands for an integer. Then the set of even integers is

$$\{\ldots, -6, -4, -2, 0, 2, 4, 6, \ldots\}.$$

An integer that is not even is said to be **odd**. Each odd integer may be expressed in the form $2k + 1$, where k stands for an integer. Then the set of odd integers is

$$\{\ldots, -7, -5, -3, -1, 1, 3, 5, 7, \ldots\}.$$

In this section we use the properties of integers and rational numbers to prove some of the properties of odd and even integers. These proofs illustrate the type of reasoning that mathematicians use. Note that any sum, product, or difference of any two integers is an integer. We consider these same properties for even integers and odd integers to determine whether or not they are true for these sets of numbers.

EXAMPLE 1. Prove that the sum of any two even integers is an even integer.

Proof: Any two even integers m and n may be expressed as $2k$ and $2r$, where k and r stand for integers. Then

$$m + n = 2k + 2r = 2(k + r)$$

where $k + r$ stands for an integer since the sum of any two integers is an integer. Therefore $m + n$ is an even integer.

EXAMPLE 2. Prove that the square of any even integer is an even integer.

Proof: Any even integer may be expressed as $2k$, where k stands for an integer. Then the square of the integer may be expressed as $(2k)^2$, where

$$(2k)^2 = (2k)(2k) = 2(2k^2).$$

Since k, k^2, and $2k^2$ all stand for integers, $(2k)^2$ stands for an even integer.

EXAMPLE 3. Prove that any rational number may be expressed in the form $\frac{a}{b}$, where a and b are not both even.

Proof: By definition any rational number may be expressed as a quotient of integers $\frac{p}{q}$. If p and q are both even, then $p = 2k$, $q = 2m$, and

$$\frac{p}{q} = \frac{2k}{2m} = \frac{k}{m}.$$

If k and m are both even, we repeat the process. Since p was a given integer, it is finite, and a finite number of steps of the form just considered must lead to an expression of the form $\frac{a}{b}$, where a and b are not both even.

Several other properties of even integers and odd integers are considered in the exercises.

Exercises

Prove each statement:

1. The sum of any two odd integers is an even integer.

2. The product of any two even integers is an even integer.

3. The square of any odd integer is an odd integer.

4. If the square of an integer is odd, the integer is odd; if the square of an integer is even, the integer is even.

7-8 Real Numbers

In mathematics we are concerned with the four fundamental operations $(+, -, \times, \div)$. The rational numbers have been introduced so that these operations are always possible except for division by zero. We are also concerned with points on a number line. We identify the points by numbers which we call the **coordinates** of the points.

Given any line we may select any point of the line as the **origin** with coordinate 0 and any other point as the **unit point** with coordinate 1. Usually the line is taken in a horizontal position with the unit point on the right of the origin.

The length of the line segment with the origin and the unit point as end-points is the unit distance for marking off a scale on the line. The points representing any given counting numbers may be obtained by marking off successive units on the right of the origin.

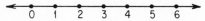

The points representing integers may be obtained by including the origin and marking off units on both the left and the right of the origin.

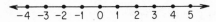

Notice that the points with positive integers as coordinates are on the same side of the origin as the unit point (that is, on the half-line that has the origin as an end-point and includes the unit point); the points with negative integers as coordinates are on the opposite side of the origin from the unit point (that is, on the half-line that has the origin as an end-point and does not include the unit point). The origin divides the line into two half-lines and does not belong to either half-line; when the integers are ordered as on the number line, 0 divides the integers into the set of positive integers and the set of negative integers and does not belong to either set.

Consider the line segment with the origin and unit point as end points. The point with coordinate $\frac{1}{2}$ divides this segment into two equal segments. The points with coordinates $\frac{1}{3}$ and $\frac{2}{3}$ divide this segment into 3 equal parts. The points with coordinates $\frac{1}{5}$, $\frac{2}{5}$, $\frac{3}{5}$, $\frac{4}{5}$, divide this line segment into five equal parts.

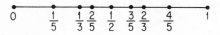

There are many rational numbers between 0 and 1. If we try to place dots for each point with a rational number as a coordinate, the line segment, and in general the line, appears to be solid. This solid appearance is due to the "density" of the rational numbers. The rational numbers are said to be **dense,** since there is a rational number between any two given rational numbers.

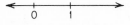

The appearance of a solid line of points with rational numbers as coordinates is misleading. For example, if we assume there is a number that represents the length of a diagonal of a unit square, the square of that number must be 2. We call the number $\sqrt{2}$ and can locate a point

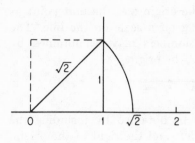

with coordinate $\sqrt{2}$ on the number line. However, the number $\sqrt{2}$ cannot be a rational number. Suppose that $\frac{a}{b}$ is a rational number, where a and b are not both even numbers (see Example 3 of § 7-7) and

$$\frac{a}{b} \times \frac{a}{b} = 2; \quad \text{that is,} \quad \frac{a}{b} = \sqrt{2}.$$

Then $a^2 = 2b^2$ and a is an integer whose square is even. Therefore, as in § 7-7, Exercise 4, a must be even; that is, $a = 2k$, where k stands for an integer. If we use $2k$ for a, we have

$$(2k)^2 = 2b^2, \quad 4k^2 = 2b^2, \quad 2k^2 = b^2;$$

b is an integer whose square is even, and b must be an even integer. This is contrary to the assumption that a and b were not both even. Our assumption that there exists a rational number whose square is 2 has led to a contradiction. In other words, if there is a number whose square is 2, that number cannot be a rational number.

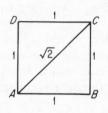

There exist line segments of length $\sqrt{2}$. For example, as we have observed, the diagonal $\overline{AC}$ of a square $ABCD$ with each side 1 unit long has length $\sqrt{2}$. We need numbers to represent lengths of line segments and thus need numbers that are not rational numbers. This is equivalent to having a coordinate for each point on the positive side of the origin on a number line. These numbers that are not rational numbers are called **irrational numbers**. We need irrational numbers such as $\sqrt{2}$ in order to have coordinates for each point on a line. We call the set of rational and irrational numbers the set of **real numbers**. There is a one-to-one correspondence between elements of the set of points on a line and the elements of the set of real numbers.

Any real number is either rational or irrational. We frequently represent real numbers by decimals and recognize three types of decimals:

terminating decimals, such as $\frac{1}{4} = 0.25$;

repeating decimals, such as

$$\frac{1}{3} = 0.333\overline{3}\ldots \quad \text{and} \quad \frac{12}{7} = 1.714285\overline{714285}\ldots;$$

nonterminating, nonrepeating decimals, such as

$$\sqrt{2} = 1.4142\ldots \quad \text{and} \quad \pi = 3.1415926\ldots.$$

Note the use of a bar over the repeated digits or digit and the assumption that such a pattern of repeated digits does not occur when the bar is missing. You may, if you wish, think of any terminating decimal as having repeated zeros; $\frac{1}{4} = 0.2500\bar{0}\ldots$. Each terminating or repeating decimal represents a rational number; each nonterminating, nonrepeating decimal represents an irrational number, that is, a real number that is not a rational number.

If a decimal is terminating, you can write it as a fraction with a power of 10 as the denominator. For example, if $n = 0.7500\bar{0}\ldots$, then $100n = 75$, and $n = \frac{75}{100}$, which reduces to $\frac{3}{4}$. If a fraction can be expressed as a terminating decimal, its denominator must be a factor of a power of 10. If a decimal is repeating, it can be written as a rational number. For example, if a decimal n repeats one digit, we can find $10n - n$. For example, suppose $n = 3.244\bar{4}\ldots$. Then,

$$10n = 32.444\bar{4}\ldots$$
$$\underline{n = 3.244\bar{4}\ldots}$$
$$9n = 29.200\bar{0}\ldots$$

$$n = \frac{29.2}{9} = \frac{292}{90} = \frac{146}{45}.$$

We can also avoid the use of decimals in common fractions:

$$100n = 324.44\bar{4}$$
$$\underline{10n = 32.44\bar{4}}$$
$$90n = 292$$

$$n = \frac{292}{90} = \frac{146}{45}.$$

If a decimal n repeats two digits, we find $10^2 n - n$; if it repeats three digits, we find $10^3 n - n$; and so forth.

EXAMPLE. Express $0.78346\overline{346}\ldots$ as a quotient of integers.

Solution:

$$1,000n = 783.46\overline{346}\ldots$$
$$\underline{n = 0.78346\overline{346}\ldots}$$
$$999n = 782.68$$

$$n = \frac{782.68}{999} = \frac{78,268}{99,900} = \frac{19,567}{24,975}.$$

We have seen how any repeating decimal can be written as a rational number. Now consider any rational number such as $\frac{12}{7}$. When we divide by 7, the possible remainders are 0, 1, 2, 3, 4, 5, 6. If the remainder is 0, the division is exact; if any remainder occurs a second time, the terms after it will repeat also. Since there are only 7 possible remainders when you divide by 7, the remainders must repeat or be exact by the seventh decimal place. Consider the determination of the decimal value of $\frac{12}{7}$ by long division:

$$
\begin{array}{r}
1.\overline{714285}\ldots \\
7\,\overline{\smash{)}\,12.000000\ldots} \\
\underline{7} \\
\textcircled{5}0 \\
\underline{49} \\
10 \\
\underline{7} \\
30 \\
\underline{28} \\
20 \\
\underline{14} \\
60 \\
\underline{56} \\
40 \\
\underline{35} \\
\textcircled{5}
\end{array}
$$

The fact that the remainder 5 occurred again implies that the same steps will be used again in the long division process and the digits 714285 will be repeated over and over; that is, $\frac{12}{7} = 1.714285\overline{714285}\ldots$. Similarly, any rational number $\frac{p}{q}$ can be expressed as a terminating or repeating decimal, and at most q decimal places will be needed to identify it.

The real numbers may be classified in several ways. Any real number is:

1. positive, negative, or zero;
2. a rational number or an irrational number;
3. expressible as a terminating, a repeating, or nonterminating, non-repeating decimal.

The relationship of the set of real numbers to some of the other sets of numbers that we have studied is shown in the following array:

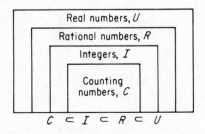

The real numbers are important because they have the property that each point on a number line has a real number as its coordinate and conversely each real number has a point on the number line as its **graph**. The real numbers may be ordered according to the order of their graphs. When the point with coordinate 1 is on the right of the point with coordinate 0, $a < b$ if and only if the point with coordinate b is on the right of the point with coordinate a.

Exercises

Tell whether or not each number is **(a)** *an integer;* **(b)** *a rational number;* **(c)** *an irrational number;* **(d)** *a real number:*

1. 5.

2. 5.76.

3. −3.

4. 1.73$\overline{73}$ . . . .

5. $\sqrt{2}$.

6. 3.1415926 . . . , i.e., π.

7. 0.0027$\overline{27}$ . . . .

8. $\frac{19}{31}$.

9. $\sqrt{8}$.

10. $\sqrt{9}$.

Tell whether each number should be represented by a terminating, a repeating, or a nonterminating, nonrepeating decimal:

11. $\frac{3}{4}$.

12. $\frac{2}{5}$.

13. $\frac{2}{3}$.

14. $\frac{5}{12}$.

15. $\frac{13}{16}$.

16. $\sqrt{3}$.

†**17.** $\sqrt{625}$.

†**18.** $\sqrt{12.25}$.

†**19.** $\sqrt[3]{5}$.

Express each number as a decimal:

20. $\frac{3}{5}$.

21. $\frac{1}{6}$.

22. $\frac{27}{15}$.

23. $5\frac{3}{8}$.

†**24.** $129\frac{5}{64}$.

†**25.** $\sqrt{30.25}$.

Express each number as a quotient of integers:

26. 2.11$\overline{1}$ . . . .

27. 5.22$\overline{2}$ . . . .

28. 2.14$\overline{14}$ . . . .

29. 4.25$\overline{25}$ . . . .

30. 0.123$\overline{123}$ . . . .

31. 65.268$\overline{268}$ . . . .

32. 0.00345$\overline{345}$ . . . .

33. 0.00127926$\overline{926}$ . . . .

34. 7.1234$\overline{1234}$ . . . .

35. 256.46244$\overline{6244}$ . . . .

all

AN INTRODUCTION TO ALGEBRA

Algebra is an extension of the arithmetic of the integers, rational numbers, and real numbers that we studied in Chapter 7. In our study of algebra we first consider statements. Statements involving only numbers and operations on numbers can be identified as true or as false. Algebra differs from arithmetic in that statements in algebra also include *variables*; that is, symbols that may be replaced by any member of a set of elements. Statements that involve variables may be true for some replacements for the variables and false for others.

8-1 Sentences and Statements

We assume that the reader understands from his study of English what is meant by a sentence. We shall consider two types of sentences. Sentences such as $2 + 3 = 5$, which can be identified as true, and such as $2 \times 3 = 7$, which can be identified as false, are called **statements**. Sentences such as $x + 2 = 5$, which cannot be identified as true or as false without the introduction of additional information, are called **open sentences**.

We also assume that a sentence cannot be both true and false. Here are some examples of statements; that is, sentences that are true and sentences that are false:

(a) George Washington was the first President of the United States;
(b) Abraham Lincoln is President of the United States;
(c) $8 \times 2 = 16$ (a true statement of equality);
(d) $7 - 3 = 5$ (a false statement of equality).

We may also write statements of inequality using the symbolism introduced in § 7-3. Consider these examples:

(a) $5 - 2 \neq 4$ (a true statement of inequality);
(b) $8 \times 3 \neq 24$ (a false statement of inequality);
(c) $12 > -3$ (a true statement of inequality);
(d) $-3 < -5$ (a false statement of inequality).

Below are some examples of open sentences (neither true nor false):

(a) _____ is President of the United States;
(b) Mr. _____ is a teacher in this school;
(c) $x + 2 = 7$;
(d) $x - 3 = 4$.

In the preceding examples of open sentences, the blank spaces and the symbols x are called *variables*. In each case, the sentence is neither true nor false until a replacement is made for the variable. After such a replacement is made, we have a statement, that is, a sentence that can be classified as either true or false.

A **variable** is a placeholder for its replacements. Each blank in Examples (a) and (b) holds a place for the name of a person. Each x in Examples (c) and (d) holds a place for the name of a number, that is, for a numeral such as 5 or 7. When a replacement is a number, it is often called a **value** for the variable. We may abbreviate such statements and say that the variable is a placeholder for the name of a person or a number. Given any open sentence, there are certain names of people, numbers, and so forth, that may be used as possible replacements. In each case, this given set of possible replacements is called the **domain** of the variable. For example:

Christmas is in the month of _____.

The domain of the variable in this open sentence is the set of names of the 12 months. The statement is true when the replacement is "December"; the statement is false for other replacements. Here is another example:

A two-digit number may be represented as $10x + y$.

In this open sentence the domain of x is the set of digits $\{1, 2, 3, 4, 5, 6, 7, 8, 9\}$ and the domain of y is the set $\{0, 1, 2, 3, 4, 5, 6, 7, 8, 9\}$. Why is 0 excluded from the domain of x?

A variable that may be replaced by any real number is called a **real variable**. A variable that may be replaced by any rational number is called a **rational variable**. A variable that may be replaced by any integer is called an **integral variable**. A variable that may be replaced by any positive integer is called a **positive integral variable**.

There exist general statements that include variables and that are true for all possible replacements of the variables. For example, if x and y are real variables, then the statement

$$x + y = y + x$$

is a true statement of equality for all possible replacements of the variables. Such a general statement is often called a *law*; our example gives the commutative law for addition.

Exercises

Tell whether each statement is **(a)** *a statement of equality or a statement of inequality;* **(b)** *a true statement, a false statement, or an open sentence.*

1. $7 \times 8 = 54$.   **2.** $17 + 13 = 30$.

3. $\frac{2}{3} < \frac{5}{6}$.   **4.** $\frac{1}{2} > \frac{4}{7}$.

5. $\frac{8}{12} \geq \frac{2}{3}$.   **6.** $\frac{25}{30} \leq \frac{5}{6}$.

7. $7 \times 11 \neq 75$.   **8.** $19 \times 21 = 20^2 - 1$.

9. $39 \times 41 = 40^2 - 1$.   **10.** $(x - 1)(x + 1) = x^2 - 1$.

11. $8(5 + 3) = 8 \times 5 + 8$.   **12.** $(3) - (2) = (-2) - (3)$.

13. $7 - 3 \neq 9 - 5$.   **14.** $\frac{2}{3} - \frac{1}{2} \neq 4\frac{2}{3} - 4\frac{1}{2}$.

15. $\frac{432}{796} > \frac{432}{795}$.   **16.** $-\frac{432}{796} < -\frac{432}{795}$.

Write an expression for each of the following and give the domain of each variable used:

17. A number that exceeds 5 by a positive integral number of units.

18. A number that is two units more than a real variable x.

19. A number that is equal to the product of two rational numbers b and h.

20. A number that is three less than an integer n.

21. The perimeter of a square of side s.

22. The perimeter of an equilateral triangle of side s.

23. An odd integer.

24. A positive even integer.

25. The cost in dollars of n five-cent stamps and t eight-cent stamps.

†**26.** A three-digit integer.

8-2 Solution Sets

Given an open sentence, the set of replacements that makes the sentence true is called the **solution set** of the sentence. Each of the elements of the solution set is said to satisfy the open sentence. Thus, consider the sentence:

_____ is a vowel.

The solution set consists of the elements of the set {a, e, i, o, u}.

The following examples are presented in detail to illustrate the meaning of solution sets and their graphs in equations and inequalities. In each one, we are asked to find and graph the solution set.

EXAMPLE 1. $x + 3 = 5$. Domain of x: integers.

Solution: The solution set consists of the single element {2}. We can graph this solution set on a number line by drawing a solid dot at 2.

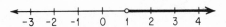

EXAMPLE 2. $x + 3 = 5$. Domain of x: negative integers.

Solution: We have an impossible equation; that is, no element in the domain will produce a true statement when used as a replacement for x. We say that the solution set is the empty set.

EXAMPLE 3. $x + 2 > 3$. Domain of x: real numbers.

Solution: The solution set consists of all the real numbers greater than 1. The graph of the solution set is drawn by placing a hollow dot at 1 on the number line to indicate that this is not a member of the solution set, and drawing a heavily shaded arrow to show that all numbers greater than 1 satisfy the given inequality.

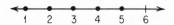

EXAMPLE 4. $x \le 5$ (read "x is less than or equal to 5"). Domain of x: positive integers.

Solution: The solution set of this inequality consists of the elements {1, 2, 3, 4, 5}. The graph of the solution set follows:

The sentence "$x \le 5$" may also be written as "$x < 5$ or $x = 5$." Notice the use of "or" in these open sentences. If *at least one* of these two open sentences is true when x is replaced by a numeral, the number is a member of the solution set of $x \leq 5$. For instance, when x is replaced by 5 in $x = 5$, the true statement $5 = 5$ is obtained; hence, 5 is a member of the solution set even though replacing x by 5 in $x < 5$ gives the false statement $5 < 5$. Similarly, when x is replaced by 3 in $x < 5$, the true statement $3 < 5$ is obtained; hence, 3 is a member of the solution set, even though replacing x by 3 in $x = 5$ gives a false statement.

For the domain given in this example, the solution set for $x < 5$ is $\{1, 2, 3, 4\}$; the solution set for $x = 5$ is $\{5\}$. Then the solution set for $x \leq 5$ may be considered as the *union* of these two sets.

EXAMPLE 5. $x \not> 5$ (read "x is not greater than 5"). Domain of x: positive integers.

Solution: Since, for any real number x, exactly one of the statements $x < 5$, $x = 5$, or $x > 5$ must hold, here x must be less than or equal to 5. This reduces to the same statement as in Example 4 and has the same domain. Thus, the solution set is the same as for Example 4.

EXAMPLE 6. $-1 < x \leq 3$. Domain of x: integers.

Solution: This inequality states that x is greater than -1, but is less than or equal to 3. The solution set consists of the elements $\{0, 1, 2, 3\}$. The graph of the solution set is:

For the domain given in this example, the solution set for $x \leq 3$ is $\{\ldots, -1, 0, 1, 2, 3\}$; the solution set for $-1 < x$ is $\{0, 1, 2, 3, 4, \ldots\}$. Then the solution set for $-1 < x \leq 3$ may be considered as the *intersection* of these two sets.

EXAMPLE 7. $-1 < x \leq 3$. Domain of x: real numbers.

Solution: This is the same sentence as in Example 6, but with a different domain. The graph of the solution set now includes all of the points on the number line between -1 and $+3$, including $+3$ but not -1:

EXAMPLE 8. $x + 3 < 5$. Domain of x: negative integers.

Solution: The solution set consists of the elements $\{-1, -2, -3, -4, -5, \ldots\}$. The graph of the solution set is:

EXAMPLE 9. $x + 2 = 2 + x$. Domain of x: real numbers.

Solution: This sentence is true for all replacements of x and thus is classified as an identity. The solution set is the entire domain, that is, the set of all real numbers. The graph of the solution set follows:

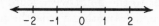

The symbol $|-3|$ is read "the *absolute value* of -3" and is equal to $+3$. In general, $|k|$ is read "the absolute value of k." On a number line, the point with coordinate k is at a distance $|k|$ from the origin. For example, the point with coordinate 3 is 3 units from the origin; also the point with coordinate -3 is 3 units from the origin. Notice that any number symbol with a plus sign may be written without the sign; any number symbol without a sign is assumed to have a plus sign. Thus, $3 = +3$, and $k = +k$ whether k is positive, negative, or zero. We define the **absolute value** of any real number k as follows:

$$|k| = k, \quad \text{if } k \text{ is positive;}$$
$$|k| = -k, \quad \text{if } k \text{ is negative;}$$
$$|k| = 0, \quad \text{if } k = 0.$$

Notice in the second case that if k represents a negative number, then $-k$ represents a positive number.

EXAMPLE 10. $|x| = 2$. Domain of x: real numbers.

Solution: The solution set of the statement $|x| = 2$ is the set of coordinates of points that are on a number line and at a distance of 2 units from the origin. Thus the solution set is $\{2, -2\}$ and is graphed as:

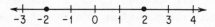

Notice that $|x| = 2$ may be considered as $|x - 0| = 2$ to emphasize the consideration of the distance from the origin.

EXAMPLE 11. $|x - 1| = 2$. Domain of x: real numbers.

Solution: The solution set consists of the coordinates of points that are on a number line and at a distance of 2 units from the point with coordinate 1. Thus $x - 1 = 2$ and $x = 3$ or $x - 1 = -2$ and $x = -1$. The solution set is $\{3, -1\}$ and may be graphed as:

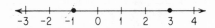

EXAMPLE 12. $|x - 1| < 2$. Domain of x: real numbers.

Solution: The solution set consists of the coordinates of points that are on a number line and at a distance of less than 2 units from the point with coordinate 1. From Example 11 each such point with coordinate x is nearer to the point with coordinate 1 than the points with coordinates -1 and 3. In other words, the points with coordinate x such that $|x - 1| < 2$ are between the point with coordinate -1 and the point with coordinate 3; each real number between -1 and 3 is a member of the solution set (that is, $-1 < x < 3$). This solution set may be graphed as:

Notice that the hollow dots show that the indicated end-points are not included in the graph of the solution set.

We now summarize the concepts considered in this section. An open sentence in one variable divides the domain of the variable into two *subsets:* one subset consists of replacements that make the sentence true; the other subset consists of the replacements that make the sentence false. A replacement that makes the sentence true is a *solution* of the sentence. The set of all solutions is the *solution set* of the sentence; the solution set is a subset of the domain. The complement of the solution set relative to the domain is the set of replacements that make the sentence false. The *graph* of an equation or an inequality is the graph of its solution set.

We can think of an equation such as $x + 2 = 5$ as a **set-selector**; it selects from the domain of x just those members which make the sentence true when used as replacements for x. The selected set is the solution set of the equation. The solution set $\{3\}$ is "the set of all x such that $x + 2 = 5$." We may designate this solution set in **set-builder notation** as

$$\{x \mid x + 2 = 5\}.$$

Then $\{x \mid x + 2 = 5\} = \{x \mid x = 3\} = \{3\}$; that is, the set of all x such that $x + 2 = 5$ equals the set of all x such that $x = 3$. Notice that the variable is given at the left of the bar; the set-selector sentence is given at the right. (Some texts use a colon instead of a bar; however, the meaning is the same.)

The domain of the variable may be indicated in the set-builder notation as in the following statements of the solution sets for the twelve examples considered in this section:

(1) $\{x \mid x + 3 = 5,\ x$ an integer$\}$.
(2) $\{x \mid x + 3 = 5,\ x$ a negative integer$\}$.
(3) $\{x \mid x + 2 > 3,\ x$ a real number$\}$.
(4) $\{x \mid x \leq 5,\ x$ a positive integer$\}$.
(5) $\{x \mid x \not> 5,\ x$ a positive integer$\}$.
(6) $\{x \mid -1 < x \leq 3,\ x$ an integer$\}$.
(7) $\{x \mid -1 < x \leq 3,\ x$ a real number$\}$.
(8) $\{x \mid x + 3 < 5,\ x$ a negative integer$\}$.
(9) $\{x \mid x + 2 = 2 + x,\ x$ a real number$\}$.
(10) $\{x \mid |x| = 2,\ x$ a real number$\}$.
(11) $\{x \mid |x - 1| = 2,\ x$ a real number$\}$.
(12) $\{x \mid |x - 1| < 2,\ x$ a real number$\}$.

Exercises

(a) *Write the solution set for each statement in set-builder notation including the domain of the variable;* (b) *describe each solution set for the given domain;* (c) *graph each solution set on a number line:*

1. $2x - 1 = 11$ Domain of x: real numbers.
2. $2y < 12$ Domain of y: positive integers.
3. $y + 3 \geq 5$ Domain of y: negative integers.
4. $9 + x < 9$ Domain of x: real numbers.
5. $x < -3$ Domain of x: negative numbers.
6. $3x \neq 15$ Domain of x: real numbers.
7. $-2 \leq x < 3$ Domain of x: real numbers.
8. $4 > x > -1$ Domain of x: real numbers.
9. $|x| < 2$ Domain of x: real numbers.
10. $|x| \geq 3$ Domain of x: real numbers.
11. $x^2 = 16$ Domain of x: real numbers.
12. $x + 2 \neq x$ Domain of x: real numbers.
13. $5x \geq 10$ Domain of x: real numbers.
14. $2m \geq 6$ Domain of m: positive integers.
15. $x + 2 < 5 + 2$ Domain of x: negative integers.
16. $2t + 1 = 4$ Domain of t: positive integers.

17. $3 + r = r + 2$ Domain of r: real numbers.

18. $x^2 \neq 9$ Domain of x: real numbers.

19. $x^2 < 9$ Domain of x: real numbers.

20. $x^2 > 9$ Domain of x: real numbers.

Graph each solution set on a number line where the variables are real variables:

21 $\{x \mid 9 \geq x - 2\}$.

22. $\{k \mid 13 \leq 2 - k\}$.

23. $\{k \mid 6 + k \geq k\}$.

24. $\{x \mid 9 + x \leq x\}$.

25. $\{x \mid x \nleq 10\}$.

26. $\{x \mid -1 < x \leq 3\}$.

27. $\{u \mid u \ngeq -3\}$.

28. $\{t \mid -3 \leq t \leq 0\}$.

29. $\{u \mid u + 5 \geq 7\}$.

30. $\{u \mid u + 3 \nleq 8\}$.

31. $\{u \mid u + 3 > 8\}$.

32. $\{x \mid |x| \geq 3\}$.

33. $\{a \mid |a| < -2\}$.

34. $\{x \mid |x| \leq 2\}$.

35. $\{x \mid |x^2| < 4\}$.

36. $\{x \mid |x^2| > 9\}$.

†37. $\{x \mid |x + 1| < 5\}$.

†38. $\{x \mid (x - 1)(x - 3) > 0\}$.

†39. $\{x \mid x + |x| = 0\}$.

†40. $\{x \mid (x - 1)(x + 2) \geq 0\}$.

8-3 Classification of Statements

Statements involving a variable must be considered in terms of the domain of that variable. For example, if the domain of x is the set of positive integers, the solution set of the statement $x^2 = 4$ is $\{2\}$; if the domain of x is the set of all integers, the solution set of $x^2 = 4$ is $\{2, -2\}$. In general, statements involving one variable may be classified by comparing the solution sets for the statements with the domains of the variables.

Each of the following statements involving a real variable x has the set of real numbers as its solution set:

(a) $x^2 - 4 = (x - 2)(x + 2)$.   (b) $x + 2 = 2 + x$.

(c) $x + 3 \neq x$.   (d) $x + 5 > x$.

In general, an equation in one variable is an **identity** (an inequality in one variable is an **absolute inequality**) if its solution set includes all elements of the domain of the variable for which the terms are defined.

Each of the following statements involving a real variable x has at least one element in its solution set, but its solution set does not include all real numbers for which the terms are defined:

(a) $x - 2 = 5$.   (b) $x + 3 = 7$.

(c) $x \neq x^2$.   (d) $x - 1 > 5$.

In general, an equation in one variable is a **conditional equation** (an inequality is a **conditional inequality**) if its solution set is a nonempty set that does not include all elements of the domain of the variable for which the terms are defined.

Each of the following statements involving a real variable x has the empty set as its solution set:

(a) $x + 3 = x$.   (b) $x + 2 = x + 3$.

(c) $x + 1 \neq x + 1$.   (d) $x < x - 1$.

In general, an equation in one variable is an **impossible equation** (an inequality is a **false statement of inequality**) if its solution set is the empty set.

Exercises

In Exercises 1 through 10 classify each statement for a real variable x as an identity, absolute inequality, conditional equation, conditional inequality, impossible equation, or false statement of inequality:

1. $x + 5 = 3$.   2. $x + 5 > 3$.

3. $x + 3 = 3 + x$.   4. $x - 2 = 2 - x$.

5. $x - 1 \neq 1 - x$.   6. $x - 1 < 1 - x$.

7. $x < x + 1$.   8. $|x| = -2$.

9. $x + |x| = 0$.   10. $x - |x| = 0$.

11. Repeat Exercises 1 through 10 for an integral variable x.

12. Repeat Exercises 1 through 10 for a positive integral variable x.

8-4 Linear Statements in Two Variables

An open sentence such as $x + y = 8$ remains an open sentence if a replacement is made for only one of the variables. For example, if x is replaced by 5, the sentence becomes $5 + y = 8$, which is an open sentence. Thus, a pair of replacements is needed for an open sentence in two variables before we can determine whether it is true or false for these replacements.

If x is replaced by 5 and y is replaced by 3, the sentence $x + y = 8$ is true. Usually we think of the variables as an ordered pair (x, y) and speak of the replacements as an ordered pair of numbers $(5, 3)$. By convention the variable x is assumed to be the first of the two variables, and the first number in the ordered pair of numbers is taken as the replacement for x; the variable y is then taken as the second variable, and the second number in the ordered pair is taken as the replacement for y.

Thus, the sentence $x + y = 8$ is true or false for certain ordered pairs of numbers. It is true for $(5, 3)$; it is false for $(2, 7)$. The solution set for the sentence $x + y = 8$ is a set of ordered pairs of numbers for which the sentence is true. This solution set of the sentence may be indicated in the set-builder notation as follows:

$$\{(x, y) \mid x + y = 8\}.$$

This is read as "the set of ordered pairs (x, y) such that $x + y = 8$." The solution set for any sentence in two variables is a set of ordered pairs.

A set of ordered pairs may be obtained from any set of numbers. For example, consider the set of numbers:

$$U = \{1, 2, 3\}.$$

Then the set of all ordered pairs of numbers from U consists of those pairs of numbers whose members are both elements of U. This set of ordered pairs is called the **Cartesian product** of U and U, is written as $U \times U$, and is read *"U cross U."* The set of all ordered pairs whose coordinates belong to the given set U is:

$$\{(1, 1), (1, 2), (1, 3), (2, 1), (2, 2), (2, 3), (3, 1), (3, 2), (3, 3)\}.$$

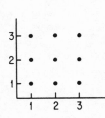

The graph of $U \times U$ is given by the nine points in the accompanying figure; such a set of points is sometimes called a **lattice**. When U is the set of all real numbers, $U \times U$ has as its graph the entire Cartesian coordinate plane.

Next we shall consider a number of specific examples of equations and inequalities in two variables. For each we are to draw the graph of the solution set.

EXAMPLE 1. $\{(x, y) \mid y = x + 1\}$; $U = \{1, 2, 3, 4\}$.

Solution: Here the set of possible replacements consists of a set of 16 ordered pairs of numbers, that is, a lattice of 16 points. The set of ordered pairs that make the sentence true—the solution set—is:

$$\{(1, 2), (2, 3), (3, 4)\}.$$

These are indicated by heavily shaded dots in the accompanying graph of the solution set.

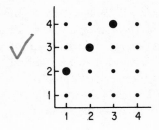

EXAMPLE 2. $\{(x, y) \mid x + y \geq 6\}$; $U = \{1, 2, 3, 4\}$.

Solution: For $x = 1$, there is no value in the domain of y that will satisfy this inequality. For $x = 2$, $y = 4$; for $x = 3$, $y = 3$ or 4; and for $x = 4$, $y = 2, 3$, or 4. The solution set is:

$$\{(2, 4), (3, 3), (3, 4), (4, 2), (4, 3), (4, 4)\}.$$

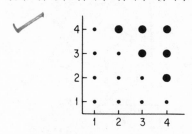

EXAMPLE 3. $\{(x, y) \mid y \geq x + 2\}$; $U = \{-3, -2, -1, 0, 1, 2, 3\}$.

Solution: The set of ordered pairs $U \times U$ is represented by a lattice of 49 points. The graph of the solution set is given in the accompanying figure.

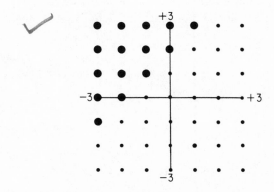

The lattice of points used need not be a square one. Thus, consider the following sets of numbers:

$$A = \{1, 2, 3\};$$
$$B = \{1, 2\}.$$

Then $A \times B = \{(1, 1), (1, 2), (2, 1), (2, 2), (3, 1), (3, 2)\}$.

EXAMPLE 4. $\{(x, y) \mid y \geq x\}$; the domain of x is $\{1, 2, 3\}$ and the domain of y is $\{1, 2\}$.

Solution: The solution set consists of the ordered pairs:

$$(1, 1), (1, 2), (2, 2).$$

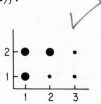

When we make the extension of U to the set of real numbers, our solution sets usually become infinite sets of ordered pairs. Note the following illustrations:

EXAMPLE 5. $\{(x, y) \mid y \leq x - 1\}$; U is the set of real numbers.

Solution:

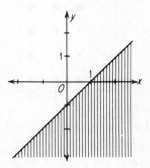

Here the solution set consists of all the points on the line $y = x - 1$ as well as the points in the half-plane indicated by the shaded portion of the graph.

EXAMPLE 6. $\{(x, y) \mid y = |x|\}$; U is the set of real numbers.

Solution:

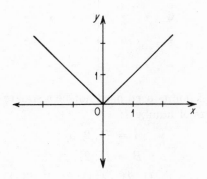

Notice that if $x = 0$, then $y = 0$; if $x = 1$ or -1, then $y = 1$; if $x = 2$ or -2, then $y = 2$; and so forth.

EXAMPLE 7. $\{(x, y) \mid y = |x + 1|\}$; U is the set of real numbers.

Solution:

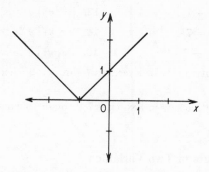

Notice that if $x = -1$, then $y = 0$; if $x = 0$ or -2, then $y = 1$; if $x = 1$ or -3, then $y = 2$; and so forth.

Any sentence in two variables can be considered as a *set-selector*. The set of ordered pairs selected is a *subset* of $U \times U$. If U is the set of real numbers, the solution set corresponds to the set of points satisfying a given condition on a coordinate plane. Thus, the graph of an equation or inequality is commonly called the **locus** of the equation or inequality; that is, the locus is the set of points that correspond to the solution set. Accordingly, we shall speak of graphing statements and mean thereby the graphing of the solution set for the statement.

When the graph of a statement is a straight line, the statement is called a **linear statement** and may be expressed in the form

$$ax + by = c$$

where x and y are real variables; a, b, and c are real numbers; and a and b are not both zero. In this section we consider linear statements and a few other related statements. Several other types of statements are considered in § 8-5.

Exercises

Graph each solution set on a plane lattice where $U = \{1, 2, 3, 4\}$:

1. $\{(x, y) \mid x + y = 5\}$.   **2.** $\{(x, y) \mid y = x - 1\}$.

3. $\{(x, y) \mid y \leq x - 1\}$.   **4.** $\{(x, y) \mid y < x\}$.

5. $\{(x, y) \mid y \geq x\}$.   **6.** $\{(x, y) \mid y \geq x + 1\}$.

In Exercises 7 through 16 graph each solution set with $U = \{-3, -2, -1, 0, 1, 2, 3\}$:

7. $\{(x, y) \mid y = x\}$.   **8.** $\{(x, y) \mid y \leq x\}$.

9. $\{(x, y) \mid x - y = 1\}$.   **10.** $\{(x, y) \mid y - x = 2\}$.

11. $\{(x, y) \mid y < x - 1\}$.   **12.** $\{(x, y) \mid y \geq x\}$.

13. $\{(x, y) \mid x + y = 7\}$.   **14.** $\{(x, y) \mid y \geq |x|\}$.

15. $\{(x, y) \mid y = |x - 1|\}$.   **16.** $\{(x, y) \mid y > |x - 1|\}$.

17. Graph the solution sets in Exercises 1 through 6 where U is the set of real numbers.

18. Graph the solution sets in Exercises 7 through 16 where U is the set of real numbers.

8-5 Other Statements in Two Variables

Statements in two variables may involve powers of the variables. Consider the following examples, in each of which the statement is to be graphed for the specified domains of the variables.

EXAMPLE 1. $\{(x, y) \mid x^2 + y^2 = 25\}$; $U = \{0, 1, 2, 3, 4, 5\}$.

Solution: The solution set consists of the ordered pairs:

$$(0, 5), (3, 4), (4, 3), (5, 0).$$

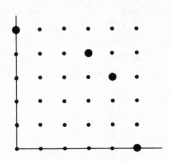

EXAMPLE 2. $\{(x, y) \mid x^2 + y^2 = 25\}$; U = the set of real numbers.

Solution: If $x = 0$, then $y = 5$ or -5; if $x = 3$, then $y = 4$ or -4; similarly, if $x = 4$ or -4, then $y = 3$ or -3. The graph is a circle of radius 5 and center at the origin.

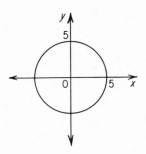

EXAMPLE 3. $\{(x, y) \mid x^2 + y^2 \leq 25\}$; $U =$ the set of real numbers.

Solution: Notice that the solid line for the circle of radius 5 and center at the origin indicates that the boundary of the region is part of the graph.

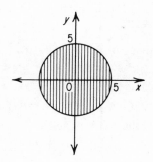

EXAMPLE 4. $\{(x, y) \mid y < x^3\}$; $U = \{1, 2, 3\}$.

Solution: The solution set consists of the ordered pairs:

$$(2, 1), (2, 2), (2, 3), (3, 1), (3, 2), (3, 3).$$

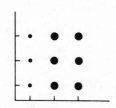

Other examples are considered in the exercises.

Exercises

Graph each statement on a plane lattice where $U = \{1, 2, 3, 4\}$:

1. $\{(x, y) \mid y = x^2\}$.   **2.** $\{(x, y) \mid y > x^2\}$.

3. $\{(x, y) \mid y < (x + 1)^2\}$.   **4.** $\{(x, y) \mid y < x^3 - 1\}$.

Graph each statement when U *is the set of real numbers:*

5. $\{(x, y) \mid y = x^2\}$.   **6.** $\{(x, y) \mid y = x^2 + 2\}$.

7. $\{(x, y) \mid y = x^2 - 1\}$.   **8.** $\{(x, y) \mid x^2 + y^2 = 0\}$.

9. $\{(x, y) \mid x^2 + y^2 = 9\}$.   **10.** $\{(x, y) \mid y \geq x^2\}$.

11. $\{(x, y) \mid y > x^2 \text{ and } x \geq 0\}$.

12. $\{(x, y) \mid x^2 + y^2 \leq 9 \text{ and } y \geq 0\}$.

13. $\{(x, y) \mid y = x^2 \text{ and } x = y^2\}$.

†**14.** $\left\{(x, y) \mid y = \dfrac{x}{|x|}\right\}$.

†**15.** $\{(x, y) \mid x + y = y + x \text{ and } x - y = y - x\}$.

8-6 Relations and Functions

A **relation** may be defined as any subset of $U \times U$; thus, a relation is a set of ordered pairs of numbers. It is most often defined as a rule. Consider, for example,

$$\{(x, y) \mid y > x - 1\}, \qquad \text{where } U = \{1, 2, 3\}.$$

This solution set is:

$$\{(1, 1), (1, 2), (1, 3), (2, 2), (2, 3), (3, 3)\}.$$

It may be graphed as in the accompanying figure.

The relation may be defined by the solution set, by the **graph**, or by a table of values for the variable:

x	1	1	1	2	2	3
y	1	2	3	2	3	3

Here is the table and graph for another relation:

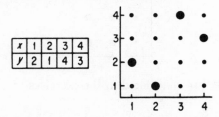

x	1	2	3	4
y	2	1	4	3

Note that the second relation differs from the first in that, for any value of x, there is at most one value for y. We call this special type of relation a *function*.

A **function** is a set of ordered pairs (x, y) such that for each value of x there is at most one value of y; that is, no first element appears with more than one second element. You may think of the first element as the independent variable and the second element as the dependent variable. Each variable has a set of possible values. The set of all first elements of the ordered pairs of numbers is called the **domain** of the function; the set of all second elements is called the **range** of the function. In terms of its graph, any vertical line drawn meets the graph of a function in at most one point.

Here are the graphs of two relations, $\{(x, y)\}$, which are also functions:

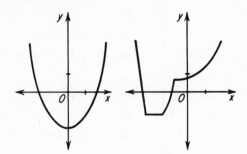

Notice that no vertical line intersects the graph in more than one point.

Here are the graphs of two relations, $\{(x, y)\}$, which are not functions:

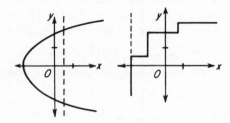

Notice that in each case there exists at least one vertical line that intersects the graph in two or more points.

Although formulas such as $y = x^2$ may define a function, they are not strictly functions. We have defined the function to be a set of ordered pairs (x, y), such as those obtained from the formula $y = x^2$ for the real variable x. Thus, a formula may provide a rule by which the function may be determined. In other words, a formula may provide a means for associating a unique element in the range with each element in the domain.

Note: Unfortunately the word "function" is used in several ways. Basically, the term does not yet have a universally accepted definition. There are several quite different and equally proper definitions. Whenever you encounter the word "function" in the literature, you should check to see what definition (or definitions) the author is using.

Exercises

Draw the graph of each relation and identify those which are functions; U is the set of real numbers.

1. $\{(x, y) \mid y^2 = x - 1\}$.   **2.** $\{(x, y) \mid x + y = y + x\}$.

3. $\{(x, y) \mid y = x^2 - 1\}$.   **4.** $\{(x, y) \mid xy = 1\}$.

5. $\{(x, y) \mid y \leq x^2\}$.   **6.** $\{(x, y) \mid |x + y| = 1\}$.

7. $\{(x, y) \mid y \geq |x|\}$.   **8.** $\{(x, y) \mid xy = 0\}$.

9. $\{(x, y) \mid x = 2\}$.

10. $\{(x, y) \mid |x - 1| = 2\}$.

11. $\{(x, y) \mid |x + y| = 2\}$.

12. $\{(x, y) \mid |y - x| = 2\}$.

†**13.** $\{(x, y) \mid |y - (x - 1)| = 2\}$.

†**14.** $\{(x, y) \mid |y - (x + 1)| = 3\}$.

Describe the graphs of:

†**15.** $\{(x, y) \mid |x| = k\}$.

†**16.** $\{(x, y) \mid |x - b| = k\}$.

†**17.** $\{(x, y) \mid |x + y| = k\}$.

†**18.** $\{(x, y) \mid |y - x| = k\}$.

†**19.** $\{(x, y) \mid |y - (x + b)| = k\}$.

†**20.** $\{(x, y) \mid |y - (mx + b)| = k\}$.

✓ 8-7 Inverse Relations

Given any relation, the **inverse relation** is the set of ordered pairs obtained by interchanging the elements of each of the ordered pairs of the given relation. Thus, suppose we are given the relation:

$$R = \{(2, 1), (3, 2), (4, 3), (4, 5)\}.$$

The inverse relation of R then consists of the set of ordered pairs

$$\{(1, 2), (2, 3), (3, 4), (5, 4)\}.$$

In a similar manner, we may find the inverse of a function, inasmuch as a function is nothing more than a special type of relation. That is, the inverse of a function is obtained by interchanging the elements of each of the ordered pairs of numbers that comprise the function. The inverse of a function is a relation; however, it may or may not be a function. It will be a function if and only if, for each y of the original function, we have at most one x.

EXAMPLE 1. Find the inverse of the function

$$F = \{(1, 2), (2, 3), (3, 4)\}.$$

Solution: The inverse of this function is another function, F', where

$$F' = \{(2, 1), (3, 2), (4, 3)\}.$$

EXAMPLE 2. Find the inverse of the function

$$A = \{(1, 3), (2, 4), (3, 4), (4, 7)\}.$$

Solution: The inverse, A', of this function is a relation, but it is not a function.

$$A' = \{(3, 1), (4, 2), (4, 3), (7, 4)\}.$$

If a relation is given by a formula, then a formula for its inverse may be obtained by interchanging the variables.

EXAMPLE 3. Find a formula for the inverse of the function

$$F = \{(x, y) \mid y = 2x\}.$$

Solution: The inverse of F is $F' = \{(x, y) \mid x = 2y\}$. We may also write it as $F' = \left\{ (x, y) \mid y = \dfrac{x}{2} \right\}$. Here the inverse of the given function is also a function.

EXAMPLE 4. Find the inverse of $F = \{(x, y) \mid y = x^2\}$.
Solution: $\{(x, y) \mid x = y^2\}$. We may also write the solution as $\{(x, y) \mid y = \pm\sqrt{x}\}$. Note that the inverse of the given function is a relation but it is not a function. Explain why not.

Exercises

Find the inverse for each of the following relations. Tell whether or not each inverse is a function.

1. $\{(1, 2), (3, 2), (5, 3)\}$. **2.** $\{(2, 1), (3, 4), (5, 2)\}$.

3. $\{(1, 1), (2, 2), (3, 3), (4, 4)\}$. **4.** $\{(1, 2), (2, 2), (3, 4), (5, 3)\}$.

Draw the graph of each relation and the graph of the inverse of each relation. For Exercises 7 through 14, the universe is the set of real numbers.

5. $\{(x, y) \mid y = x\}$; $U = \{1, 2, 3\}$.

6. $\{(x, y) \mid y = x + 1\}$; $U = \{1, 2, 3, 4\}$.

7. $\{(x, y) \mid y = x\}$. **8.** $\{(x, y) \mid y = x + 1\}$.

9. $\{(x, y) \mid y = x - 2\}$. **10.** $\{(x, y) \mid y = 2x\}$.

11. $\{(x, y) \mid y = 3x\}$. **12.** $\{(x, y) \mid y = x - 3\}$.

13. $\{(x, y) \mid y = 4x^2\}$. **14.** $\{(x, y) \mid y = |x|\}$.

8-8 Arithmetic and Algebra

The numbers of arithmetic were considered in Chapter 7 and used as a basis for our study of the sets of integers, rational numbers, and real numbers. In this chapter we have used sets of numbers as the domains of variables and the domains of functions in algebra. In a sense each variable in algebra may be considered as a generalization of the numbers of arithmetic. Notice that each variable has many of the properties of the numbers that form its domain. For example, the commutative and associative laws for addition and multiplication are true for real variables as well as for real numbers. Similarly, statements in algebra may be regarded as generalizations of statements in arithmetic. In this chapter we have observed that a statement in one variable may have a solution set; a statement in two variables may determine a relation.

The operations of addition, subtraction, multiplication, and division, which are considered in arithmetic, are extended in algebra to include several other operations including taking the squares and square roots of numbers, finding other powers and roots of numbers, and finding the power of a number that gives a specified result. For example, what power of 2 is equal to 8? A little calculation will show that the third power of 2 (that is, 2^3) is equal to 8. We say that 3 is the *logarithm* of 8 to the base 2. Logarithms are among the many topics of algebra which we have not had an opportunity to consider.

The use of statements in algebra and other subjects is considered in Chapter 9. The use of algebra in geometry is considered in Chapter 10 where the graphing of algebraic statements is considered further.

Arithmetic, algebra, and geometry are all parts of mathematics. The study of separate courses in arithmetic, algebra, and geometry is misleading since it makes them appear as separate subjects rather than as parts of the same subject, mathematics. One aim of this book is to help you visualize algebra as an extension of arithmetic. We hope that many of you will also be able to visualize algebra and geometry as two ways of considering mathematics. In algebra we may use numbers, variables, and other elements of algebra to represent whatever we are studying. In geometry we may use points, lines, line segments, and other elements of geometry to represent whatever we are studying. Then, as we have observed in a few cases in this chapter, algebraic statements may be graphed in geometry, and many geometrie figures are the graphs of algebraic statements. In Chapter 10 we shall consider further the concept of algebra and geometry as two ways of studying, or looking at, mathematics.

LOGIC AND STATEMENTS

Any logical system is concerned with elements, relations among the elements, and statements. The elements may be numbers, variables, points, lines, and so forth. The relations may be addition, subtraction, congruence, parallelism, and so forth. An element and the relations may be either defined or undefined (that is, assumed). The statements may be either proved or assumed. In Chapter 8 we discussed statements in algebra. Here we shall discuss statements in a more abstract manner, and we shall explore various aspects of abstract logic and methods of logical thinking.

9-1 Statements

The distinguishing feature of any statement is that it is either *true* or *false*. Each of the following is an example of a **simple statement:**

"Today is Friday."
"The sun is shining."

Notice that a command such as "Stand up and be counted" is neither true nor false and is not considered to be a statement as we are using the word here.

A **compound statement** is formed by combining two or more simple statements. An example is the following:

"Today is Friday and the sun is shining."

In this illustration the two simple statements are combined by the connective "and." Other connectives could also have been used. Consider the same simple statements using the connective "or":

"Today is Friday or the sun is shining."

We shall consider such compound statements and determine the conditions under which they are true or false, assuming that the simple statements are true. In doing this we use letters or variables to represent statements and symbols to represent connectives. For example, we may use p and q to represent these simple statements:

p: Today is Friday.
q: The sun is shining.

The following connectives are commonly used:

$\wedge$: and
$\vee$: or
$\sim$: not

We may use p and q as previously defined and write several statements in symbolic form together with their translations in words:

$p \wedge q$: Today is Friday and the sun is shining.
$p \vee q$: Today is Friday or the sun is shining.
$\sim p$: Today is not Friday.

EXAMPLE 1. Translate $p \wedge (\sim q)$ where p and q are as given in this section.

Solution: Today is Friday and the sun is not shining.

EXAMPLE 2. Write, in symbolic form: Today is not Friday or the sun is shining.

Solution: $(\sim p) \vee q$.

Exercises

1. Use p: Jim is tall; q: Bill is short. Think of "short" as "not tall," and write each of these statements in symbolic form:

(a) Jim is short and Bill is tall.
(b) Bill and Jim are both tall.
(c) Neither Jim nor Bill is tall.
(d) Jim is not tall and Bill is short.
(e) It is not true that Jim and Bill are both tall.
(f) Either Jim is short or Bill is short.
(g) Either Jim or Bill is tall.

2. Assume that Bill and Jim are both tall. Which of the statements in Exercise 1 are true?

3. Use p: I like this book; q: I like mathematics. Give each of these statements in words:

(a) $p \wedge q$.   (b) $\sim q$.

(c) $\sim p$.   (d) $(\sim p) \wedge (\sim q)$.

(e) $(\sim p) \wedge q$.   (f) $p \vee q$.

(g) $\sim (p \wedge q)$.   (h) $\sim [(\sim p) \wedge q]$.

4. Assume that you like this book and that you like mathematics. Which of the statements in Exercise 3 are true?

5. Assume that you like this book but that you do not like mathematics. Which of the statements in Exercise 3 are true?

9-2 Truth Tables

Consider the simple statements:

p: It is snowing.
q: This is the month of December.

The truth of any compound statement, such as $p \wedge q$, depends upon the truth of each of these simple statements. Since each of the statements p and q may be either true or false, there are four distinct possibilities:

p true, q true
p true, q false
p false, q true
p false, q false

For each of these possibilities we wish to determine the truth value of the statement $p \wedge q$. When we say that $p \wedge q$ is true, we mean that both p and q are true. We may define the truth values of $p \wedge q$ by means of the following **truth table** where T stands for "true" and F stands for "false":

The statement $p \wedge q$ is called the **conjunction** of p and q. The truth values of $p \wedge q$ are independent of the meanings assigned to the variables. For example, if you are told that each of two simple statements is true, it follows immediately that the conjunction of these statements is also true; in any other circumstance, it

p	q	$p \wedge q$
T	T	T
T	F	F
F	T	F
F	F	F

follows immediately that the conjunction of the statements is false.

We next consider the compound statement $p \vee q$, called the **disjunction** of p and q. We translate "$\vee$" as "or" even though we shall use the word "or" more precisely than in the ordinary English language. As we shall use it here, "p or q" means that at least one of the statements

p, q is true; that is, either p is true, or q is true, or both p and q are true. The truth values of $p \lor q$ are defined by the following truth table:

p	q	$p \lor q$
T	T	T
T	F	T
F	T	T
F	F	F

From the table we deduce the fact that the compound statement $p \lor q$ is true unless both p and q are false.

Finally we consider the negation symbol introduced in the last section. As we would expect from the meaning of the word "negation," if p is true, then $\sim p$ is false; if p is false, then $\sim p$ is true. The truth values of the statement $\sim p$ are given in the following table:

p	$\sim p$
T	F
F	T

Consider the statements:

p: It is a lemon.

q: It is a piece of fruit.

The statements p and q are called **consistent statements** since they can both be true of the same object.

Consider the statements: p: It is a lemon.

s: It is an orange.

The statements p and s are called **contrary statements** since they cannot both be true of the same object.

Consider the statements: p: It is a lemon.

$\sim p$: It is not a lemon.

The statements p and $\sim p$ are also contrary statements, but they have the additional property that they cannot both be false; either it is a lemon or it is not a lemon. Exactly one of the statements must be true; exactly one of the statements must be false. If either statement is true, the other is false. If either statement is false, the other is true. This special relationship between "p" and "$\sim p$" is indicated by calling them **contradictory statements.** Two statements are contradictory if they cannot both be true and they cannot both be false. In general, any two statements are either consistent or contrary (inconsistent). Contrary statements may or may not be contradictory. However, any two contradictory statements are also contrary.

We can use truth tables to summarize the truth values of various compound statements. To illustrate this procedure we shall construct a truth table for the statement $p \land (\sim q)$.

First set up a table with the appropriate headings as follows:

p	q	p	$\land$	$(\sim q)$
T	T			
T	F			
F	T			
F	F			

Now complete the column headed "p" by using the truth values that appear under p in the first column. In the column headed "$\sim q$" write the negation of the values given under q in the second column. (Why?) Our table now appears as follows:

p	q	p	$\wedge$	$(\sim q)$
T	T	T		F
T	F	T		T
F	T	F		F
F	F	F		T

Finally we find the conjunctions of the values given in the third and fifth columns. The completed table appears as follows, with the final results in bold print:

p	q	p	$\wedge$	$(\sim q)$
T	T	T	**F**	F
T	F	T	**T**	T
F	T	F	**F**	F
F	F	F	**F**	T

We can summarize this by saying that the statement $p \wedge (\sim q)$ is true only in the case when p is true and q is false. Thus the statement "Today is Wednesday and it is not snowing" is a true statement on a hot Wednesday in July. (We must assume, of course, that it will not snow on a hot day in July.)

Exercises

1. Indicate which of the following pairs of statements are contrary:

(a) That is John Smith. That is Henry Jones.
(b) It is a citrus fruit. It is an orange.
(c) The car is a Buick. The car is not a Cadillac.
(d) x is positive. x is negative.
(e) $x < 3$. $x \geq 3$.
(f) $x < 6$. $x = 7$.
(g) $x^2 = 9$. $x \neq 3$.

2. Indicate which of the pairs of statements in Exercise 1 are contradictory.

3. What name is used to describe the relationship between statements p and q given by $\sim (p \wedge q)$?

4. What name is used to describe the relationship between statements p and q given by

$$\sim (p \wedge q) \wedge \sim [(\sim p) \wedge (\sim q)]?$$

5. Define $p \vee q$ to mean "p or q but not both" and construct a truth table for this connective.

6. Construct a truth table for $p \mid q$, defined to mean "p and q are not both true."

7. In Exercise 6, express $p \mid q$ in terms of other connectives thus far defined.

8. Two statements that have the same truth values are said to be equivalent. Show, by means of truth tables, that the following statements are equivalent.

(a) $\sim (p \wedge q) = \sim p \vee \sim q.$ **(b)** $\sim (p \vee q) = \sim p \wedge \sim q.$

9. Construct truth tables for:

(a) $(\sim p) \wedge q.$ **(b)** $(\sim p) \wedge (\sim q).$
(c) $\sim (p \wedge q).$ **(d)** $p \vee (\sim q).$
(e) $\sim [p \vee (\sim q)].$ **(f)** $\sim [(\sim p) \vee q].$

10. Use p: I like this book; q: I like mathematics. Tell the conditions under which each of the statements of Exercise 9 is true.

9-3 Implication

Many of the statements that we make in everyday conversation are based upon a condition. For example, consider the following:

> If the sun shines, then I will cut the grass.
> If I have no homework, then I will go bowling.
> If I bribe the instructor, then I will pass the course.

Each of these statements is expressed in the **if-then** form:

> If p, then q.

Any if-then statement can be expressed in symbols as

$$p \to q,$$

which is read either as "if p, then q" or as "p implies q." The symbol "$\to$" is called the **implication symbol**; it is a connective used to form a compound statement called a **conditional statement**.

Our first task is to consider the various possibilities for p and q in order to define $p \to q$ for each of these cases. One way to do this would be to present a completed truth table and to accept this as our definition of $p \to q$. Let us, however, attempt to justify the entries in such a table. Consider again the conditional statement:

> If the sun shines, then I will cut the grass.

Now if the sun shines and I do cut the grass, then the statement is obviously true. On the other hand, the statement is false if the sun shines and I do not cut the grass. Assume now that the sun is not shining; then, whether I cut the grass or not, the original statement is true in that I only declared my intentions under the condition that the sun shines. We can summarize these assertions by means of a truth table:

p	q	$p \rightarrow q$
T	T	T
T	F	F
F	T	T
F	F	T

This table tells us that any statement of the form "if p, then q" is false only when p is true and q is false. On the other hand, if p is false, then the statement $p \rightarrow q$ is accepted as true regardless of the truth value of q. Thus each of the following statements is true by this definition:

If $2 + 3 = 7$, then George Washington is now the President of the United States.

If $2 + 3 = 7$, then the moon is made of green cheese.

If $2 + 3 = 7$, then July follows June.

If you have difficulty accepting any of these statements as true, then you should review the definition of the truth values of if-then statements. Remember also that there need be no relationship between p and q in an if-then statement, although we tend to use such statements in this way in everyday life.

There are many other forms in which a conditional statement may appear. We shall explore several of these here. Given any simple statement of implication, $p \rightarrow q$, three other related statements may be identified:

Statement:	$p \rightarrow q$	If p, then q.
Converse:	$q \rightarrow p$	If q, then p.
Inverse:	$(\sim p) \rightarrow (\sim q)$	If not p, then not q.
Contrapositive:	$(\sim q) \rightarrow (\sim p)$	If not q, then not p.

Here are several illustrative examples of the various forms that conditional statements may assume:

(a) *Statement:* If it is snowing, I leave my car in the garage.

Converse: If I leave my car in the garage, it is snowing.

Inverse: If it is not snowing, I do not leave my car in the garage.

Contrapositive: If I do not leave my car in the garage, it is not snowing.

(b) *Statement:* If $\triangle ABC \cong \triangle XYZ$, then $\triangle ABC \sim \triangle XYZ$.

Converse: If $\triangle ABC \sim \triangle XYZ$, then $\triangle ABC \cong \triangle XYZ$.

Inverse: If $\triangle ABC$ is not congruent to $\triangle XYZ$, then $\triangle ABC$ is not similar to $\triangle XYZ$.

Contrapositive: If $\triangle ABC$ is not similar to $\triangle XYZ$, then $\triangle ABC$ is not congruent to $\triangle XYZ$.

(c) *Statement:* If x is negative, then $x \neq 0$.
   Converse: If $x \neq 0$, then x is negative.
   Inverse: If x is not negative, then $x = 0$.
   Contrapositive: If $x = 0$, then x is not negative.

EXAMPLE 1. Write the converse, inverse, and contrapositive of the statement: "If $x + 2 = 5$, then $x = 3$."

Solution: Converse: If $x = 3$, then $x + 2 = 5$.
         Inverse: If $x + 2 \neq 5$, then $x \neq 3$.
         Contrapositive: If $x \neq 3$, then $x + 2 \neq 5$.

Many *fallacies* (that is, invalid examples of reasoning, § 9-5) stem from the assumption that the converse and the inverse of any true statement are necessarily true. For example, let us return to the statement:

If I bribe the instructor, then I will pass the course.

Assume that this statement is true and consider the converse:

If I pass the course, then I have bribed the instructor.

Now this latter statement may be true, but it is not necessarily true. That is, there may be other ways to pass the course without resorting to bribery! By the same token, the inverse of the original statement is not necessarily true:

If I do not bribe the instructor, then I will not pass the course.

There may be an instructor who would like you to believe this. However, the original statement only told you what would happen if you bribed the instructor, and made no mention of the results of failing to bribe him.
   Finally consider the contrapositive of the original statement:

If I do not pass the course, then I have not bribed the instructor.

This statement is equivalent to the original one. If you fail the course, then you have not bribed the instructor, because if you had bribed him then you would have been assured of passing!
   The following truth tables for these variants of a conditional statement $p \rightarrow q$ summarize this discussion and specify the truth values for each statement:

		Statement	Converse	Inverse	Contrapositive
p	q	$p \rightarrow q$	$q \rightarrow p$	$(\sim p) \rightarrow (\sim q)$	$(\sim q) \rightarrow (\sim p)$
T	T	T	T	T	T
T	F	F	T	T	F
F	T	T	F	F	T
F	F	T	T	T	T

Two statements are **equivalent** if they have the same truth values. Note that a statement is equivalent to its contrapositive. Also note that the converse and the inverse of any simple statement of implication are equivalent.

EXAMPLE 2. Write the converse, inverse, and contrapositive of the statement: $p \to (\sim q)$.

Solution:

Converse: $(\sim q) \to p$.

Inverse: $(\sim p) \to \sim (\sim q)$, which can be simplified as $(\sim p) \to q$.

Contrapositive: $\sim (\sim q) \to (\sim p)$, which can be simplified as $q \to (\sim p)$.

Exercises

1. Write each statement in if-then form:

(a) The boy is a Johnson, if he has red hair.

(b) All ducks are birds.

(c) Vertical angles are equal.

(d) Complements of the same angle are equal.

(e) Supplements of equal angles are equal.

(f) Any two parallel lines are coplanar.

2. Consider the statements:

p: You will study hard.
q: You will get an A.

Translate each of the following symbolic statements into an English sentence:

(a) $p \to q$.   **(b)** $q \to p$.

(c) $(\sim p) \to (\sim q)$.   **(d)** $(\sim q) \to (\sim p)$.

3. Repeat Exercise 2 for the statements:

p: The triangle is equilateral.
q: The triangle is isosceles.

4. Which of the parts of Exercise 3 are always true?

Write the converse, inverse, and contrapositive of each statement:

5. If we can afford it, then we buy a new car.

6. If we play pingpong, then you win the game.

7. If two sides and the included angle of one triangle are equal to two sides and the included angle of another triangle, then the triangles are congruent.

8. If $x > 2$, then $x \neq 0$.

9. If $x(x - 1) = 0$, then $x = 1$.

For each of the Exercises 7 through 9, tell whether or not you accept as always true:

10. The converse statement.

11. The inverse statement.

[*Note:* Compare your answers for Exercises 10 and 11.]

12. The contrapositive statement.

Discuss each of the following, using symbolic form:

13. Any statement is the contrapositive of its contrapositive statement.

14. The contrapositive of the converse of a statement is the inverse of the statement.

Construct truth tables for each of the following:

15. $(p \rightarrow q) \wedge (q \rightarrow p)$.

16. $q \rightarrow [(\sim p) \vee q]$.

17. $[(\sim p) \wedge q] \rightarrow (p \vee q)$.

18. Show, by means of truth tables, that each of the following statements has the same truth values as $p \rightarrow q$:

    (a) $(\sim p) \vee q$.   **(b)** $\sim [p \wedge (\sim q)]$.

19. Write the converse, inverse, and contrapositive for the statement $(\sim p) \rightarrow q$.

20. Use p: The sun shines; q: I cut the grass. Write each of the following statements in symbolic form:

    (a) If the sun shines, then I cut the grass.
    (b) I will cut the grass only if the sun shines.
    (c) If the sun does not shine, then I do not cut the grass.
    (d) The sun's shining is a necessary condition for me to cut the grass.
    (e) I cut the grass if and only if the sun shines.

†**21.** Compare the following statements:

    (a) $p \rightarrow q$.
    (b) If p, then q.
    (c) p is a sufficient condition for q.
    (d) q is a necessary condition for p.
    (e) p, only if q.

9-4 Necessary and Sufficient Conditions.

Conditional statements may be written in a variety of forms. In mathematics this is often done through use of the words *"necessary"* and *"sufficient."* Consider the statement:

Working hard is a sufficient condition for passing the course.

Let us use p to mean "work hard" and q to represent "pass the course."

We need to decide whether the given statement means "if p, then q" or "if q, then p." The word sufficient can be interpreted to mean that working hard is adequate or enough—but not necessary—for passing. That is, there may be other ways to pass the course, but working hard will do it! Thus we interpret the statement to mean:

If you work hard, then you will pass the course.

The symbolic statement $p \rightarrow q$ may thus be used for each of these statements:

If p, then q.
p is a sufficient condition for q.

Next consider the statement:

Working hard is a necessary condition for passing the course.

Here you are told that working hard is necessary or essential in order to pass. That is, regardless of what else you do, you had better work hard if you wish to pass. However there is no assurance that working hard alone will do the trick! It is necessary, but not sufficient. (You may also have to get good grades!) Therefore we interpret the statement to mean:

If you pass the course, then you have worked hard.

The symbolic statement $q \rightarrow p$ may thus be used for each of these statements:

If q, then p.
p is a necessary condition for q.

Still another form to consider is the statement "q, only if p." In terms of the example used in this section we may write this as:

You will pass the course only if you work hard.

Note that this does *not* say that working hard will insure a passing grade! It does mean that if you have passed, then you have worked hard. That is, "q, only if p" is equivalent to the statement "if q, then p."

We can also interpret this in another way. This statement "q, only if p" means "if not p, then not q." The contrapositive of this last statement, however, is "if q, then p." In terms of our illustration this means that if you do not work hard, then you will not pass. Therefore if you pass, then you have worked hard.

To summarize our discussion to date, each of the following statements represents an equivalent form of writing the statement $p \rightarrow q$:

$p \rightarrow q$.
If p, then q.
p is a sufficient condition for q.
q is a necessary condition for p.
p, only if q.

EXAMPLE 1. Use p: I will work hard; q: I will get an A. Translate into symbolic form:

(a) I will get an A only if I work hard.
(b) Working hard is a sufficient condition for getting an A.

Solution: (a) $q \rightarrow p$;   (b) $p \rightarrow q$.

EXAMPLE 2. Use p and q as in Example 1 and translate into symbolic form:

> If I work hard then I will get an A and if I get an A then
> I will work hard.

Solution: $(p \rightarrow q) \land (q \rightarrow p)$.

In this last example we have essentially said that p is a sufficient condition for q and also that p is a necessary condition for q. We may condense this by saying that p is a **necessary and sufficient condition** for q. In symbols this is written as $p \leftrightarrow q$, which may be read "p, if and only if q." This conjunction, $\leftrightarrow$, is referred to as the **biconditional** or the **equivalence symbol.** Basically it tells us that p is equivalent to q; that is, it says "if p, then q and if q, then p." Notice that the equivalence symbol is used for equivalent statements; that is, statements with the same truth values.

EXAMPLE 3. Complete a truth table for the statement: $(p \rightarrow q) \land (q \rightarrow p)$.

Solution:

p	q	$(p \rightarrow q)$	$\land$	$(q \rightarrow p)$
T	T	T	T	T
T	F	F	F	T
F	T	T	F	F
F	F	T	T	T

(The final set of truth values is given in boldface print in the table.)

In Example 3 we constructed a truth table for the statement $(p \rightarrow q) \land (q \rightarrow p)$. However, we have previously agreed that this conjunction of statements is equivalent to $p \leftrightarrow q$. This enables us to construct a truth table for $p \leftrightarrow q$ as follows:

p	q	$p \leftrightarrow q$
T	T	T
T	F	F
F	T	F
F	F	T

From the truth table we see that $p \leftrightarrow q$ is true when p and q are both true or are both false. Thus each of these statements is true:

$2 \times 2 = 4$ if and only if $7 - 5 = 2$. (Both parts are true.)
$2 \times 2 = 5$ if and only if $7 - 5 = 3$. (Both parts are false.)

Each of the following statements is false because exactly one part of each statement is false:

$$2 \times 2 = 4 \quad \text{if and only if} \quad 7 - 5 = 3.$$
$$2 \times 2 = 5 \quad \text{if and only if} \quad 7 - 5 = 2.$$

As we have previously noted, we use the symbol "$\leftrightarrow$" to show that two statements are equivalent. Consider these statements:

p: I cut the grass this afternoon.
q: The sun is shining.

Then the statement "$p \leftrightarrow q$," that is, p if and only if q, is true in these two cases:

(a) if I cut the grass and the sun is shining, or
(b) if I do not cut the grass and the sun is not shining.

In all other cases, the statement "$p \leftrightarrow q$" is false. Briefly, two statements "p" and "q" are equivalent if each implies the other; in other words, we may write "$p \leftrightarrow q$" if it is true that $p \rightarrow q$ and also that $q \rightarrow p$.

EXAMPLE 4. Under what conditions is the following statement true?

I will get an A if and only if I work hard.

Solution: The statement is true in each of two cases:

(a) You get an A and you work hard.
(b) You do not get an A and you do not work hard.

Exercises

1. Write each statement in if-then form:
(a) You will like this book only if you like mathematics.
(b) A necessary condition for liking this book is that you like mathematics.
(c) To like this book it is sufficient that you like mathematics.
(d) A sufficient condition for liking this book is that you like mathematics.
(e) Liking this book is a necessary condition for liking mathematics.

2. Use p: The sun shines; q: I cut the grass. Write each of the following statements in symbolic form:
(a) If the sun shines, then I do not cut the grass.
(b) I cut the grass only if the sun shines.
(c) A necessary condition for me to cut the grass is that the sun shines.

(d) For me to cut the grass it is sufficient that the sun shines.

(e) A necessary and sufficient condition for me to cut the grass is that the sun shines.

3. Use p: I miss my breakfast; q: I get up late. Write each of the following statements in symbolic form:

(a) I miss my breakfast if and only if I get up late.

(b) A necessary condition for me to miss my breakfast is that I get up late.

(c) For me to miss my breakfast it is sufficient that I get up late.

(d) A necessary and sufficient condition for me to miss my breakfast is that I get up late.

(e) For me not to miss my breakfast it is necessary that I do not get up late.

4. Write each statement in if-then form:

(a) All triangles are polygons.

(b) All circles are round.

(c) All mathematics books are dull.

(d) All teachers are boring.

(e) All p are q.

5. Classify as true or false:

(a) A necessary condition for 2×2 to be equal to 5 is that $8 - 5 = 3$.

(b) $7 \times 6 = 40$ only if $8 \times 5 \neq 40$.

(c) $7 \times 6 = 42$ only if $8 \times 5 \neq 40$.

(d) $11 - 3 > 8$ if and only if $9 + 3 < 10$.

(e) For 7×4 to be equal to 25 it is sufficient that $5 + 3 = 8$.

6. Construct a truth table for each of the following:

(a) $p \leftrightarrow (\sim q)$.   **(b)** $(\sim p) \leftrightarrow q$.

(c) $(\sim p) \leftrightarrow (\sim q)$.   **(d)** $(p \vee q) \leftrightarrow (p \rightarrow q)$.

7. Show, by means of a truth table, that the statement $p \leftrightarrow q$ is equivalent to:

$$[(\sim p) \rightarrow (\sim q)] \wedge [(\sim q) \rightarrow (\sim p)].$$

8. Show, by means of truth tables, that the following statements are equivalent.

(a) $\sim (p \leftrightarrow q)$.   **(b)** $p \leftrightarrow (\sim q)$.

9. Suppose a young man makes the bold assertion: "I will marry your daughter only if you give me \$10,000." Furthermore assume that he receives the money yet fails to marry the young lady. Should he be sued for breach of promise?

10. Repeat Exercise 9 if the following assertion had been made instead: "A sufficient condition for me to marry your daughter is that you give me \$10,000."

9-5 The Nature of Proof

We are now ready to apply the concepts of logic developed thus far to a study of the nature of proof. In examining proofs we need to be careful to base our judgments on rules of inference rather than on personal biases. One rule that we use in organizing proofs is the **law of detachment** or **modus ponens**. This law may be expressed as follows:

If a statement of the form "If p, then q" is assumed to be true, and if p is known to be true, then q must be true.

Symbolically, we may write this rule as

$$p \rightarrow q \qquad \text{If } p, \text{ then } q; \text{ and}$$
$$\underline{p \qquad\qquad} \quad p$$
$$\therefore q \qquad \text{imply } q.$$

We may also write the rule in the form

$$[(p \rightarrow q) \wedge p] \rightarrow q.$$

Consider these specific examples of this valid form of reasoning:

(a) Use p: Mary is a junior; q: Mary is taking algebra; and apply the rule of modus ponens:

If Mary is a junior, then she is taking algebra.	$p \rightarrow q$
Given: Mary is a junior.	p
Therefore, she is taking algebra.	$\therefore q$

(b) Use $p: 3x - 1 = 8$; $q: 3x = 9$; and apply the rule of modus ponens:

If $3x - 1 = 8$, then $3x = 9$.	$p \rightarrow q$
Given: $3x - 1 = 8$.	p
Therefore, $3x = 9$.	$\therefore q$

(c) Use p: $KLMN$ is a parallelogram; q: its opposite sides are equal; and apply the rule of modus ponens:

If $KLMN$ is a parallelogram, then its opposite sides are equal.	$p \rightarrow q$
Given: $KLMN$ is a parallelogram.	p
Therefore, its opposite sides are equal.	$\therefore q$

(d) Use $p: n = 2k + 1$; $q: n$ is an odd number; and apply the rule of modus ponens:

If $n = 2k + 1$, then n is an odd number.	$p \rightarrow q$
Given: $n = 2k + 1$.	p
Therefore, n is an odd number.	$\therefore q$

The important point to note here is that each chain of reasoning consists of two premises, or hypotheses. If you accept these premises, you are then *forced* to accept the conclusion.

Consider the statement:

If you like mathematics, then you are crazy.

If you accept this premise as true, and furthermore if you agree that you like mathematics, then you must accept the conclusion that you are crazy. You do so without regard to the meaning or significance of the words used in the statement. You do so only because the law of detachment and the acceptance of the premises force you to accept the conclusion.

We have referred to such examples as valid forms of reasoning. An argument, or proof, is said to be **valid** if its conclusion is a necessary logical consequence of its premises (assumptions). That is, an argument is valid if the conjunction of the premises implies the conclusion. Wherever the premises are all true, the conclusion is also true.

It is important to emphasize again the fact that validity has nothing to do with the question of whether the conclusion is true or false. The conclusion may be false, yet the argument may be valid if the chain of reasoning is correct. On the other hand, the conclusion may be true, yet the argument may not be valid if the reasoning is incorrect.

Consider the following example of a valid argument where the conclusion is obviously false:

> If you like dogs, then you will live to the age of 120.
> You like dogs.
> Therefore, you will live to the age of 120.

The following is an example of a form of reasoning that is not valid:

> If you are reading this book, then you like mathematics.
> You like mathematics.
> Therefore, you are reading this book.

The conclusion in this example is true, but the argument is not valid and is called a **fallacy.** Actually here we are assuming that the converse of a statement is true, and we have seen that this is not always so. The form of this fallacy is:

$$p \to q \qquad \text{If } p, \text{ then } q, \text{ and}$$
$$\underline{q} \qquad\qquad q$$
$$\therefore p \qquad\quad \text{imply } p.$$

Another example of a fallacy may be obtained by using the inverse of a statement. An example of this type of reasoning, which is not valid, is:

> If you are reading this book, then you like mathematics.
> You are not reading this book.
> Therefore, you do not like mathematics.

In symbols, the form of this fallacy is:

$$p \to q \qquad \text{If } p, \text{ then } q; \text{ and}$$
$$\underline{\sim p} \qquad\quad \text{not } p$$
$$\therefore \sim q \qquad \text{imply not } q.$$

EXAMPLE 1. Use p: you work hard; q: you pass the course; and give both a valid argument and one that is not valid.

Solution:

(a) A valid argument is:

If you work hard, then you pass the course.	$p \rightarrow q$
You work hard.	p
Therefore, you pass the course.	$\therefore q$

(b) One argument that is not valid is:

If you work hard, then you pass the course.	$p \rightarrow q$
You pass the course.	q
Therefore, you have worked hard.	$\therefore p$

Another nonvalid argument that might be given is:

If you work hard, then you pass the course.	$p \rightarrow q$
You do not work hard.	$\sim p$
Therefore, you do not pass the course.	$\therefore \sim q$

There are other forms of valid arguments besides the law of detachment. Argument by contraposition is valid. Symbolically, we may write this as:

$p \rightarrow q$	If p, then q; and
$\sim q$	not q
$\therefore \sim p$	imply not p.

EXAMPLE 2. Use p: You work hard; q: you will pass the course; and give a valid argument by contraposition.

Solution:

If you work hard, then you pass the course.	$p \rightarrow q$
You do not pass the course.	$\sim q$
Therefore, you did not work hard.	$\therefore \sim p$

A final form of valid reasoning we shall consider is of the "chain-reaction" type. Symbolically we write:

$p \rightarrow q$	If p, then q; and
$q \rightarrow r$	if q, then r
$p \rightarrow r$	implies if p, then r.

Again, the truth of the conclusion does not enter into the discussion in any way. The argument is valid only because of its form. Consider these specific examples of this valid form of reasoning:

(a) If you like this book, then you like mathematics.
    If you like mathematics, then you are intelligent.
    Therefore, if you like this book, then you are intelligent.

(b) If a polygon is a square, then it has 3 sides.
If a polygon has 3 sides, then it has 4 angles.
Therefore, if a polygon is a square, then it has 4 angles.

Note that both premises are false, the conclusion is true, and the argument is valid.

(c) If a polygon is a square, then it has 4 sides.
If a polygon has 4 sides, then it has 3 angles.
Therefore, if a polygon is a square, then it has 3 angles.

Here the conclusion is false, yet the argument is valid. It is again of the form

$$[(p \rightarrow q) \wedge (q \rightarrow r)] \rightarrow (p \rightarrow r).$$

Exercises

1. Complete the following truth table and show that whenever $p \rightarrow q$ and p are both true, then q is also true.

p	q	$(p \rightarrow q)$	$\wedge$	p
T	T			
T	F			
F	T			
F	F			

2. Show, by means of a truth table, that whenever $p \rightarrow q$ and $\sim q$ are both true, then $\sim p$ is also true.

Classify each of the following arguments as valid or not valid.

3. If Elliot is a freshman, then Elliot takes mathematics.
Elliot is a freshman.
Therefore, Elliot takes mathematics.

4. If Jean is a boy, then Jean loves girls.
Jean loves girls.
Therefore, Jean is a boy.

5. If the Yanks win the game, then they win the pennant.
They do not win the pennant.
Therefore, they did not win the game.

6. If you like mathematics, then you will like this book.
You do not like mathematics.
Therefore, you do not like this book.

7. If you work hard, then you will be a success.
You are not a success.
Therefore, you did not work hard.

8. If you work hard, then you will pass the course.
If you pass the course, then your teacher will praise you.
Therefore, if you work hard, then your teacher will praise you.

9. If you like this book, then you like mathematics.
If you like mathematics, then you are intelligent.
Therefore, if you are intelligent, then you like this book.

10. If you are a blonde, then you are lucky.
If you are lucky, then you will be rich.
Therefore, if you do not become rich, then you are not a blonde.

Supply a conclusion so that each of the following arguments will be valid.

11. If you drink milk, then you will be healthy.
You are not healthy.
Therefore, . . .

12. If you eat a lot, then you will gain weight.
You eat a lot.
Therefore, . . .

13. If you like to fish, then you enjoy swimming.
If you enjoy swimming, then you are a mathematician.
Therefore, . . .

14. If you do not work hard, then you will not get an A.
If you do not get an A, then you will have to repeat the course.
Therefore, . . .

15. If you like this book, then you are not lazy.
If you are not lazy, then you will become a mathematician.
Therefore, . . .

9-6 Euler Diagrams

In the eighteenth century the Swiss mathematician Leonhard Euler
used diagrams to present a visual approach to the question of validity of
arguments. Although the diagrams he used were not necessarily circles,
they are frequently referred to as **Euler's circles.** These diagrams, which
we shall explore in this section, are an aid to reasoning but are not essential
to the process.

First consider the statement $p \rightarrow q$ (if p, then q). This statement is
equivalent to saying "all p are q," that is, p is a subset of q; if you have p
then you must have q. We show this by drawing circles to represent p and
q with p drawn as a subset of q.
Consider the statements:

p: It is a lemon.
q: It is a piece of fruit.

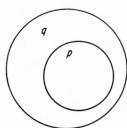

Then the preceding figure may be used as a visualization of the statement "All lemons are pieces of fruit." Note that statements p and q are consistent statements.

Next consider the statements:

> p: It is a lemon.
> s: It is an orange.

Recall that the statements p and s are called contrary statements since they cannot both be true of the same object. If we wish to draw a diagram to represent the statement "No lemon is an orange," then we may draw two circles whose intersection is the empty set:

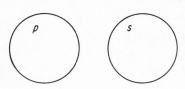

Note that this same diagram can be used to represent either of the following equivalent statements:

If it is a lemon, then it is not an orange.
If it is an orange, then it is not a lemon.

We may also represent contradictory statements by means of Euler diagrams. Consider the statements:

> p: It is a lemon.
> $\sim p$: It is not a lemon.

If we draw a circle to represent the statement p, then $\sim p$ may be represented by the set of points outside of p, that is, by the complement of p.

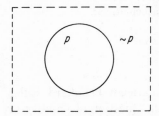

Let us now return to the question of validity and explore a visual approach to this problem. Consider the argument:

$$p \rightarrow q \qquad \text{If } p, \text{ then } q; \text{ and}$$
$$\underline{q \rightarrow r} \qquad \text{if } q, \text{ then } r$$
$$\therefore p \rightarrow r \qquad \text{implies if } p, \text{ then } r.$$

We have seen that the statement "if p, then q" is equivalent to saying "all p are q" and may be drawn with p as a subset of q. Similarly, the statement "if q, then r" can be written in the form "all q are r"; that is, q is a subset of r. To represent these two statements we construct circles in such a way that p is contained within q, and q is contained within r, as follows:

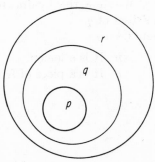

We have followed instructions carefully for our two premises. From the diagram it is clear that p must be a subset of r. That is, we conclude that "all p are r" or "if p, then r," which is what we set out to demonstrate as the conclusion of our argument.

From the final diagram it should also be clear that each of the following conclusions would *not* be valid:

$$\text{All } r \text{ are } q; \qquad r \to q.$$
$$\text{All } q \text{ are } p; \qquad q \to p.$$

Can you see that each of the following conclusions follows logically from the diagram drawn?

$$\text{If not } r, \text{ then not } p; \qquad \sim r \to \sim p.$$
$$\text{If not } q, \text{ then not } p; \qquad \sim q \to \sim p.$$

EXAMPLE 1. Show, by means of Euler circles, that the law of detachment is a valid form of argument.

Solution: The law of detachment states:

$$\begin{array}{ll} p \to q & \text{If } p, \text{ then } q; \text{ and} \\ \underline{p } & p \\ \therefore q & \text{imply } q. \end{array}$$

Draw a circle with p as a subset of q. It is clear that if you have p, then you must have q since all p are in q. Furthermore, the contrapositive is likewise clear from the figure. If you are not in q, then you cannot be in p. That is, $\sim q \to \sim p$.

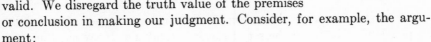

Once again, as in the preceding section, it is important to note that it is the structure of the diagram that tells us whether or not an argument is valid. We disregard the truth value of the premises or conclusion in making our judgment. Consider, for example, the argument:

All undergraduates are sophomores.
All sophomores are attractive.
Therefore, all undergraduates are attractive.

A diagram of this argument follows:

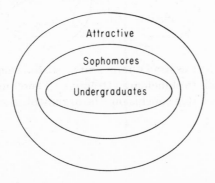

You may or may not agree with the conclusion or with the premises. The important thing is that you are *forced* to draw the diagram in this manner. The conclusion is an inescapable consequence of the given premises. You should not allow the everyday meaning of words to alter your thinking. Thus the preceding argument can be stated abstractly in this form:

> All *u*'s are *s*'s.
> All *s*'s are *a*'s.
> Therefore, all *u*'s are *a*'s.

Here we rely on logic alone rather than any unfortunate notions about the meaning of such words as "undergraduate," "sophomore," and "attractive."

EXAMPLE 2. Draw a diagram to test the validity of this argument:

> All freshmen are clever.
> All attractive people are clever.
> Therefore, all freshmen are attractive.

Solution: The first premise tells us that the set of freshmen is a subset of the set of clever individuals. This is drawn as follows:

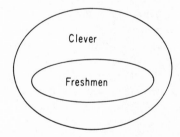

Next we need to draw a circle to represent the set of attractive people as a subset of the set of clever individuals. However, there are several possibilities here:

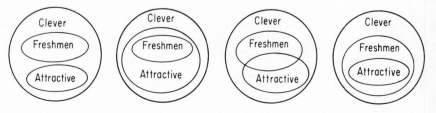

Each of the figures drawn represents a distinct possibility, but only one shows that all freshmen are attractive. Therefore, since we are not *forced* to arrive at this conclusion, the argument is said to be *not valid*.

Each of the figures, on the other hand, forces you to arrive at the following valid conclusions:

> Some clever people are attractive.
> Some clever people are freshmen.

Let us explore further the use of the word "some." We shall use the statement "some x are y" to mean that there is at least one member of x that is a member of y. In everyday language we usually use the word "some" to mean "some, but not all." No such meaning is to be attached to this word as used in a mathematical sense. For example, each of the following is a legitimate use of the word "some" as we shall use it here:

> Some live human beings breathe.
> Some normal dogs have four legs.
> Some mathematicians believe that $1 + 1 = 2$.

In these examples we used the word "some" whereas we could also have used the word "all" instead.

Consider next the statement:

> Some freshmen are attractive.

This statement means that there exists at least one freshmen who is attractive. It does not, however, preclude the possibility that all freshmen are attractive. Now consider the following argument whose validity we wish to check:

> Some freshmen are attractive.
> All girls are attractive.
> Therefore, some freshmen are girls.

To test the validity of this argument we draw Euler circles for the two premises and then see whether we are forced to accept the conclusion. Since some freshmen are attractive, we will draw the following but recognize that the set of freshmen could also be drawn as a proper subset of the set of attractive people.

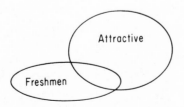

Next we draw a circle to represent the set of girls as a proper subset of the set of attractive people. Here are several possible ways to do this.

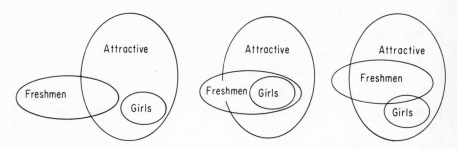

Notice that in two of the figures we find that some freshmen are girls. But we are not forced to adopt this conclusion, as seen in the first of the three figures drawn. Accordingly we conclude that the argument is not valid.

EXAMPLE 3. Test the validity of the following argument:

> All a's are b's.
> Some a's are c's.
> Therefore, some c's are b's.

Solution: The argument is valid, as seen from the diagram that follows.

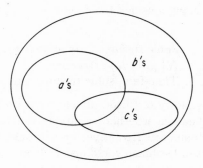

Note that since some a's are c's, then there are also some c's that are a's. However, since all a's are b's it follows that some c's must also be b's.

Exercises

Draw diagrams to test the validity of each of the following arguments.

1. All students love mathematics.
   Harry is a student.
   Therefore, Harry loves mathematics.

2. All juniors are brilliant.
   All brilliant people love mathematics.
   Therefore, if you are a junior then you are brilliant.

3. All girls are beautiful.
   All beautiful people like this book.
   Therefore, if you like this book then you are a girl.

4. All mathematics teachers are dull.
   Some Ph.D.'s are dull.
   Therefore:
   (a) Some mathematics teachers are Ph.D.'s.
   (b) Some dull people have Ph.D.'s.

5. All juniors are clever.
   Some juniors are males.
   Therefore:
   (a) Some males are clever.
   (b) Some males are juniors.
   (c) Some clever people are males.
   (d) All males are juniors.

6. All boys are handsome.
   Some boys are athletes.
   Therefore, some athletes are handsome.

7. All mathematics teachers are interesting.
   All attractive individuals are interesting.
   Some mathematics teachers are kind.
   Therefore:
   (a) Some interesting people are kind.
   (b) Some mathematics teachers are attractive.
   (c) All mathematics teachers are attractive.
   (d) All mathematics teachers are kind.
   (e) Some kind individuals are attractive.
   (f) No mathematics teachers are attractive.
   (g) No attractive individuals are interesting.

8. All x's are y's.
   Some y's are z's.
   Therefore:
   (a) Some x's are z's.
   (b) Some z's are y's.

9. All a's are b's.
   All b's are c's.
   Some d's are not c's.
   Therefore:
   (a) All a's are c's.
   (b) Some d's are not b's.
   (c) Some d's are not a's.
   (d) Some d's are c's.

10. All booms are mooms.
    Some booms are tooms.
    Some zooms are booms.
    Therefore:
    (a) Some mooms are booms.
    (b) Some zooms are mooms.
    (c) Some mooms are tooms.
    (d) No toom is a zoom.
    (e) Some zooms are moom-tooms.

CHAPTER

TEN

GEOMETRY

Geometry is a growing body of knowledge with ever widening applications and an inherent beauty in its systematic structure and organization. In this final chapter we shall consider the evolution of geometry from the practical procedures used several thousand years ago to the logical systems that are currently called geometries. We shall briefly examine some of these geometries, but our treatment will be informal and an effort will be made to convey an understanding of rather than proficiency in the subject matter discussed. We shall consider geometry within the framework of the other topics of mathematics that have been previously considered.

10-1 The Evolution of Geometry

Early geometry was a practical science and an empirical science, that is, a science based upon man's experiences and observations. General theories, postulates, and proofs came much later. We do not know the complete history of geometry; however, the following are among the major influences that have contributed to its evolution:

(a) The empirical procedures of the early Babylonians and Egyptians.
(b) The Greeks' love of knowledge for its own sake and their use of classical constructions.

(c) The organization of early geometry by Euclid.

(d) The continuation of Euclid's work during the Golden Age of Greece.

(e) The contribution of Hindu, Arabian, and Persian mathematicians during the Dark Ages in Europe.

(f) The reawakening in Europe with the growth of the universities, the development of the printing press, and the flowering of all branches of knowledge.

(g) The introduction of coordinate systems in the seventeenth century.

(h) The application of algebra (and also calculus) to geometry in the eighteenth century.

(i) The recognition of points and lines as undefined (abstract) elements giving rise to many different geometries in the nineteenth century.

(j) The emphasis upon generalizations, arithmetizations, and axiomatic foundations in the twentieth century.

At each stage of the development of geometry we find extensive use and application of geometry to the mathematics of its time. We also find the impact of other mathematical and cultural concepts upon geometry.

The geometry of the early Babylonians and Egyptians was concerned with areas and volumes. The Babylonians of 4000 B.C. used the product of the length and the width of a rectangular field as a measure of the field, probably for taxation purposes. The pyramids of Egypt provide striking evidence of early engineering accomplishments that probably required the use of many geometric concepts. For example, the granite roof members over the chambers of a pyramid built about 3000 B.C. are 200 feet above the ground level, weigh about 50 tons each, and were probably brought from a quarry over 600 miles away. The rules and formulas of the early Babylonians and Egyptians were empirical results. Each was considered solely on its own merits since there did not exist any underlying body of theoretical geometric knowledge. In general, the Babylonian and Egyptian concepts of geometry appear to have remained at a utilitarian and empirical level until about 600 B.C. when the influence of the Greeks began to have an effect.

The Greeks with their love of reason and knowledge left a profound impression on geometry. They encouraged its study as a science independent of its practical applications and as a part of a liberal education. They enlarged the scope of geometry to include not only empirical formulas for areas and volumes but also

(a) the use of line segments to represent numbers;

(b) the study of properties of polygons and parallel lines;

(c) properties of circles and other conic sections;

(d) classical constructions with straightedge and compasses;
(e) ratios and proportions arising from a study of similar polygons; and
(f) proofs of the consequences of a set of postulates.

Most of the intellectual progress of the early Greeks came from schools centered around such outstanding scholars and groups of scholars as Thales, Pythagoras, the Sophists, and Plato.

About 300 B.C. the center of mathematical activity shifted from Greece to Egypt, and especially to the newly established university of Alexandria where Euclid was a professor of mathematics. Euclid wrote at least ten treatises covering the mathematics of his time. His most famous work is called Euclid's *Elements* and contains thirteen books in which he presents an elegant organization of

(a) plane geometry (Books I to IV);
(b) the theory of proportions (Books V and VI);
(c) the theory of numbers (Books VII to IX);
(d) the theory of incommensurables (Book X); and
(e) solid geometry (Books XI to XIII).

These topics were more closely related than we now consider them. Proportions were based upon similar polygons, the theory of numbers upon the lengths of line segments, and incommensurables upon proportions and the construction of line segments. The books on geometry included nearly all of the concepts that are now considered in a high-school geometry course. They also included geometric proofs of algebraic identities and geometric solutions of equations (both linear and quadratic). In general, Euclid's *Elements* rendered geometry a tremendous service as an organization of geometry and indeed of all of the mathematical knowledge of that time. We do not know how much of this material was original with Euclid. We do know that the *Elements* represents a logical outgrowth of the geometry of the early Greeks. We shall consider the geometry of Euclid briefly in § 10-2.

The prestige of Alexandria lasted for many years after Euclid. Archimedes (about 250 B.C.) studied there and, in addition to discoveries in other fields, made many contributions to geometry. Appolonius (about 225 B.C.) and Pappus (about 300 A.D.) also enhanced the prestige of Alexandria through their work in geometry. However, by 700 A.D. the geometry of measurements of the early Babylonians and Egyptians had been modified in accordance with the Greek love of knowledge and reason and was in need of new influences.

During the Dark Ages in Europe the mathematical achievements of the Greeks were modified by Hindu, Arabian, and Persian mathematicians.

Most of these influences were of a practical and utilitarian nature. There were noteworthy advances in number notation, areas, volumes, classical constructions, astronomy, and trigonometry (that is, the measure of triangles). Euclid's parallel postulate (§ 10-3) was questioned and Omar Khayyám, the author of the Rubáiyát, wrote a treatise on algebra using a geometric approach.

In mathematics as in trade and art, the first signs of European awakening were in Italy. There were some evidences of mathematical life in England in the eighth century and in France in the tenth century. However, progress was very slow. About the end of the twelfth century Leonardo Fibonacci returned to Italy after traveling extensively, and soon published several treatises making available a vast amount of information regarding previous achievements in number notation, arithmetic, algebra, geometry, and trigonometry. These new ideas were soon picked up in the new European universities, where groups of scholars provided the mutual stimulus that is necessary for great achievements. Then in the fifteenth century the printing press provided a new means of disseminating knowledge, and intellectual activity began to spread rapidly throughout Europe. At first there was an intellectual smoldering while the scholars acquired additional knowledge of past achievements. Soon Alberti and the Italian artists developed some of the principles of descriptive geometry and provided a basis for projective geometry (§ 10-4). Letters were introduced for numbers in France. Mathematical activity gradually acquired momentum and by the end of the seventeenth century was well under way. During the last three centuries there has burst forth such an avalanche of activity, constantly expanding without any definite signs of spending its force, that we shall be hard pressed to assess or even recognize the evolution of geometric concepts.

Our coordinate systems are called Cartesian coordinate systems in recognition of the work of René Descartes in the seventeenth century. He applied algebraic notation to the study of curves and visualized all algebraic expressions as representing numbers instead of geometric objects. Previously linear terms such as x or $2y$ had been considered as line segments, quadratic terms such as x^2 or xy had been considered as areas, and cubic terms such as x^3 or x^2y had been considered as volumes. The old interpretations were restrictive in that only like quantities could be added. For example, it was permissible to add x^2 and xy (areas), but it was not permissible to add x^2 and x (that is, an area and a line segment). Descartes' interpretation of all algebraic expressions as numbers and therefore as line segments made it possible to consider sums such as $x^2 + x$. This new point of view provided a basis for the representation of curves by equations. The application of new ideas to geometry typifies the seventeenth century. There was the application of algebra initiated by Descartes and Fermat

(§ 10-6), applications of projections initiated by Desargues and Pascal (§ 10-4), and application of calculus initiated by Newton and Leibniz.

In the eighteenth and nineteenth centuries we find a broadening of the applications of the new ideas begun in the seventeenth century and the development of the non-Euclidean geometries (§ 10-3). During the last half of the eighteenth century we find increasing evidence of the forthcoming crescendo of mathematical activity that characterizes the nineteenth and twentieth centuries. Because of the increased specialization of terminology and the detailed and abstract character of many of the contributions, our treatment of the evolution of geometry will, of necessity, become very general.

In the nineteenth century the use of coordinates and the acceptance of points as undefined elements made possible the formal development of the non-Euclidean and other geometries. These have led in the twentieth century to the development of geometries as logical systems and the recognition of the equivalence of algebraic and geometric representations of mathematics. We shall try to illustrate this equivalence of algebraic and geometric representations in our discussions of coordinate geometry (§§ 10-6 through 10-11), finite geometry (§ 10-5), and linear programming (§ 10-12).

Exercises

These exercises illustrate the use by the early Greeks of areas of figures to justify statements which we now think of as algebraic. Use the given figure to explain each statement:

1. $(x + 1)^2 = x^2 + 2x + 1$.

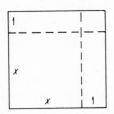

2. $(a + b)^2 = a^2 + 2ab + b^2$.

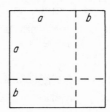

3. $(a - b)^2 = a^2 - 2ab + b^2$.

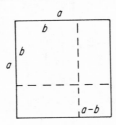

10-2 Euclidean Geometry

The geometry that is usually studied in high school is often called Euclidean geometry in recognition of Euclid's *Elements*, which provided an outstanding organization of most of the properties of this geometry. Since Euclid's time mathematicians have found improved sets of postulates and have stated many of the assumptions that Euclid assumed without mentioning them.

Euclid based his work upon five postulate and five common notions which were considered to be applicable to all sciences. His common notions were:

(i) things that are equal to the same thing are equal to each other;
(ii) if equals are added to equals, the sums are equal;
(iii) if equals are subtracted from equals, the remainders are equal;
(iv) things that coincide are equal;
(v) the whole is greater than the part.

Notice that the first three common notions are properties of the relation "equal." The fourth common notion has caused philosophical questions as to whether two distinct things may coincide and has caused logical difficulties from the use of the converse:

Things that are equal may be made to coincide.

The fifth common notion has caused difficulties since it holds only for finite sets. For example, there are as many positive even integers as there are positive integers (§ 7-1).

Euclid's first three postulates were:

(i) any two points may be joined by a line segment;
(ii) any line segment may be extended to form a line; and
(iii) a circle may be drawn with any given center and distance.

These three were probably Plato's assumptions for constructions with straightedge and compass. Euclid's remaining two postulates were:

(iv) any two right angles are equal; and
(v) if a line m intersects two lines p and q such that the sum of the interior angles on the same side of m is less than two right angles, then the lines p and q intersect on the side of m on which the sum of the interior angles is less than two right angles.

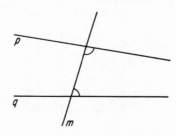

We shall consider Euclid's fifth (or parallel) postulate in more detail in § 10-3. The name *parallel postulate* arises from the use of the postulate to prove that lines are parallel and essentially to prove the existence of one and only one line parallel to a given line and through a given point.

The excellence of the logical structure of Euclid's proofs was one of his major contributions to geometry. His proofs included:

(a) a statement of the proposition that was to be proved;
(b) a statement of the given data (usually with a diagram);
(c) an indication of the use that was to be made of the data;
(d) a construction of any needed additional lines or figures;
(e) a synthetic proof; and
(f) a conclusion stating what had been done.

Lest we idealize Euclid, we should recognize that he adopted many Greek ideas including Aristotle's distinction between postulates and common notions; that he often used definitions as descriptions of terms; and that he tacitly assumed that

points and lines exist;
not all points are on the same line;
not all points are on the same plane;
two distinct lines have at most one point in common;
things that are equal may be made to coincide;
all sets of objects are finite;
there are order relations on a line;
a line is infinite in extent;
a line is a continuous set of points.

However, the results of two thousand years of experience should not be allowed to detract seriously from the significance of Euclid's work.

Euclid's difficulties with definitions may be illustrated by his first eight definitions:

(a) A *point* is that which has no part.
(b) A *line* is breadthless length.
(c) The extremities of a line are points.
(d) A *straight line* is a line that lies evenly with the points on itself.
(e) A *surface* is that which has length and breadth only.
(f) The extremities of a surface are lines.
(g) A *plane surface* is a surface that lies evenly with the straight lines on itself.
(h) A *plane angle* is the inclination to one another of two lines in a plane that meet one another and do not lie in a straight line.

We now recognize that it is not possible to define every term that we use. Some terms must be left undefined; for example, we usually leave point and line undefined. Every definition should have the following four properties:

(i) The term to be defined should be placed in its *nearest class*.

EXAMPLE: A triangle is a geometric figure.

(ii) The necessary *distinguishing properties* should be given.

EXAMPLE: A triangle consists of three noncollinear points and the line segments determined by them.

(iii) The definition should be *reversible*.

EXAMPLE: If a geometric figure consists of three noncollinear points and the line segments determined by them, it is a triangle.

(iv) The definition should involve *simpler terms* (that is, undefined or previously defined terms).

Euclid probably thought of his geometry as describing the physical universe. Modern Euclidean geometry is based upon modifications of Euclid's postulates and appears to provide a good model for the physical universe. However, we actually don't know whether Euclidean geometry is true in the physical universe or not. We suspect that Euclidean geometry does not hold when very large distances are considered, as in astronomy.

Euclidean geometry is sometimes described as the geometry of rigid motions; that is, as the geometry in which figures may be moved without changing their size and shape. Triangles are often introduced as rigid figures; that is, figures whose size and shape cannot be changed without changing the length of at least one of the sides. If we assume that triangles have this property, how many diagonals are required to make plane polygons of 3, 4, 5, . . . , n sides into rigid figures? The pattern is shown in the following array:

Number of sides	3	4	5	6	7	8	9	10	12	n
Number of diagonals needed to make rigid	0	1	2	3	4	5	6	7	9	$n-3$

When you have satisfied yourself that this is the correct pattern, consider the number of ways in which the necessary diagonals can be picked for a quadrilateral and for a pentagon. In the case of the quadrilateral, one diagonal is needed and either one may be used. Thus, the diagonal may be selected in two ways. In the case of the pentagon, the two diagonals may have a common vertex (any one of the five) or they may use four of the vertices (thus avoiding any one of the five) and, hence, may be chosen in ten ways. There are at least forty ways for a hexagon. A complete discussion of the number of ways to make a hexagon a rigid figure is beyond the scope of this book.

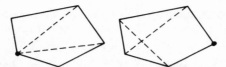

Throughout the study of Euclidean geometry, and indeed any geometry, it is helpful to make conjectures and to test them in the postulational system under discussion. When a theorem is proved on a plane, consider it also in space. Consider the converse of the theorem on a plane and in space. The treatment in space can be either deductive or informal; usually the informal, or intuitive, approach provides sufficient insight. As an example of the extension of concepts on a plane to concepts in space, consider perpendicularity (that is, intersections at right angles). Under what conditions do perpendicular figures exist on a plane? Under what conditions are the perpendiculars *unique* (that is, determined so that one and only one exists which satisfies the given conditions)? Now extend each of these considerations to space figures. Parallels may be treated in the same way. These ideas are developed further in Exercises 7 through 10.

Exercises

Does each definition have the four properties listed in this section? Explain.

1. A point is that which has no part.

2. A line is length without breadth.

3. A duck is a bird.

4. A circle is the locus of points at a given distance from a given point.

5. A triangle is a three-sided polygon.

6. A polygon is convex if the entire figure is on the same half-plane or its edge when each of the sides of the polygon is taken as the common edge of two half-planes.

7. Describe the ways in which perpendiculars exist **(a)** on a plane; **(b)** in space.

8. Describe the situations under which perpendiculars exist and seem to be unique **(a)** on a plane; **(b)** in space.

9. Describe the ways in which parallelism exists **(a)** on a plane; **(b)** in space.

10. Describe the situations under which parallels exist and seem to be unique **(a)** on a plane; **(b)** in space.

10-3 Non-Euclidean Geometries*

The fifth postulate of Euclid appears to have been a "child of necessity." Euclid postponed his use of it as long as possible but couldn't

---

* This section may be omitted without disrupting the continuity of the chapter.

complete his proofs without it. For over two thousand years mathematicians tried to avoid using the fifth postulate. However, each time they either made a mistake or (often unknowingly) made an equivalent assumption. Here are a few of the equivalent assumptions that were used:

(a) If a (straight) line intersects one of two parallel lines, it will intersect the other also (Proclus, fifth century).

(b) Given any line m and any point P that is not on m, there is one and only one line through P and parallel to m (Playfair's axiom).

(c) There exists a pair of coplanar (straight) lines that are everywhere equidistant from one another.

(d) There exists at least one triangle having the sum of its three angles equal to 180°.

(e) There exists a pair of similar triangles that are not congruent.

(f) A circle can be drawn through any three points that are not on the same (straight) line.

Each assumption could be proved as a theorem in Euclidean geometry. However, at some stage in the proof the fifth postulate or a statement whose proof requires the use of the fifth postulate would be needed as a reason.

There are two non-Euclidean geometries, called *elliptic geometry* and *hyperbolic geometry* respectively. They are based upon modifications of Euclid's fifth postulate, his other postulates being kept. For example, consider the fifth postulate in the form of Playfair's axiom and notice these two other possibilities:

Given any line m and any point P that is not on m, there is no line through P and parallel to m. (Elliptic geometry.)

Given any line m and any point P that is not on m, there are at least two lines through P and parallel to m. (Hyperbolic geometry.)

These are the postulates that distinguish elliptic and hyperbolic geometries from Euclidean geometry. Euclid's other postulates are satisfied in all three geometries.

There are many geometries that are different from Euclidean, that is, *not* Euclidean. However, only the elliptic and hyperbolic geometries are called *non*-Euclidean. This distinction between "not Euclidean" and "non-Euclidean" reflects the growth of man's concept of geometry.

We often think of the physical universe as a model of Euclidean geometry. Accordingly we now consider the points and lines on a plane as a model of Euclidean two-dimensional geometry and seek models of the non-Euclidean two-dimensional geometries.

A model for two-dimensional elliptic geometry may be obtained by thinking of the diametral lines (lines through the center) and the diametral planes (planes through the center) of a sphere. The diametral lines represent points of elliptic geometry; the diametral planes represent lines of elliptic geometry. Then, since in Euclidean geometry any two lines with a point in common determine a plane, we have in elliptic geometry:

any two points (diametral lines) determine a line (diametral plane).

The absence of parallel lines is evidenced by the fact that in elliptic geometry we also have:

any two lines (diametral planes) determine a point (diametral line).

There are also other models for elliptic geometry. Different models are used for different purposes. Elliptic geometry is sometimes called Riemannian geometry in recognition of the work on it by Bernard Riemann (1826–1866).

A model for two-dimensional hyperbolic geometry may be obtained by thinking of the circles that intersect a given (fixed) circle at right angles and considering only the interior points of the fixed circle. This model is based upon the work of Henri Poincaré (1854–1912). He visualized the physical universe as the interior of a sphere of radius R such that the absolute temperature t at any point at a distance r from the center of the sphere is given by the formula

$$t = c(R^2 - r^2),$$

where c is a constant of proportionality. He made an assumption (which is not accepted at present) that physical bodies decrease in volume with decreasing temperature and vanish altogether at the bounding surface of the above-mentioned sphere where the temperature is absolute zero. Under this assumption the shortest path between two given points may be shown to be along an arc of a circle that intersects the sphere at right angles.

We now obtain a model for two-dimensional hyperbolic geometry by considering the interior points of the circle in which a plane through the center of Poincaré's sphere intersects the sphere. The arcs of circles that intersect this fixed circle at right angles represent lines. Two lines intersect if they have an interior point of the fixed circle in common, are parallel if they have a point of the fixed circle in common, and are nonintersecting if they are neither intersecting nor parallel. In this model the diameters of the fixed circle are treated as arcs of circles of infinite radius.

Intersecting
lines

Parallel
lines

Non-intersecting
lines

Euclidean, elliptic, and hyperbolic geometries have many different properties. However, in the neighborhood of any point the three geometries approximately coincide. Notice also that the geometry on a sphere in the neighborhood of a point P is essentially the same as the geometry in the neighborhood of that point P on the plane that is tangent to the sphere at P. Relative to the physical universe we know that the geometry in the neighborhood of any point appears to be Euclidean. We do not know whether the neighborhood of the point that we are able to observe is relatively so small that what we are in fact observing is the geometry in the neighborhood of a point in elliptic or hyperbolic space. The three geometries are equally consistent and in a sense equally likely as the geometries of the physical universe.

We know that Euclidean geometry is at least a good approximation to the geometry of the portion of physical space in which man is able to make measurements. It is a relatively simple geometry with numerous theorems and applications, and accordingly, until there is overwhelming evidence that the physical universe has a different geometry, we shall undoubtedly continue to study Euclidean geometry.

Exercises

Identify the two-dimensional geometry or geometries (Euclidean, elliptic, hyperbolic) in which each statement holds:

1. Any two distinct lines intersect in at most one point.
2. Any two distinct lines intersect in exactly one point.
3. Parallel lines are equidistant.
4. Parallel lines do not exist.
5. Two lines perpendicular to the same line are parallel.
6. Two lines perpendicular to the same line do not intersect.
7. Two lines perpendicular to the same line are intersecting.
8. The sum of the angles of a triangle is equal to two right angles.
9. Any two triangles with corresponding angles equal are congruent.
10. The area of a triangle depends upon the sum of its angles.

10-4 Projective Geometry

The early Greeks knew that straight lines often did not appear to be straight. For example, they knew that if the edges of the steps of a large temple were to appear straight, then the edges of the steps had to be curved. We observe the same phenomenon when we stand near a long,

straight, level road and notice that
the edges of the road appear to come
together at a point P on the horizon.

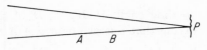

Perhaps you have also seen roads that were straight but not level.
Then, assuming that the part between A and B is behind a hill and the
rest of the road is in sight, the edges
of the road appear as in the next
figure. The change in the apparent
width of the road from AC to BD
helps a person at R driving along the
road to estimate the distance from A to B.

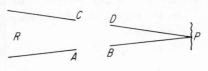

The Renaissance artists thought of the horizon points as vanishing
points and developed a system of *focused perspective* to make their paintings
appear realistic; that is, to enable them to paint pictures of our three-
dimensional world on a two-dimensional canvas. The extent of their use
of mathematics is indicated by the opening statement in Leonardo da
Vinci's *Trattato della Pittura*: "Let no one who is not a mathematician
read my works." The artists of the late fifteenth century realized that
perspective must be studied scientifically and that this could only be done
using geometry.

Alberti, Leonardo da Vinci, Dürer, and others thought of the artist's
canvas as a glass screen through which he looked at the object or scene
to be painted. The artist held the position of one eye fixed, looked only
through that eye, and thought of the lines of light from his eye to each
point of the scene. He marked a point on the glass screen where each line
pierced it. These points make the same impression on the eye as the scene
itself. We call the set of lines from the eye to the object the *projection;*
we call the set of points on the glass screen a *section* of the projection.

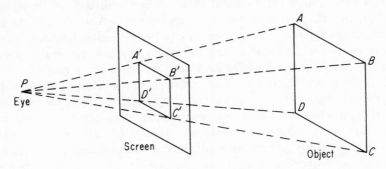

Notice that each point A, B, C, D of the object or scene being painted
is on the same line (collinear) with the point P at the eye and a corres-

ponding point A', B', C', D' of the screen. We describe this situation by saying that the two figures $ABCD$ and $A'B'C'D'$ are *perspective* from the point P.

Perspective figures are also used in many ways today. If we use a pin-hole camera to avoid the necessity of considering a lens, the picture on the film is perspective with the object or scene being photographed. Thus the object and its image on the film are perspective with respect to the pin-hole.

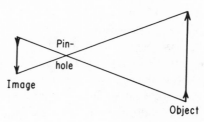

Projections may also be illustrated by the projection of a camera slide or movie. Think of a point source of light and notice that the image on the film and the image on the screen are perspective with respect to the source of light.

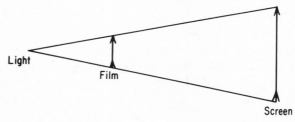

The Renaissance artists could think of their canvases as transparent, but actually the canvases were not transparent. Also the artists often wished to paint scenes that existed only in their imagination. Accordingly, it was necessary to develop the principles of their system of focused perspectivity. These principles provided the basis for a geometry based upon projections, which we call *projective geometry*. The postulates (rules) for projective geometry are relatively simple and the theorems are useful to artists, mechanical draftsmen, mapmakers, photographers, mathematicians, and many others. We shall not attempt to develop the theory of projective geometry; rather we shall conclude this section by pointing out a few of its properties. Projective geometry is a very general geometry which can be restricted by adding appropriate postulates to obtain Euclidean geometry or either of the non-Euclidean geometries.

We have seen that the artists drew parallel lines so that they intersected at vanishing points on the horizon. The horizon line is an ideal line or a line at infinity in the sense that it is not a line of our physical universe and is not a line of a Euclidean plane. Thus in projective geometry a new line has been added to the Euclidean plane so that any two coplanar lines intersect; in other words, since the lines that were considered to be parallel in Euclidean geometry now intersect on this new line, there are no parallel lines in projective geometry. This means that the usual statement,

Any two points on a plane determine a line,

now has a corresponding statement,

Any two lines on a plane determine a point.

In general, any valid statement about points and lines on a plane in projective geometry may be used to obtain a valid statement about lines and points simply by interchanging the words "point" and "line." This property of projective plane geometry is known as the **principle of planar duality.**

There is a corresponding **principle of space duality** which states that in projective geometry any valid statement about points, lines, and planes may be used to obtain a valid statement about planes, lines, and points simply by interchanging the words "point" and "plane" and leaving the word "line" unchanged. Since there are no parallels in projective geometry:

Any two points are on a line.

Any two planes are on a line.

Also:

Any three points are on at least one plane.

Any three planes are on at least one point.

As described by the Renaissance artists, two figures are **perspective from a point** P if the lines through corresponding vertices of the figures all pass through the point P. For example, triangle ABC is perspective from P with triangle $A'B'C'$ since the lines AA', BB', and CC' all pass through P.

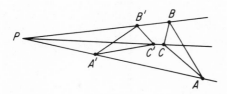

Let us now use the principle of planar duality and the definition of figures perspective from a point to define figures perspective from a line.

Two figures are **perspective from a line** p if the points of intersection of corresponding sides of the figure are all on m. For example, triangle ABC is perspective from p with triangle $A'B'C'$ since the points $\overleftrightarrow{AB} \cap \overleftrightarrow{A'B'}$, $\overleftrightarrow{BC} \cap \overleftrightarrow{B'C'}$, and $\overleftrightarrow{AC} \cap \overleftrightarrow{A'C'}$ are all on p.

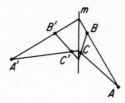

In a detailed study of projective geometry we could prove the **Theorem of Desargues:** If two triangles are perspective from a point, they are perspective from a line, and conversely. (See Exercises 8 and 9.)

We conclude this section with a brief description of two other theorems from projective geometry. Notice that the theorems of projective geometry involve lines and intersections of lines but do not involve measures of distances.

We define a **hexagon** as a plane figure consisting of six lines a, b, c, d, e, f, no three of which are on the same point, and the six points (vertices) $a \cap b$, $b \cap c$, $c \cap d$, $d \cap e$, $e \cap f$, $f \cap a$ obtained by taking the intersections of the lines in cyclic order. Notice that a hexagon may appear in many ways:

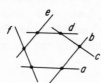 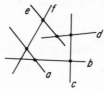 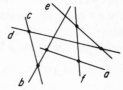

Our final two theorems involve the diagonal points of hexagons that are inscribed in intersecting lines or in a conic (that is, in a circle, parabola, ellipse, or hyperbola). The sides a and d, b and e, c and f of any hexagon $abcdef$ are called **opposite sides.** The three points of intersection of the pairs of opposite sides of a hexagon are its **diagonal points.** (Remember that in projective geometry any two lines on a plane must intersect.) A hexagon is said to be **inscribed** in a figure if the vertices of the hexagon are points of the figure.

Each of the following theorems may be proved in projective geometry. We shall consider only figures illustrating the theorems.

Theorem of Pappus: If a hexagon is inscribed in two lines that are not lines of the hexagon, then the diagonal points of the hexagon are

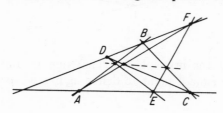

collinear. (In the figure the hexagon $ABCDEF$ is inscribed in the intersecting lines m and m'; the line through the diagonal points is dashed.)

Theorem of Pascal: If a hexagon is inscribed in a conic, then the diagonal points of the hexagon are collinear. (In the figure the hexagon $ABCDEF$ is inscribed in a circle; the line through the diagonal points is dashed.)

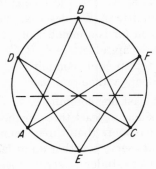

Exercises

1. Write the plane dual of the statement: Any two distinct lines on the same plane determine a unique point.

2. Write the space dual of the statement given in Exercise 1.

3. Write the plane dual of the statement that was obtained as an answer for Exercise 1.

4. Write the space dual of the statement that was obtained as an answer for Exercise 1.

5. The figure consisting of four coplanar points (vertices), no three of which are on the same line, and the six lines (sides) determined by them is called a complete quadrangle on the plane. Sketch a complete quadrangle and label the given points A, B, C, D.

6. The plane dual of a complete quadrangle is a complete quadrilateral. Use the plane dual of the definition given in Exercise 5 to obtain a definition for a complete quadrilateral.

7. Sketch a complete quadrilateral and label the given lines a, b, c, d.

8. (a) Draw triangle RST and triangle $R'S'T'$ perspective from a point M.
(b) In your drawing show that there exists a line m such that these triangles are also perspective from m.

9. (a) Draw triangle XYZ and triangle $X'Y'Z'$ perspective from a line t.
(b) In your drawing show that there exists a point T such that these triangles are also perspective from T.

10. Draw a figure for the Theorem of Pappus.

11. Draw a figure for the Theorem of Pascal.

10-5 A Finite Geometry

We now consider a finite projective geometry; that is, a projective geometry with only a finite number of elements. In our geometry there are two types of undefined elements and one undefined relation among those elements. We call the elements of the first type of undefined elements students in a certain class; we call the elements of the second type of undefined elements committees. We describe the undefined relation by saying that a student is on (or is a member of) a committee. As a matter of convenience we shall use capital letters A, B, C, . . . to represent students and columns of letters to represent committees. Here are the postulates for our geometry of students and committees:

    I. There exists at least one committee.

    II. Each committee has at least three members.

    III. No committee has more than three members.

    IV. Any two students serve together on at least one committee.

    V. Any two distinct students serve together on at most one committee.

    VI. Not all students are members of the same committee.

    VII. Any two committees have at least one member in common.

We may use Postulates I through VII to determine the number of students in the class and the committee structure of the class. By Postulates I and II there exists at least one committee with at least three members A, B, C and which we may designate as committee

$$A$$
$$B$$
$$C$$

By Postulate III this committee does not have any other members. By Postulate VI there must be a student D who does not serve on this committee. By Postulates IV and V student D must serve on exactly one committee with each of the students A, B, and C. The committee on which A and D serve together must have a third member (Postulate II) and (by Postulate V) this third member cannot be B or C. Thus the third member must be a fifth student, E.

The preceding discussion may be continued to determine the complete committee structure of the class. (See Exercises 1 through 44 for the determination of this structure in terms of points and lines.) We conclude the present discussion with a sequence of figures in which students are represented as points and committees as collinear sets of points where the lines are not necessarily straight. The figures are given to illustrate the sequence of steps used in the exercises to prove that there are exactly seven points and seven lines in the geometry obtained when Postulates I through VII are restated for points and lines:

   I. There exists at least one line.
  II. Each line has at least three points.
 III. No line has more than three points.
  IV. Any two points are both on at least one line.
   V. Any two distinct points are both on at most one line.
  VI. Not all points are on the same line.
 VII. Any two lines have at least one point in common.

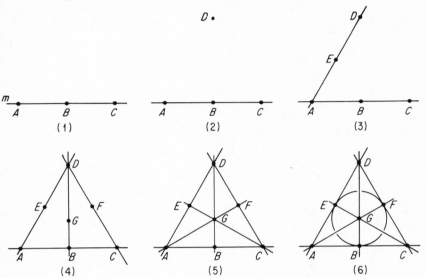

Notice that each of the seven postulates is a correct statement for the seven points and seven lines in Figure 6, where one of the lines appears as an oval. In more advanced courses this two-dimensional finite geometry of 7 points and 7 lines may be extended to obtain a three-dimensional finite geometry of 15 points, 35 lines, and 15 planes.

Exercises

Use Postulates I through VII as restated for points and lines and prove each statement in the order given:

   1. There exists a line m. (See Figure 1.)

   2. The line m has at least three points which we shall call A, B, C.

   3. The line m has no points other than A, B, and C.

   4. The line m has exactly three points.

   5. There is a point D which is not on AB; that is, which is not on the line through A and B. (See Figure 2.)

   6. There is a line AD. (See Figure 3.)

7. There is a third point E on the line AD.

8. $E \neq B$; that is, the point E is distinct from the point B.

9. $E \neq C$ and thus E is a fifth point of the set.

10. There are lines DB and DC. (See Figure 4.)

11. There is a third point G on the line DB and a third point F on the line DC.

12. $F \neq A$.

13. $F \neq B$.

14. $F \neq E$ and thus F is a sixth point of the set.

15. $G \neq A$.

16. $G \neq C$.

17. $G \neq E$.

18. $G \neq F$ and thus G is a seventh point of the set.

19. There is a line AF. (See Figure 5.)

20. The lines AF and DB must have a point P in common.

21. $P \neq B$.

22. $P \neq D$.

23. P must coincide with one of the points B, D, G and therefore P coincides with G; that is, AF and DB are both on G.

24. There is a line CE.

25. The lines CE and AF must have a point S in common.

26. $S \neq A$.

27. $S \neq F$.

28. $S = G$; that is, CE and AF are both on G.

29. There is a line EF. (See Figure 6.)

30. The lines EF and AC must have a point R in common.

31. $R \neq A$.

32. $R \neq C$.

33. $R = B$; that is, the lines AC and EF are both on B.

34. If there were an eighth point H, there would be a line AH.

35. The line AH would intersect the line BD in a point O.

36. $O \neq B$.

37. $O \neq D$.

38. $O \neq G$.

39. AH cannot intersect BD.

40. There cannot exist a line AH.

41. There cannot exist an eighth point H and thus the set consists of exactly seven points which we call A, B, C, D, E, F, and G.

42. There exist at least seven lines as shown by these columns:

$$
\begin{array}{ccccccc}
A & A & B & C & A & C & E \\
B & D & D & D & F & E & F \\
C & E & G & F & G & G & B
\end{array}
$$

43. There exist exactly seven points and seven lines.

44. When Postulates I through VII are stated for students and committees there are seven students in the class and seven committees.

10-6 Coordinate Geometry

Each point on a line in Euclidean geometry has a real number as its coordinate; each real number has a point on a Euclidean line as its graph (§ 7-8). We used a number line in Chapter 7 to help us understand the properties of sets of numbers. In Chapter 8 we used a number line to graph statements in one variable; then we used a Cartesian coordinate plane to graph statements in two variables and to help us understand relations, functions, and inverse relations. We now use a coordinate plane to help us understand the properties of geometric figures.

In the study of geometry the location of any point (x, y) on a coordinate plane may be determined after parallel lines have been introduced and a unit of measure has been given. For example, the points that are one unit from the x-axis are on the lines $y = 1$ and $y = -1$ parallel to the x-axis. The points that are two units from the y-axis are on the lines $x = 2$ and $x = -2$ parallel to the y-axis. The point $(2, 1)$ is at the intersection of the lines $x = 2$ and $y = 1$.

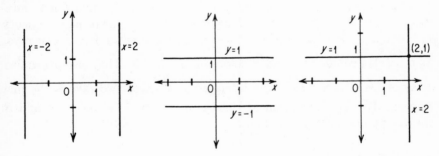

Any two points with the same first coordinate are on the same line parallel to the y-axis; any two points with the same second coordinate are on the same line parallel to the x-axis. Lines parallel to the y-axis have equations of the form $x = k$; lines parallel to the x-axis have equations of the form $y = n$. Each line is a locus; that is, a set of points satisfying a given condition. We locate points (k, n) as the intersection of these loci. The x-coordinate is sometimes called the **abscissa** of the point and the y-coordinate is sometimes called the **ordinate** of the point.

The distance from the origin of a point $(x, 0)$ on the x-axis may be expressed as $|x|$, or as $|x - 0|$. Also, on the x-axis the length of any line segment with end-points $(x_1, 0)$ and $(x_2, 0)$ may be expressed as $|x_2 - x_1|$. On the coordinate plane, the length of any line segment with end-points (x_1, y_1) and (x_2, y_1) may be expressed as $|x_2 - x_1|$; the length of any line segment with end-points (x_1, y_1) and (x_1, y_2) may be expressed as $|y_2 - y_1|$.

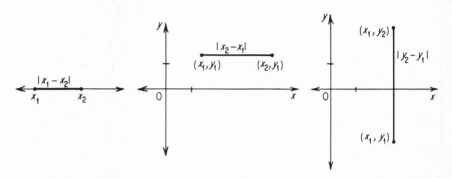

The exercises that follow illustrate the development of the desired concepts. Notice that this material is very susceptible to explorations, conjectures, and discoveries; also, that additional relations among points may be developed by determining whether or not three points having given coordinates lie on a straight line. For example, consider three points A, B, and C on a line. The point B is said to be **between** A and C if the lengths of the line segments satisfy the equation $AB + BC = AC$.

The concept of betweenness has been essentially undefined until recent times. It may be defined for points using lengths of line segments as just noted. It may also be defined using the intersection of two rays. As in § 5-1, two points A and B determine a line $\overleftrightarrow{AB}$. They also determine a ray $\overrightarrow{AB}$ and a ray $\overrightarrow{BA}$. The intersection of these two rays is the line segment $\overline{AB}$. This line segment consists of the two end points A and B and the points *between* A and B.

Exercises

Plot on the same coordinate plane:

1. $(2, 5)$.   **2.** $(-2, 5)$.   **3.** $(-3, -4)$.   **4.** $(3, -4)$.

5. $(0, -2)$.   **6.** $(-3, 0)$.   **7.** $(5, -2)$.   **8.** $(-2, -3)$.

Draw coordinate axes, sketch each locus, and give its equation:

9. The points 2 units above the x-axis.

10. The points 3 units to the left of the y-axis.

11. The points 2 units from the origin and on the x-axis.

12. The points with coordinates that are equal.

Graph each equation or inequality on a coordinate plane and give the coordinates of any three points of the graph:

13. $y = 2$.   **14.** $x = -3$.   **15.** $x = y$.

16. $x + y = 1$.   **17.** $y = 2x - 1$.   **18.** $x > 3$.

19. $x > 3$ and $y < 4$.   †**20.** $|x| + |y| = 1$.   †**21.** $|x - y| < 1$.

Find the equation of the line through and the lengths of the line segment determined by each pair of points:

22. $(2, 1)$ and $(2, 5)$.   **23.** $(-3, 2)$ and $(-3, 7)$.

24. $(2, 1)$ and $(5, 1)$.   **25.** $(-3, 2)$ and $(-7, 2)$.

26. $(5, -2)$ and $(5, 7)$.   **27.** $(-1, -3)$ and $(5, -3)$.

10-7 The Mid-point Formula

The mid-point formula for the line segment determined by any two given points (x_1, y_1) and (x_2, y_2) is derived using the fact that if three parallel lines cut off equal segments on one transversal, they cut off equal segments on every transversal. To do this, we need to be able to find the mid-point of a line segment on a coordinate axis, that is, on a number line.

Consider the points with coordinates 5 and 11 on a number line; the length of the line segment determined by them is $11 - 5$, that is, 6. The mid-point of the line segment has coordinate $5 + \frac{1}{2}(6)$, that is, 8. Notice that $8 = \frac{1}{2}(5 + 11)$. The points with coordinates 3 and -5 on a number line determine a line segment of length $3 - (-5)$, that is, 8; the mid-point has coordinate $-5 + \frac{1}{2}(8)$, that is, -1. Notice that $-1 = \frac{1}{2}(-5 + 3)$.

Suppose that R and S are points on a number line with coordinates r and s. Then the line segment $\overline{RS}$ has length $|r - s|$. When $r < s$, as in the figure, the length is $s - r$; the mid-point has coordinate $r + \frac{1}{2}(s - r)$, that is, $\frac{1}{2}(r + s)$. This formula holds for any two points R and S on a number line.

Now consider any two points A: (x_1, y_1) and B: (x_2, y_2) on a coordinate plane. The line that passes through A and is parallel to the y-axis has the equation $x = x_1$ and crosses the x-axis at $(x_1, 0)$; the line that passes

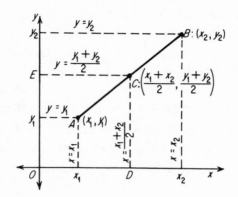

through B and is parallel to the y-axis has the equation $x = x_2$ and crosses the x-axis at $(x_2, 0)$. These points with coordinates x_1 and x_2 on the x-axis determine a line segment; the mid-point D of this line segment has x-coordinate $\frac{1}{2}(x_1 + x_2)$. The line that passes through D and is parallel to the y-axis has equation $x = \frac{1}{2}(x_1 + x_2)$. Notice that the three parallel lines

$$x = x_1, \qquad x = \tfrac{1}{2}(x_1 + x_2), \qquad \text{and} \qquad x = x_2$$

cut off equal segments on the x-axis; therefore, they cut off equal segments on the line AB. In other words, the line $x = \frac{1}{2}(x_1 + x_2)$ passes through the mid-point C of the line segment $\overline{AB}$, and C has x-coordinate $\frac{1}{2}(x_1 + x_2)$.

Similarly, the lines that pass through A and B and are parallel to the x-axis have equations $y = y_1$ and $y = y_2$. These lines intersect the y-axis in points $(0, y_1)$ and $(0, y_2)$; they determine a line segment with mid-point $\left(0, \dfrac{y_1 + y_2}{2}\right)$. The three parallel lines

$$y = y_1 \qquad y = \tfrac{1}{2}(y_1 + y_2), \qquad \text{and} \qquad y = y_2$$

cut off equal segments on the y-axis and therefore cut off equal segments on the line AB. In other words, the line $y = \frac{1}{2}(y_1 + y_2)$ passes through the mid-point C of the line segment $\overline{AB}$, and C has y-coordinate $\frac{1}{2}(y_1 + y_2)$.

We have now completed the derivation of the **mid-point formula:** Any line segment with end-points (x_1, y_1) and (x_2, y_2) has mid-point

$$\left(\frac{x_1 + x_2}{2}, \frac{y_1 + y_2}{2}\right).$$

Notice that after the coordinate plane has been introduced, the mid-point formula can be derived without any additional assumptions. This development is based upon the theorem: If three parallel lines cut off equal segments on one transversal, then they cut off equal segments on any transversal. Applications of the mid-point formula will be considered in the following example and the exercises.

EXAMPLE. Represent the figure on a coordinate plane and prove that the diagonals of a rectangle bisect each other.

Solution: Any rectangle may be represented on a coordinate plane with vertices at R: $(0, 0)$, S: $(a, 0)$, T: (a, b), and U: $(0, b)$. (See

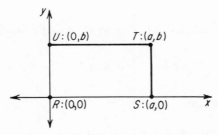

Exercise 6.) Then the mid-point of $\overline{RT}$ is $\left(\dfrac{a + 0}{2}, \dfrac{b + 0}{2}\right)$; that is, $\left(\dfrac{a}{2}, \dfrac{b}{2}\right)$. Similarly, the mid-point of $\overline{US}$ is $\left(\dfrac{a}{2}, \dfrac{b}{2}\right)$. Thus the two diagonals have the same point as mid-point. Then each diagonal contains the mid-point of the other and the diagonals are said to bisect each other.

Exercises

Find the mid-point of the line segment with the given end-points:

1. $(1, 2)$ and $(3, 8)$.   **2.** $(2, -3)$ and $(4, 7)$.

3. $(-5, 4)$ and $(3, -2)$.   **4.** $(-3, -7)$ and $(5, 9)$.

Show that, for suitable values of the coordinates, any figure of the given type may be represented with vertices at the indicated points on a coordinate plane having mutually perpendicular axes:

5. Right triangle; $(0, 0)$, $(b, 0)$, $(0, a)$.

6. Rectangle; $(0, 0)$ $(a, 0)$, (a, b), $(0, b)$.

7. Square; $(0, 0)$, $(a, 0)$, (a, a), $(0, a)$.

8. Rhombus; $(a, 0)$, $(0, b)$, $(-a, 0)$, $(0, -b)$.

9. Parallelogram; $(0, 0)$, $(a, 0)$, $(a + b, c)$, (b, c).

10. Triangle; $(0, 0)$, $(a, 0)$, (b, c).

11. Quadrilateral; $(0, 0)$, $(a, 0)$, (b, c), (d, e).

In Exercises 12 through 15, represent the figure on a coordinate plane and prove:

12. The line segment joining the mid-points of two sides of a triangle is parallel to the third side and equal to half of it.

13. The median of a trapezoid is parallel to the bases and equal to one-half their sum.

14. The diagonals of a parallelogram bisect each other.

15. The lines joining the mid-points of the opposite sides of a quadrilateral bisect each other.

16. A line segment $\overline{RS}$ has end point R: $(1, 3)$ and mid-point M: $(2, 7)$. Find the coordinates of S.

17. Repeat Exercise 16 for R: $(2, -5)$ and M: $(5, -8)$.

10-8 The Slope of a Line

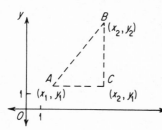

Given any two points A: (x_1, y_1) and B: (x_2, y_2), either the line AB is parallel to a coordinate axis or a right triangle ACB with legs parallel to the co-ordinate axes may be formed by using C: (x_2, y_1) as the third vertex. Then the sides $\overline{AC}$ and $\overline{BC}$ have lengths $|x_2 - x_1|$ and $|y_2 - y_1|$. The ratio $\dfrac{y_2 - y_1}{x_2 - x_1}$ of the directed segments $\overline{CB}$ and $\overline{AC}$ is defined to be the slope of the line segment $\overline{AB}$.

Slope is important primarily as a property of lines rather than of line segments. Any two points A: (x_1, y_1) and B: (x_2, y_2) determine a line AB. This line is parallel to the y-axis if and only if $x_2 = x_1$. If $x_2 = x_1$, the ratio $\dfrac{y_2 - y_1}{x_2 - x_1}$ is undefined, since we cannot divide by zero. If $x_2 \neq x_1$, the ratio $\dfrac{y_2 - y_1}{x_2 - x_1}$ is defined for any points A and B on the line. Prop-erties of similar figures are needed to prove that the ratio $\dfrac{y_2 - y_1}{x_2 - x_1}$ has the same value whatever points A and B are selected on the line. This value is called the **slope** m of the line; we write

$$m = \frac{y_2 - y_1}{x_2 - x_1}.$$

Notice that the slope is defined for any line that is not parallel to the
y-axis; the slope of any line parallel to the x-axis is zero. Slope is usually
introduced for lines through the origin; then defined in general, as we
have done; then it is proved that, for lines that are not parallel to the
y-axis, two lines are parallel if and only if they have the same slope.

The equation of any line that is "determined" may now be found.
We shall consider these cases:

(a) a line through two arbitrary points;
(b) a line through two points on the coordinate axes;
(c) a line through any given point and parallel to a given line; and
(d) a line through a point on the y-axis and parallel to a given line.

Let A: (x_1, y_1) and B: (x_2, y_2) be any two given points. If $x_1 = x_2$,
the line AB has equation $x = x_1$. If $x_1 \neq x_2$, a point P: (x, y) is on the
line AB if and only if the slope $\dfrac{y - y_1}{x - x_1}$ of the line segment $\overline{AP}$ is equal to

the slope $\dfrac{y_2 - y_1}{x_2 - x_1}$ of the line segment $\overline{AB}$. This assertion is equivalent to

the statement that through a given point
A there is one and only one line parallel
to the given line AB; that is, with a given
slope. We use the expressions for the
slopes and write

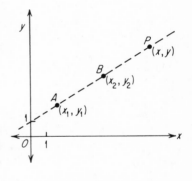

$$\frac{y - y_1}{x - x_1} = \frac{y_2 - y_1}{x_2 - x_1}$$

as the equation of a line through any two
points A: (x_1, y_1) and B: (x_2, y_2), where
$x_1 \neq x_2$. This equation is called the **two-
point form** of the equation of the line.

Let A: $(a, 0)$ and B: $(0, b)$ be two given points on the coordinate axes.
If $a = 0$, both A and B are on the y-axis and the line AB has equation
$x = 0$. If $a \neq 0$, the line AB consists of points (x, y) such that

$$\frac{y - 0}{x - a} = \frac{b - 0}{0 - a},$$

that is, the points with coordinates satisfying the two-point form of the
equation of the line. We may rewrite this equation in the forms

$$(-a)y = b(x) + (-a)b,$$

$$\frac{y}{b} = -\frac{x}{a} + 1,$$

$$\frac{x}{a} + \frac{y}{b} = 1.$$

The last equation is called the **intercept form** of the equation of the line. The number a is the x-coordinate of the point at which the line cuts the x-axis and is called the **x-intercept** of the line. The number b is the y-coordinate of the point at which the line cuts the y-axis and is called the **y-intercept** of the line. Notice that a line parallel to a coordinate axis fails to have two intercepts and cannot be written in intercept form.

Let $A: (x_1, y_1)$ be any given point, and let m be the slope of a given line. The coordinates of each point $P: (x, y)$ on the line through A with slope m satisfy the equation

$$\frac{y - y_1}{x - x_1} = m.$$

When written in the form

$$y - y_1 = m(x - x_1),$$

this equation is called the **point-slope form** of the equation of the line.

Let $A: (0, b)$ be any point on the y-axis, and let m be the slope of any given line. Then the point-slope form of the equation is

$$y - b = m(x - 0)$$

and may be written in the form

$$y = mx + b.$$

This equation is called the **slope-intercept form** of the equation of the line. Notice that it is the y-intercept, that is, the y-coordinate of the point at which the line cuts the y-axis, that is used.

Practice in using these four forms of the equations of a line is provided in the exercises. Notice that, if an equation of a line is given in one form, it may be rewritten in each of the other forms. For example, this equation in two-point form,

$$\frac{y - 1}{x - 1} = \frac{3 - 1}{2 - 1},$$

may be written in point-slope form as

$$y - 1 = 2(x - 1),$$

in slope-intercept form as

$$y = 2x - 1,$$

and in intercept form as

$$\frac{x}{\frac{1}{2}} + \frac{y}{-1} = 1.$$

Notice also that, for any given equation, it is possible to find as many points as desired on the line. For example, if the equation is $y = 2x + 3$, then each point has coordinates of the form $(x, 2x + 3)$. If $x = 1$, $y = 5$;

if $x = -1$, $y = 1$; if $x = 5$, $y = 13$, and so forth. Each of the points $(1, 5)$, $(-1, 1)$, and $(5, 13)$ is on the line whose equation is $y = 2x + 3$. Any two of these points may be used to write an equation for the line in two-point form. For example,

$$\frac{y - 5}{x - 1} = \frac{13 - 5}{5 - 1}.$$

Exercises

Consider lines with the given equations. In Exercises 1 through 4, find two points on each line and write an equation for each line in two-point form.

1. $y = 3x - 5$.

2. $2x + 3y = 6$.

3. $x = 5 - y$.

4. $y = -2$.

5. Write an equation for each line in Exercises 1 through 4 in point-slope form.

6. Write an equation for each line in Exercises 1 through 4 in slope-intercept form.

7. Write an equation for each line in Exercises 1, 2, and 3 in intercept form.

8. Draw the graph of each line in Exercises 1 through 4 on a coordinate plane.

Find an equation for a line:

9. Through $(2, 3)$ and $(4, 5)$.

10. Through $(0, 3)$ and $(5, 0)$.

11. Through $(0, -2)$ with slope $\frac{3}{2}$.

12. With x-intercept 5 and y-intercept 4.

Assume (a) that the coordinate axes have been selected so that none of the lines under discussion is parallel to the y-axis, and (b) that two lines on a coordinate plane are parallel if and only if they have the same slope. Then prove each of these statements for lines on a coordinate plane:

13. If two lines are parallel to the same line, they are parallel to each other.

14. If a line intersects one of two parallel lines, then it intersects the other also.

15. If a line is parallel to one of two intersecting lines, then it intersects the other.

16. Lines parallel to intersecting lines intersect.

17. Quadrilateral $ABCD$ is a parallelogram when its vertices are A: $(0, 0)$, B: $(5, 7)$, C: $(7, 13)$, and D: $(2, 6)$.

10-9 The Distance Formula

We assume that the Pythagorean theorem is known to the reader and use it to obtain a general formula for the length of any line segment on a coordinate plane. Let the end-points of the line segment have coordinates

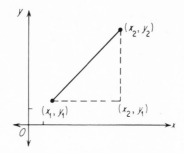

(x_1, y_1) and (x_2, y_2). As in § 10-8, either the line segment is parallel to a coordinate axis, or a right triangle may be formed with the vertex of the right angle at (x_2, y_1). The lengths of the legs of the right triangle are $|x_2 - x_1|$ and $|y_2 - y_1|$; by the Pythagorean theorem, the length of the hypotenuse is

$$d = \sqrt{(x_2 - x_1)^2 + (y_2 - y_1)^2}.$$

This is the **distance formula** on a plane. It holds also when the line segment is parallel to a coordinate axis, since

$$|x_2 - x_1| = \sqrt{(x_2 - x_1)^2} \quad \text{and} \quad |y_2 - y_1| = \sqrt{(y_2 - y_1)^2}.$$

The treatment of circles can now be considered from both a synthetic and a coordinate point of view.

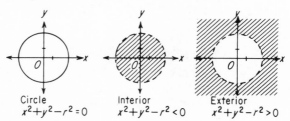

Circle $x^2+y^2-r^2=0$ Interior $x^2+y^2-r^2<0$ Exterior $x^2+y^2-r^2>0$

The distance formula can be used to obtain proofs of many common theorems in coordinate geometry. Several of these are considered in exercises. The proof of the following theorem provides an opportunity to use inequalities as well as equations.

If two chords of a circle are unequal, the longer chord is nearer the center.

Consider the lengths of the chords as $2q$ and $2t$, where $2q > 2t$. Call their distances from the center of the circle p and s, respectively. The radius of the circle with equation $x^2 + y^2 = r^2$ is r. Consider the chord with end-points (p, q) and $(p, -q)$ and the chord with end-points (s, t) and $(s, -t)$. These chords are equal to the given chords, since in the same circle or equal circles chords equally distant from the center

are equal. The statement that the end-points of the
chords are on the circle is $p^2 + q^2 = r^2$ and $s^2 + t^2 = r^2$. Thus, $p^2 + q^2 = s^2 + t^2$. Given that $2q > 2t$, and
that p, q, s, and t are distances (that is, nonnega-
tive), then $q > t$, $q^2 > t^2$, and, subtracting the inequality from the equality, we have

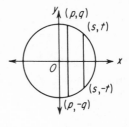

$$p^2 + q^2 = s^2 + t^2$$
$$\underline{\qquad q^2 > \qquad\qquad t^2 \qquad}$$
$$p^2 \qquad < s^2$$

whence $p < s$ as was to be proved. Obviously, the statements require
previous consideration of inequalities (§ 7-4).

The converse of this theorem may be proved in a similar manner
(Exercise 7). Other applications are also considered in the exercises.

The distance formula enables us to classify triangles when the coordinates of their vertices are given. A triangle is isosceles if at least two
of its sides are equal, equilateral if all three sides are equal, and right if
the sum of the squares of two sides is equal to the square of the third
side.

Exercises

Find the length of the line segment with end-points:

1. (1, 3) and (4, 7).   **2.** (2, −3) and (7, 9).

3. (−1, 5) and (2, −3).   **4.** (−3, −4) and (−7, −15).

*Find the lengths of the sides and tell whether the triangle with the given vertices is
(a) an isosceles triangle, (b) an equilateral triangle, (c) a right triangle:*

5. (4, 5), (3, 7), and (6, 6).

6. (−1, 15), (7, −12), and (−3, −5).

Prove on a coordinate plane:

7. A line $x = p$ is tangent to the circle with equation $x^2 + y^2 = r^2$ if $p^2 = r^2$;
is a secant if $p^2 < r^2$; does not intersect the circle if $p^2 > r^2$.

8. The diagonals of a rectangle are equal.

9. An isosceles triangle has two equal medians.

10. The sum of the squares of the distances from any point P on the plane of a
rectangle to the end-points of one diagonal of the rectangle is equal to the sum of
the squares of the distances from P to the end-points of the other diagonal.

10-10 Perpendicular Lines

Two lines on a coordinate plane are parallel if and only if they are both parallel to the y-axis or if they have the same slope (§ 10-8). We now use the Pythagorean theorem and prove that if neither of two lines is parallel to the x-axis and if the lines are perpendicular, then the product of their slopes is -1.

Consider two lines p and q on a coordinate plane. If at least one of the lines is parallel to the x-axis, then the lines are perpendicular if and only if the other line is parallel to the y-axis. If neither line is parallel to the x-axis, then each line intersects the x-axis. Suppose that one line intersects the x-axis at A: $(a, 0)$ and that the other line intersects the x-axis at B: $(b, 0)$, where $b > a$. This assumption implies that the lines do not intersect on the x-axis. When the lines intersect on the x-axis, either a new coordinate system may be used with a different choice of the x-axis or a new proof may be given with A and B selected on a line $y = k$, $k \neq 0$.

If $p \perp q$, call their point of intersection C and draw the altitude $\overline{CD}$ of triangle ABC. Since $b > a$, we may choose $r > 0$ such that $\overline{AD} = r^2$, and thus D has coordinates $(a + r^2, 0)$. In any right triangle ABC with right angle at C and altitude $\overline{CD}$, we know that $\overline{CD}^2 = (\overline{AD})(\overline{DB})$, since the altitude to the hypotenuse is the mean proportional between the segments of the hypotenuse. Therefore, we may choose s such that

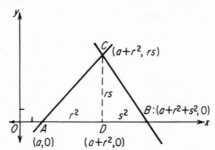

$\overline{CD} = rs$ and $\overline{DB} = s^2$. Then we have

$$C: (a + r^2, rs) \quad \text{and} \quad B: (a + r^2 + s^2, 0),$$

as in the figure. The slope of $\overleftrightarrow{AC}$ is

$$\frac{rs - 0}{(a + r^2) - a},$$

that is, $\dfrac{s}{r}$. The slope of $\overleftrightarrow{BC}$ is

$$\frac{rs - 0}{(a + r^2) - (a + r^2 + s^2)},$$

that is, $-\dfrac{r}{s}$. The product of the slopes of the two lines is

$$\frac{s}{r}\left(-\frac{r}{s}\right),$$

that is, -1. We have proved that the product of the slopes of the perpendicular lines p and q is -1. As a matter of convenience, in this text we shall assume the converse statement without proof: If the product of the slopes of two lines is -1, then the lines are perpendicular.

Exercises

Assume that the lines are not parallel to coordinate axes and prove:

1. A line perpendicular to one of two parallel lines is perpendicular to the other.

2. Two lines perpendicular to the same line are parallel.

3. Two lines perpendicular, respectively, to two intersecting lines intersect.

Prove:

4. The diagonals of a square are mutually perpendicular.

5. The altitudes of a triangle are concurrent.

10-11 The Conic Sections

In § 10-9 the distance formula was used to classify triangles with given vertices on a coordinate plane as isosceles, equilateral, or right. We now use the distance formula to derive the equations of figures which are defined in terms of distances.

A **circle** may be defined as the set of points $P: (x, y)$ at a distance r from a given point (h, k); these points satisfy the equation

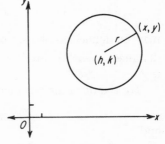

$$(x - h)^2 + (y - k)^2 = r^2.$$

An **ellipse** with center at the origin and major axis along the x-axis may be defined as the set of points $P: (x, y)$ such that the sum of the distances of each point P from the points $F_1: (-\sqrt{a^2 - b^2}, 0)$ and $F_2: (+\sqrt{a^2 - b^2}, 0)$ is $2a$. By the distance formula,

$$\overline{PF_1}^2 = (x + \sqrt{a^2 - b^2})^2 + y^2 \quad \text{and} \quad \overline{PF_2}^2 = (x - \sqrt{a^2 - b^2})^2 + y^2.$$

Then, since $\overline{PF}_1 + \overline{PF}_2 = 2a$, we have

$$\sqrt{(x + \sqrt{a^2 - b^2})^2 + y^2} + \sqrt{(x - \sqrt{a^2 - b^2})^2 + y^2} = 2a,$$

which can be written in the form

$$\frac{x^2}{a^2} + \frac{y^2}{b^2} = 1. \tag{1}$$

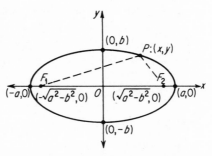

In general, an ellipse with center (h, k) has an equation of the form

$$\frac{(x - h)^2}{a^2} + \frac{(y - k)^2}{b^2} = 1. \tag{2}$$

A **hyperbola** with center at the origin and major axis along the x-axis

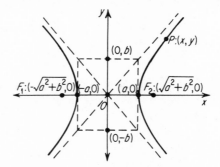

may be defined as the set of points $P: (x, y)$ such that a difference of the distances of each point P from $F_1: (-\sqrt{a^2 + b^2}, 0)$ and $F_2: (+\sqrt{a^2 + b^2}, 0)$ is $2a$.

By the distance formula,

$$\overline{PF}_1^2 = (x + \sqrt{a^2 + b^2})^2 + y^2$$

and

$$\overline{PF}_2^2 = (x - \sqrt{a^2 + b^2})^2 + y^2.$$

Then, since $\overline{PF}_1 - \overline{PF}_2 = \pm 2a$, we have

$$\sqrt{(x + \sqrt{a^2 + b^2})^2 + y^2} - \sqrt{(x - \sqrt{a^2 + b^2})^2 + y^2} = \pm 2a,$$

which can be written in the form

$$\frac{x^2}{a^2} - \frac{y^2}{b^2} = 1. \tag{3}$$

In general, a hyperbola with center (h, k) and major axis parallel to the x-axis has an equation of the form

$$\frac{(x - h)^2}{a^2} - \frac{(y - k)^2}{b^2} = 1; \tag{4}$$

a hyperbola with center (h, k) and major axis parallel to the y-axis has an equation of the form

$$\frac{(y - k)^2}{a^2} - \frac{(x - h)^2}{b^2} = 1. \tag{5}$$

A **parabola** with focus at F: $(0, a)$ and the line $y = -a$ as directrix may be defined as the set of points P: (x, y) such that $\overline{PF}$ is equal to

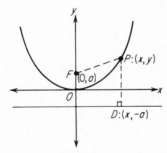

the distance of P from the directrix. As in the figure, draw PD with D: $(x, -a)$. Then the lines PD and $y = -a$ are perpendicular, $\overline{PD}$ is the distance of P from the directrix, and we have

$$\overline{PD} = y + a,$$
$$\overline{PF} = \sqrt{x^2 + (y - a)^2}.$$

Since $\overline{PD} = \overline{PF}$, we have

$$y + a = \sqrt{x^2 + (y - a)^2},$$
$$y^2 + 2ay + a^2 = x^2 + y^2 - 2ay + a^2,$$

which can be expressed as

$$x^2 = 4ay. \tag{6}$$

In general, a parabola with vertex (h, k) and directrix parallel to the x-axis has an equation of the form

$$(x - h)^2 = 4a(y - k); \tag{7}$$

a parabola with vertex (h, k) and directrix parallel to the y-axis has an equation of the form

$$(y - k)^2 = 4a(x - h). \tag{8}$$

These curves (circle, ellipse, hyperbola, and parabola) are called conic sections because they may be obtained as plane sections of a cone, as in the figure. Think of a cone as generated by revolving a line m through

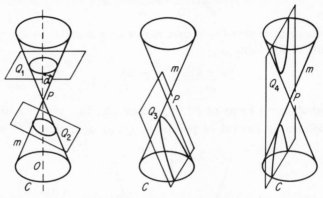

a fixed point P so that the line traverses a circle C which has center $O \neq P$ and is on a plane perpendicular to the line PO. The line m will then make a constant angle α with the line OP. Let Q be any point different from P on the cone. The cone has two nappes; the positions of m are called the elements of the cone. A plane through Q_1 and perpendicular to OP intersects the cone in a circle. A plane through Q_2 and intersecting all of the elements of the cone on one of the nappes (the lower one in the figure) but not perpendicular to $\overleftrightarrow{OP}$ intersects the cone in an ellipse. A plane through Q_3 and parallel to an element of the cone intersects the cone in a parabola. Any other plane through a point Q_4 and that does not contain an element of the cone intersects the cone in a hyperbola. In other words, a plane through Q intersects the cone in a circle if the plane is perpendicular to $\overleftrightarrow{OP}$; intersects the cone in an ellipse if the angle θ between the plane and $\overleftrightarrow{OP}$ is greater than α, intersects in a hyperbola if $\theta < \alpha$, and intersects in a parabola if $\theta = \alpha$.

It is usually desirable to base any geometric proof on the most general possible case of the statement to be proved. For this reason, some people might object to the arbitrary selection of the origin as the center of the ellipse, the center of the hyperbola, and the vertex of the parabola in the development of their equations. Such an objection is not a significant one, since the center or vertex may be considered in any other position after a translation of the axes.

$$x' = x + h, \qquad y' = y + k.$$

Notice that the form of the equations for each conic section in terms of (h, k) may be obtained by the substitution

$$x = x' - h, \qquad y = y' - k.$$

Any objection to the selection of an axis or directrix of a conic section parallel to a coordinate axis may be similarly resolved by rotating the axes through some angle θ.

Exercises

Prove:

1. Any parabola with vertex (h, k) and directrix parallel to the x-axis has an equation of the form (7).

2. Any parabola with vertex (h, k) and directrix parallel to the y-axis has an equation of the form (8).

3. Any ellipse with center at (h, k) has an equation of the form (2).

4. Any hyperbola with center (h, k) and major axis parallel to the x-axis has an equation of the form (4).

5. Any hyperbola with center (h, k) and major axis parallel to the y-axis has an equation of the form (5).

10-12 Linear Programming

Graphs of linear statements in two variables (§ 8-4) provide a very important tool for solving modern problems. Although mathematicians are developing theories for statements that are not necessarily linear, we shall consider only the linear case. Thus we assume that the conditions of the problem have been represented by or approximated by linear statements. Then the solution of the problem depends upon the solution of a system (that is, a set) of linear statements. The usual method of solution is by graphing; that is, the method is geometrical. Accordingly, we first consider two examples of graphs of systems of linear statements in two real variables.

EXAMPLE 1. Graph the system: $x \geq 0$, $y \geq 0$, $y \geq x - 1$.

Solution: The solution set of the given system consists of the ordered pairs of real numbers (x, y) that satisfy all three of the statements. To graph the system we graph each one of the three statements and then take the intersection of their graphs. As in § 8-4 we graph an inequality by first graphing the equality (using a solid line if its graph is part of the solution set, a dashed line otherwise).

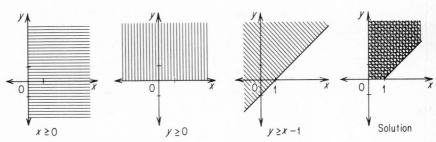

EXAMPLE 2. Graph the system: $x \geq 0, y \geq 0, x \leq 6, y \leq 7, x + y \leq 10$.

Solution:

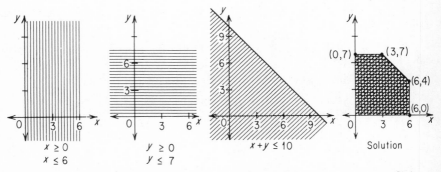

In a linear program problem we not only need to set up our conditions but we also need to maximize or minimize an expression for profit, cost, or other quantity. Consider the conditions in Example 2 and the expression

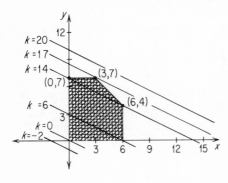

$x + 2y$. For each value k of the expression $x + 2y$, the graph of $x + 2y = k$ is a straight line. As k takes on different values we have a set of parallel lines. When several of these lines are graphed with the solution of the conditions in Example 2, we see that under these conditions k may have any value from 0 to 17 inclusive. The maximum (largest) value that is possible for k under these conditions is 17 and occurs at

$(3, 7)$. The minimum (smallest) possible value for k is 0 and occurs at $(0, 0)$. Suppose that the conditions are for the manufacture of products (say x metal boxes and y glass jars) in a given time and $x + 2y$ represents the manufacturer's profit. Then if we assume that the manufacturer can sell all that he can make, he would make the most profit by manufacturing 3 boxes and 7 jars per unit of time.

In any linear programming problem the maximum or minimum always occurs at a vertex (possibly at two vertices; that is, along a side) of the polygonal region. Intuitively, the reason is that the region is convex (§ 5-3) and thus the lines of a set of parallel lines first intersect the region either by passing through a vertex as in our example or by passing along a side of the region. Accordingly, in our example we could have found the maximum value of $x + 2y$ for points of the region by testing the values corresponding to the vertices $(0, 0)$, $(6, 0)$, $(6, 4)$, $(3, 7)$, and $(0, 7)$ of the region. The corresponding values of $x + 2y$ are 0, 6, 14, 17, and 14 respectively. Thus, as we observed before, the minimum value of $x + 2y$ is 0 and occurs as $(0, 0)$; the maximum value of $x + 2y$ is 17 and occurs at $(3, 7)$.

Exercises

Graph each set of statements as a system:

1. $x \geq 1$, $x \leq 3$, $y \geq 0$, $x + y \leq 10$.

2. $x \geq 0$, $y \geq 0$, $x + 2y \leq 12$, $3x + y \leq 21$.

Find the values of x and y such that under the set of conditions in the specified exercise the given expression has **(a)** *a maximum value;* **(b)** *a minimum value.*

3. $x + 2y$; Exercise 1.

4. $3x + y$; Exercise 1.

5. $x + y$; Exercise 2.

6. $x + 5y$; Exercise 2.

Use linear programming to solve these hypothetical problems:

7. A college is experimenting with a combination of teaching methods, using both teachers in the classroom and closed-circuit TV. The college has facilities for handling five sections of a class at once using closed-circuit TV. For the five sections of a class that meets three clock hours per week the conditions appear to be as follows: The cost per minute of regular teaching is $5; the cost per minute of closed-circuit TV is $3. For a certain week at most $750 can be spent on the instruction of these classes. Assume that the class hour can be spent in part with a teacher and in part with TV. When neither the teacher nor the TV is on the students are free to discuss anything they wish. If the value to the students of x minutes of regular teaching and y minutes of closed-circuit TV may be expressed as $3x + 2y$, how many minutes of regular teaching and how many minutes of closed-circuit TV would be best for the students during the week?

8. Repeat Exercise 7 with the additional condition that the instructor must be present at least 30 minutes each week.

9. Use the conditions as for Exercise 8 and find the number of minutes of regular teaching and of closed-circuit TV when the value to the students may be expressed as $x + 2y$.

10. Repeat Exercise 9 when the value to the students may be expressed as $2x + y$.

10-13 Algebra and Geometry

We have seen that algebra may be used in the study of geometry as, for example, in the use of coordinates. Also geometry may be used in the study of algebra as, for example, in the use of a number line (Chapter 7). The very close relationship between algebra and geometry may be observed by noticing that the algebra of the real numbers and the geometry of points on a Euclidean line are basically the same. Indeed, the early Greeks represented numbers by line segments before more convenient notations were developed. Thus algebra provides one approach or point of view for the study of mathematics and geometry provides another approach or point of view. Both algebra and geometry are concerned with the same basic subject matter—mathematics. We hope that your study of this book has given you a better understanding of this subject matter, and an introduction to mathematics.

The bibliography that follows is for readers who have special interests in one or more of the topics that we have considered. Each reference may be used effectively as supplementary reading or as a source of additional exercises.

BIBLIOGRAPHY

Abbott, Edwin A., *Flatland*. New York: Dover, 1952.
A readable and thought-provoking account of life in a two-dimensional world.

Adler, Irving, *The New Mathematics*. New York: Day, 1958.
A brief overview for the general reader of some aspects of modern mathematics.

Bakst, Aaron, *Mathematics: Its Magic and Mastery*. Princeton, N.J.: Van Nostrand, 1952.
Puzzles, recreations, interesting aspects of mathematics.

Banks, J. Houston, *Elements of Mathematics*. Boston: Allyn & Bacon, 1956.
A survey of various aspects of mathematics for the general reader.

Bell, E. T., *Men of Mathematics*. New York: Simon and Schuster, 1937.
The lives, loves, and works of some of the outstanding mathematicians of all times.

Bergamini, David, *Mathematics*. Life Science Library. New York: Time Incorporated, 1963.
An exceptionally well-illustrated treatment of various aspects of mathematics.

Freund, John E., *A Modern Introduction to Mathematics*. Englewood Cliffs, N.J.: Prentice-Hall, 1956.
An overview of mathematics for the reader with a good background.

Fugi, John N., *An Introduction to the Elements of Mathematics*. New York: Wiley, 1961.
There is a strong emphasis upon sets and logic for the general reader.

Gamow, George, *One, Two, Three—Infinity*. New York: Viking, 1947.
A good discussion of large numbers and infinity.

Gardner, Martin, *The Scientific American Book of Mathematical Puzzles and Diversions*. New York: Simon and Schuster, 1959.
A good collection of puzzles and mathematical recreations.

——————, *The Second Scientific American Book of Mathematical Puzzles and Diversions*. New York: Simon and Schuster, 1961.
Another fine collection of puzzles and mathematical recreations.

Hogben, Lancelot, *Mathematics in the Making*. New York: Doubleday, 1960.
A beautifully illustrated history of mathematics.

Huff, Darrell, *How to Lie with Statistics*. New York: Norton, 1954.
The misuses of statistics.

——————, *How to Take a Chance*. New York: Norton, 1959.
A fascinating popular treatment of probability.

Infeld, Leopold, *Whom the Gods Love: The Story of Evariste Galois*. New York: Whittlesey House, 1948.
The romantic life of a brilliant mathematician killed in a duel at the age of 21.

Jones, Burton W., *Elementary Concepts of Mathematics*, 2nd ed. New York: Macmillan, 1963.
Well-written accounts of such varied topics as sets, logic, probability, and topology.

Kasner, E., and J. R. Newman, *Mathematics and the Imagination*. New York: Simon and Schuster, 1940.
A very popular treatment of elementary topics of mathematics.

Kemeny, J. G., J. L. Snell, and G. L. Thompson, *Introduction to Finite Mathematics*. Englewood Cliffs, N.J.: Prentice-Hall, 1957.
Logic, sets, probability, matrices, and game theory for the mature reader.

Kline, Morris, *Mathematics—A Cultural Approach*. Reading, Mass.: Addison-Wesley, 1962.
The role of mathematics in science and culture for the mature reader.

——————, *Mathematics in Western Culture*. Reading, Mass.: Addison-Wesley. 1953.
A historical survey of the role of mathematics in such fields as art, music, literature, and religion.

Richardson, Moses, *Fundamentals of Mathematics*. New York: Macmillan, 1958.
A general survey of elementary mathematics for the reader with a moderate mathematical background.

Schaaf, William L., *Basic Concepts of Elementary Mathematics*. New York: Wiley, 1960.
Logic, geometry, and the number system are stressed in this survey of elementary mathematics.

Stein, Sherman K., *Mathematics, The Man-made Universe*. San Francisco: W. H. Freeman, 1963.
A collection of unique and interesting patterns for the reader with some mathematical background.

Steinhaus, Hugo, *Mathematical Snapshots.* New York: Oxford U.P., 1950.
  A collection of illustrations concerning important mathematical principles.

Wallis, W. A., and H. V. Roberts, *Statistics: A New Approach.* New York: The
  Free Press of Glencoe, 1956.
  The uses and misuses of statistics interestingly presented.

ANSWERS FOR ODD-NUMBERED
EXERCISES

Chapter 1

1-1 Mathematical Patterns

1. The text shows the diagrams for 3×9, 7×9, and 4×9 respectively. Here are the others:

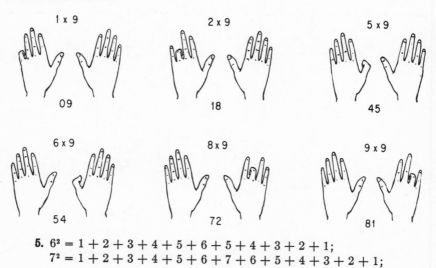

1 x 9   2 x 9   5 x 9

09   18   45

6 x 9   8 x 9   9 x 9

54   72   81

5. $6^2 = 1 + 2 + 3 + 4 + 5 + 6 + 5 + 4 + 3 + 2 + 1;$
$7^2 = 1 + 2 + 3 + 4 + 5 + 6 + 7 + 6 + 5 + 4 + 3 + 2 + 1;$

$8^2 = 1 + 2 + 3 + 4 + 5 + 6 + 7 + 8 + 7 + 6 + 5 + 4 + 3 + 2 + 1;$
$9^2 = 1 + 2 + 3 + 4 + 5 + 6 + 7 + 8 + 9 + 8 + 7 + 6 + 5 + 4 + 3 +$
$2 + 1.$

7. (a) $9 \times 47 = 423.$ **(b)** $9 \times 36 = 324.$

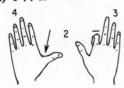   

(c) $9 \times 18 = 162.$ **(d)** $9 \times 29 = 261.$

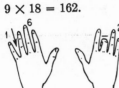   

9. (a) $25 \times 51 = 1,275;$ **(b)** $100 \times 201 = 20,100;$ **(c)** $\frac{25}{2} \times 50 = 625;$ **(d)** $25 \times 100 = 2,500;$ **(e)** $50 \times 202 = 10,100.$

1-2 Finite and Infinite

1. It would take one billion seconds; that is, about 11,574 days.

3. (a) Approximately three billion; **(b)** 3,153,600,000 for 365 days and 3,155,760,000 for 365¼ days.

5. Multiples of 5: $\{ 5, 10, 15, 20, 25, \ldots, 5n, \ldots \}$
Counting numbers: $\{ 1, 2, 3, 4, 5, \ldots, n, \ldots \}$

7. 200; $10^{100} \times 10^{100} = 10^{200}.$ This number is much smaller than a googolplex, which is 10 raised to the googol power; that is, 10 with 10^{100} zeros.

1-3 Mathematical Recreations

1. (a) 12. **(b)** Only one, if it's long enough. **(c)** Only half way; then you start walking out. **(d)** *One* of them is not a nickel, but the other one is. **(e)** There is no dirt in a hole. **(f)** Brother-sister.

3. There are eleven trips needed. First one Indian and one missionary go over; the missionary returns. Then two Indians go over and one returns. Next two missionaries go over; one missionary and one Indian return. Two missionaries go over next and one Indian returns. Then two Indians go over and one of them returns. Finally, the last two Indians go over.

5. After 27 days the cat still has 3 feet to go.   **7.**
It does this the next day and is at the top after
28 days.

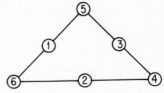

9. Both A's and B's will say that they are B's. Therefore when the second man said that the first man said he was a B, the second man was telling the truth. Thus the first two men told the truth and the third man lied.

11. If the penny is in the left hand and the dime in the right hand, the computation will give $3 + 60 = 63$, an odd number. If the coins are reversed, we have $30 + 6 = 36$, an even number.

13. There really is no missing dollar. The computation may be done in one of two ways: $(30 - 3) - 2 = 25$, or $25 + 2 + 3 = 30$. In the problem the arithmetic was done in a manner that is not legitimate, that is, $(30 - 3) + 2$.

15. $4 = 4 + \dfrac{4 - 4}{4}$; $5 = (4 \times 4 + 4) \div 4$; $6 = \dfrac{4 + 4}{4} + 4$; $7 = 4 + 4 - \dfrac{4}{4}$;

$8 = 4\left(\dfrac{4 + 4}{4}\right)$; $9 = 4 + 4 + \dfrac{4}{4}$; $10 = 4 + 4 + \dfrac{4}{\sqrt{4}}$. There are other ways as well.

17. 15 moves are needed.

1-4 Impossible and Unsolved Problems

1. (a) 5; (b) 9; (c) $D = \dfrac{n(n - 3)}{2}$.

3. (a) Multiply the tens digit by the next consecutive integer and then by 100; add 25; (b) Let the number be written as $10n + 5$. Then

$$(10n + 5)^2 = 100n^2 + 100n + 25 = 100n(n + 1) + 25.$$

We may then rearrange factors to write this last expression as $n(n + 1)(100) + 25$, which is the pattern given in words for (a).

5. (a) 6; (b) 1, 6, 12, 8, 0.　　　　**7.** 6.　　　　**9.** $\dfrac{n(n - 1)}{2}$.

Chapter 2

2-1 Egyptian Numeration

1. ∩∩ ⏐ ⏐ ⏐ ⏐ ⏐

3. 𝄢 ℭ ℭ ℭ ℭ ∩∩ ⏐⏐⏐⏐⏐

5. ⤳𝄢𝄢 ℭ ℭ ℭ ℭ ⏐⏐⏐⏐⏐⏐⏐

7. 211.　　　　**9.** 2,211.

11.

$$\begin{array}{r} \cap\cap\cap\cap\ \mathrm{I}\ \mathrm{I} \\ +\quad \cap\cap\ \mathrm{I} \\ \hline \cap\cap\cap\cap\cap\cap\ \mathrm{I}\ \mathrm{I}\ \mathrm{I} \end{array}$$

13.

$$\begin{array}{r} \mathrm{CC}\cap\cap\cap\ \mathrm{IIIIIIII} \\ -\quad \mathrm{C}\cap\cap\cap\ \mathrm{IIIII} \\ \hline \mathrm{C}\qquad \mathrm{III} \end{array}$$

15.

$$\begin{array}{r} \mathrm{\mathring{E}\ C\ C}\cap\cap\cap\cap\ \mathrm{III} \\ -\quad \mathrm{C}\cap\cap\cap\ \mathrm{IIIIII} \end{array}$$

$$\begin{array}{r} \mathrm{\mathring{E}\ C\ C}\cap\cap\cap\ \mathrm{III}^{\ \mathrm{IIIIIIIII}} \\ -\quad \mathrm{C}\cap\cap\cap\ \mathrm{IIIIIII} \\ \hline \mathrm{\mathring{E}}\qquad \mathrm{C}\qquad \mathrm{IIIIII} \end{array}$$

2-2 Other Methods of Computation

1.

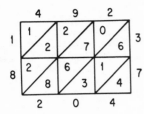

Answer: 18,204

3.

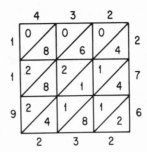

Answer: 119,232

5.

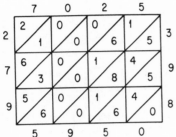

Answer: 2,795,950

7.

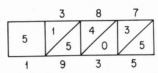

Answer: 1,935

9.

Answer: 58,048

2-3 Decimal Notation

1. 125.   **3.** 0.001.   **5.** 1.   **7.** 0.04.   **9.** 2,000.

11. $(4 \times 10^2) + (3 \times 10^1) + (2 \times 10^0)$.

13. $(4 \times 10^0) + (2 \times 10^{-1}) + (3 \times 10^{-2})$.

15. $(2 \times 10^3) + (3 \times 10^2) + (4 \times 10^1) + (5 \times 10^0)$.

17. $(4 \times 10^2) + (2 \times 10^1) + (3 \times 10^0) + (8 \times 10^{-1}) + (3 \times 10^{-2})$.

19. (7×10^{-3}).

21. 3,253.   **23.** 52.173.   **25.** 0.025.

2-4 Other Systems of Notation

1. 22_{five}.   **3.** 30_{four}.   **5.** ⟨＊ ＊ ＊ ＊ ＊⟩
                                                                  ⟨＊ ＊ ＊ ＊ ＊⟩
                                                                  ＊ ＊ ＊＊

7. ⟨＊ ＊ ＊ ＊ ＊ ＊ ＊⟩   **9.** 23.
       ⟨＊ ＊ ＊ ＊ ＊ ＊ ＊⟩
          ＊ ＊ ＊ ＊ ＊

11. 26.   **13.** 32_{five}.   **15.** 32_{six}.

2-5 Base Five Numeration

1. 113. **3.** 124. **5.** 86. **7.** 141. **9.** 41.88. **11.** $3,012_5$. **13.** $11,112_5$. **15.** $10,000_5$. **17.** $1,022_5$. **19.** 0.2_5. **21.** 0.22_5. **23.** 0.001_5. **25.** $3,004.002_5$. **27.** 135. **29.** 457. **31.** 116.5. **33.** 98.25.

2-6 Other Bases

1. 215. **3.** 1,248. **5.** 43. **7.** 268. **9.** $23,110_4$. **11.** $2,104_6$. **13.** 123_{12}. **15.** $12,041_5$.

2-7 Computation in Base Five Notation

1. 43_5. **3.** $1,112_5$. **5.** $1,423_5$. **7.** 14_5. **9.** 143_5. **11.** 342_5. **13.** $1,331_5$. **15.** $1,423_5$. **17.** 22_5. **19.** 13_5.

21.

+	0	1	2	3
0	0	1	2	3
1	1	2	3	10
2	2	3	10	11
3	3	10	11	12

X	0	1	2	3
0	0	0	0	0
1	0	1	2	3
2	0	2	10	12
3	0	3	12	21

23. All numbers are expressed in base 12 notation.

+	0	1	2	3	4	5	6	7	8	9	t	e
0	0	1	2	3	4	5	6	7	8	9	t	e
1	1	2	3	4	5	6	7	8	9	t	e	10
2	2	3	4	5	6	7	8	9	t	e	10	11
3	3	4	5	6	7	8	9	t	e	10	11	12
4	4	5	6	7	8	9	t	e	10	11	12	13
5	5	6	7	8	9	t	e	10	11	12	13	14
6	6	7	8	9	t	e	10	11	12	13	14	15
7	7	8	9	t	e	10	11	12	13	14	15	16
8	8	9	t	e	10	11	12	13	14	15	16	17
9	9	t	e	10	11	12	13	14	15	16	17	18
t	t	e	10	11	12	13	14	15	16	17	18	19
e	e	10	11	12	13	14	15	16	17	18	19	$1t$

X	0	1	2	3	4	5	6	7	8	9	t	e
0	0	0	0	0	0	0	0	0	0	0	0	0
1	0	1	2	3	4	5	6	7	8	9	t	e
2	0	2	4	6	8	t	10	12	14	16	18	1t
3	0	3	6	9	10	13	16	19	20	23	26	29
4	0	4	8	10	14	18	20	24	28	30	34	38
5	0	5	t	13	18	21	26	2e	34	39	42	47
6	0	6	10	16	20	26	30	36	40	46	50	56
7	0	7	12	19	24	2e	36	41	48	53	5t	65
8	0	8	14	20	28	34	40	48	54	60	68	74
9	0	9	16	23	30	39	46	53	60	69	76	83
t	0	t	18	26	34	42	50	5t	68	76	84	92
e	0	e	1t	29	38	47	56	65	74	83	92	ll

2-8 Binary Notation

1. $11,100_2$. **3.** $10,011_2$. **5.** $10,011,000_2$. **7.** 42. **9.** 1,755. **11.** $101,000_2$. **13.** $11,110_2$. **15.** $1,101,110_2$.

2-9 Just for Fun

1. The numerals at the top of each column represent powers of 2: $2^0 = 1$; $2^1 = 2$; $2^2 = 4$; $2^3 = 8$. Every number less than 15 can be represented in binary notation in exactly one way. Each such number will or will not contain one of these powers of 2. For each such power of 2 that it contains it will appear in the corresponding column A, B, C, or D.

3. There are many references. One is: Burton W. Jones, *Elementary Concepts of Mathematics* (New York: Macmillan, 1963).

5. The procedure is exactly the same as in Exercise 4.

Chapter 3

3-2 An Abstract System

1. #. **3.** Σ. **5.** Commutative property for multition. **7.** Identity element (*). **9.** Associative property for multition. **11.** Inverse element. **13.** $\triangle$. **15.** Yes. **17.** Yes. **19.** No; it must hold for all possible choices of three elements. **21.** Yes; the inverse of $\triangle$ is Q, the inverse of $\square$ is $\square$, the inverse of Q is $\triangle$. **23.** No; the entries within the table contain elements $\bigcirc$ and $\sim$, which are not members of the original set of elements. **25.** Yes; $\cdot$.

3-3 The Distributive Property

1. 3, 3, 3, 7. **3.** 7, 7. **5.** 3, 3. **7.** Take the sum of the two numbers. **9.** Add 1 to the sum of the two numbers. **11.** Subtract the second number from twice the first number. **13.** Subtract 2 from the sum of the first two numbers. **15.** No.

3-4 Clock Arithmetic

1. (a) Yes. (b) Yes. **3.** The identity with respect to addition is 12; the identity with respect to multiplication is 1. **5.** 3. **7.** 9. **9.** 3. **11.** 5. **13.** 10. **15.** 11. **17.** 1, 5, or 9. **19.** 4. **21.** An impossible equation; that is, there is no value of t for which this equation is true. **23.** An identity; that is, this equation is true for all possible replacements of t.

3-5 Modular Arithmetic

1. Two specific cases are: $2 \times 3 = 3 \times 2 = 1$ and $4 \times 2 = 2 \times 4 = 3$. There are many others. **3.** 1. **5.** 3. **7.** 3. **9.** 3. **11.** 3. **13.** 4. **15.** 4. **17.** 4. **19.** 4. **21.** 4. **23.** An impossible equation; that is, there is no value of x for which this equation is true. **25.** Here are two specific cases:

$$3(2 + 4) = 3 \cdot 2 + 3 \cdot 4 = 3 \quad \text{and} \quad 2(4 + 1) = 2 \cdot 4 + 2 \cdot 1 = 0.$$

There are many others.

Supplementary Exercises

1.

+	0	1	2	3
0	0	1	2	3
1	1	2	3	0
2	2	3	0	1
3	3	0	1	2

X	0	1	2	3
0	0	0	0	0
1	0	1	2	3
2	0	2	0	2
3	0	3	2	1

This system is closed, commutative, and associative with respect to both addition and multiplication. It satisfies the distributive property for multiplication with respect to addition. There are identity elements for both addition (0) and multiplication (1). Each element has an inverse with respect to addition; not every element has an inverse with respect to multiplication.

3. 0. **5.** 1, 3, 5, 7. **7.** 2. **9.** 5. **11.** 5. **13.** 3. **15.** 9.

17. $185 - 150 = 35 \equiv 0 \pmod 7$. Therefore July 4 is an integral number of complete weeks after Memorial Day and thus falls on the same day of the week as Memorial Day; that is, on Thursday. In a similar manner, $359 - 150 = 209 \equiv 6$

(mod 7). Therefore Christmas is six days more than an integral number of complete weeks after Memorial Day and thus falls six days after a Thursday; that is, on Wednesday

19. (a)

∘	E	R	L	A
E	E	R	L	A
R	R	A	E	L
L	L	E	A	R
A	A	L	R	E

(b) A, E, A. (c) Yes. (d) Yes. (e) Yes. (f) E. (g) The inverse of E is E; the inverse of R is L; the inverse of L is R; the inverse of A is A. (h) Yes.

Chapter 4

4-1 Set Notation

1. Well-defined. **3.** Not well-defined. **5.** Well-defined. **7.** {January, February, March, . . . , December}. **9.** $\{1, 2, 3, 4, . . . , 9\}$. **11.** $\{51, 52, 53, . . .\}$. **13.** The set of integers 1 through 5. **15.** The set of integers greater than 50. **17.** The set of multiples of 10 from 10 through 100. **19.** The set of numbers of the form $n(n - 1)$ where n ranges from 0 through 10. **21.** Yes. No. Any two identical sets can be placed in one-to-one correspondence and are thus equivalent. Two sets that are equivalent may be placed in one-to-one correspondence but need not have the same elements in each set.

4-2 Subsets

1. $\varnothing$, $\{1\}$, $\{2\}$, $\{3\}$, $\{4\}$, $\{1, 2\}$, $\{1, 3\}$, $\{1, 4\}$, $\{2, 3\}$, $\{2, 4\}$, $\{3, 4\}$, $\{1, 2, 3\}$, $\{1, 2, 4\}$, $\{1, 3, 4\}$, $\{2, 3, 4,\}$, $\{1, 2, 3, 4\}$. **3.** $N = 2^n$. **5.** No. The empty set has no members; the set $\{0\}$ has the single element 0. **7.** A' is the set of odd counting numbers.

4-3 Relationship Between Sets

1. (a) $\{1, 2, 3, 5\}$; (b) $\{1, 3\}$. **3.** (a) $\{1, 3, 5, 7, 9\}$; (b) $\{7\}$. **5.** (a) $\{1, 2, 3, 4\}$; (b) $\varnothing$. **7.** (a) $\{1, 2, 3, . . .\}$; (b) $\varnothing$. **9.** (a) $\{1, 2, 3, 4\}$; (b) $\varnothing$. **11.** (a) $\{2, 3, 4, 5\}$; (b) $\{4\}$. **13.** (a) $\{1, 2, 3, . . .\}$; (b) $\varnothing$. **15.** (a) $\{1, 2, 3, 4, 5, 6, 7\}$; (b) $\varnothing$. **17.** (a) $\{1, 2, 3\}$; (b) $\{2\}$. **19.** $\{6, 8\}$. **21.** $\{2, 4, 5, 6, 8, 9, 10\}$. **23.** $\{4, 5, 9\}$.

4-4 Venn Diagrams

1. A' is shaded with horizontal lines; B is shaded with vertical lines. The union of these two sets is the subset of U that is shaded with lines in either or both directions.

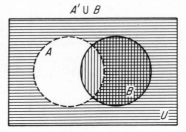

$A' \cup B$

3. *A* is shaded with vertical lines; *B'* is shaded with horizontal lines. The intersection of these two sets is the subset of *U* that is shaded with lines in both directions.

$A \cap B'$

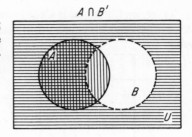

5. Set $(A \cup B)$ is shaded with vertical lines. The complement of the set, $(A \cup B)'$, is the remaining portion of *U*, shaded with horizontal lines.

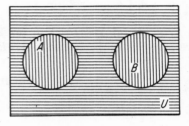

In each of the following pairs of diagrams, the final result is the same, showing the equivalence of the statements given.

7.

$(A \cap B)'$

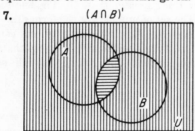

$A' \cup B'$

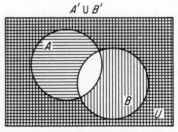

The set $(A \cap B)$ is shaded with horizontal lines. Its complement, $(A \cap B)'$, is the remaining portion of *U* shaded with vertical lines.

The set *A'* is shaded with vertical lines; the set *B'* is shaded with horizontal lines. Their union, $A' \cup B'$, is the portion of *U* shaded with lines in either or both directions.

9.

$A \cap (B \cap C)$

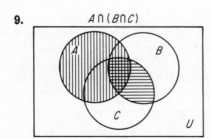

$(A \cap B) \cap C$

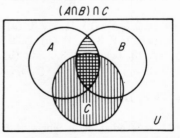

The set *A* is shaded with vertical lines; the set $B \cap C$ is shaded with hori-

The set $A \cap B$ is shaded with lines in the horizontal direction; the set *C* is

zontal lines. Their intersection, $A \cap$ $(B \cap C)$, is the portion of U that has lines in both directions.

shaded with lines in the vertical direction. Their intersection, $(A \cap B)$ $\cap C$, is the portion of U that has lines in both directions.

11. There are 11 students not taking any of the three subjects, 10 taking only chemistry, and 2 taking physics and chemistry but not biology. The given data are shown in the following Venn diagram:

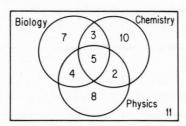

4-5 Graphs on a Line

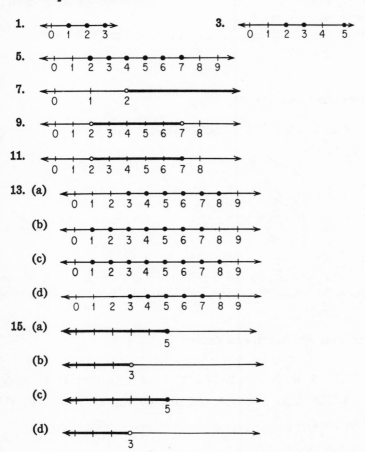

1.

3.

5.

7.

9.

11.

13. (a)

(b)

(c)

(d)

15. (a)

(b)

(c)

(d)

Supplementary Exercises

1. $\{1, 2, 3, 4, 5\}$.

3. $\{3, 4, 5\}$.

5. $\{3, 4, 5, 6\}$.

7. $[3, 5]'$.

9. $[-7, 2]$ and $[3, 5]$ are disjoint sets; their intersection is the empty set. The complement of the empty set is the universal set, namely, $[-10, 10]$.

11. $[-2, 5] \cup [3, 8] = [-2, 8]$; $[-5, 7] \cap [-3, 3] = [-3, 3]$; $[-2, 8] \cap [-3, 3] = [-2, 3]$.

Chapter 5

5-1 Points, Lines and Planes

1.

3.

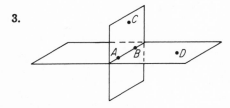

5. No; the point P is not a member of the union of the half-lines. **7.** No; the points of the given line are not members of the union of the half-planes. **9.** As many as you wish.

5-2 Rays, Line Segments, and Angles

1. $\overline{AD}$. **3.** $\overline{BC}$. **5.** $\overline{BC}$. **7.** $\overline{BC}$. **9.** $\overrightarrow{BC}$. **11.** B. **13.** Empty set. **15.** Interior of $\angle ABD$. **17.** $\overrightarrow{AB}$ with point B missing. **19.** Half-line PA. **21.** $\angle BPC$. **23.** The line $\overleftrightarrow{AC}$ and the half-line PB.

5-3 Plane Figures

1.   **3.**

5.   **7.**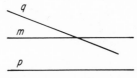

9. Empty set. **11.** M. **13.** P. **15.** Line segment $\overline{MN}$ with points M and N missing. **17.** Triangle RMN. **19.** The points of the line $\overleftrightarrow{MN}$ that are not on $\overline{MN}$. **21.** $\overline{MN}$. **23.** Interior of triangle MRN. **25.** Interior of quadrilateral $STNM$. **27.** Interior of triangle RST.

5-4 Space Figures

1. M, N, O, P. **3.** The interiors and sides of triangles MNO, PMN, PNO, PMO. **5.** A, B, C, D, E, F, G, H. **7.** The interiors and sides of rectangles $ABCD$, $EFGH$, $ABFE$, $CDHG$, $BCGF$, $ADHE$. **9.** $\overleftrightarrow{EF}$, $\overleftrightarrow{CD}$, $\overleftrightarrow{HG}$. **11.** $\overleftrightarrow{AB}$, $\overleftrightarrow{BC}$, $\overleftrightarrow{CD}$, $\overleftrightarrow{DA}$. **13.** $\overleftrightarrow{AE}$, $\overleftrightarrow{BF}$, $\overleftrightarrow{CG}$, $\overleftrightarrow{DH}$. **15.** $\overline{XY}$, $\overline{XZ}$, $\overline{XW}$, $\overline{XT}$, $\overline{YZ}$, $\overline{ZW}$, $\overline{WT}$, $\overline{TY}$.

17.

	V	E	F
Exercises 1 through 4	4	6	4
Exercises 5 through 13	8	12	6
Exercises 14 through 16	5	8	5

19. 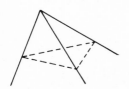   **21.**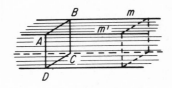

23. 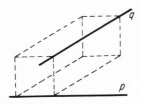   **25.**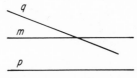

5-5 Plane Curves

Each of these exercises may be done in many ways.

1.

3.

5.   **7.**

5-6 Networks

1. Yes. **3.** No. **5.** No; it has 8 odd vertices. **7.** Add one more bridge joining any two of the points A, B, C, D.

Chapter 6

6-1 Counting Problems

1. 25; 20. **3.** 60.

5. New York   Chicago   Los Angeles

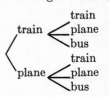

7. 90,000. **9.** (a) 12; (b) 3. **11.** (a) 450; (b) 180; (c) 648; (d) 200. [*Note:* A three-digit number has a units, a tens, and a hundreds digit, with the hundreds digit not equal to 0.] **13.** 117,600.

6-2 Permutations

1. (a) 56; (b) 504. **3.** $\dfrac{n!}{(n-r)!} \cdot (n-r)! = n!$ **5.** (a) 20; (b) 120. **7.** 210. **9.** 9!

6-3 Combinations

1. $_nC_r = \dfrac{n!}{r!(n-r)!};\ _nC_{n-r} = \dfrac{n!}{(n-r)![n-(n-r)]!} = \dfrac{n!}{(n-r)!\,r!} = {_nC_r}.$

3. $_nC_0 = \dfrac{n!}{0!(n-0)!} = \dfrac{n!}{1 \cdot n!} = 1$; there is only one way of not selecting any elements from a set of n elements, namely, not to select any.

5. $1 + 5 + 10 + 10 + 5 + 1 = 32 = 2^5$. In selecting subsets we may do so as in § 4–2 by either including or not including each element of a set of 5. Since there are two choices (include or don't include) for each of the five elements, the total number of subsets is $2 \cdot 2 \cdot 2 \cdot 2 \cdot 2 = 2^5$.

7. $_5C_2 = 10.$ **9.** $_{52}C_{13} = 635{,}013{,}559{,}600.$ **11.** Order is important. **13.** $_8C_4 = 70.$ **15.** $_{10}C_2 = 45.$ **17.** $_{10}C_4 = 210;$ $_7C_3 \times _3C_1 = 105.$ **19.** $\frac{1}{2} \times _8C_4 = 35.$

6-4 Definition of Probability

1. $\frac{1}{2}.$ **3.** $\frac{1}{13}.$ **5.** 0. **7.** (a) $\frac{5}{6};$ (b) 1. **9.** (a) $\frac{7}{10};$ (b) $\frac{7}{15}.$

6-5 Sample Spaces

1. (a) $\frac{1}{10};$ (b) $\frac{3}{10};$ (c) $\frac{2}{5};$ (d) $\frac{3}{10};$ (e) $\frac{3}{5}.$

3.
$(1, 1),$ $(1, 2),$ $(1, 3),$ $(1, 4),$ $(1, 5),$ $(1, 6)$
$(2, 1),$ $(2, 2),$ $(2, 3),$ $(2, 4),$ $(2, 5),$ $(2, 6)$
$(3, 1),$ $(3, 2),$ $(3, 3),$ $(3, 4),$ $(3, 5),$ $(3, 6)$
$(4, 1),$ $(4, 2),$ $(4, 3),$ $(4, 4),$ $(4, 5),$ $(4, 6)$
$(5, 1),$ $(5, 2),$ $(5, 3),$ $(5, 4),$ $(5, 5),$ $(5, 6)$
$(6, 1),$ $(6, 2),$ $(6, 3),$ $(6, 4),$ $(6, 5),$ $(6, 6)$

5. (a) $\frac{1}{6};$ (b) $\frac{1}{18};$ (c) $\frac{1}{12};$ (d) $\frac{5}{6}.$

6-6 Computation of Probabilities

1. (a) $\frac{2}{13};$ (b) $\frac{1}{2};$ (c) $\frac{4}{13};$ (d) $\frac{1}{52}.$ **3.** (a) $\frac{1}{16};$ (b) $\frac{1}{2704};$ (c) $\frac{1}{16};$ (d) $\frac{1}{676};$ (e) $\frac{1}{4}.$ **5.** $\frac{3\frac{1}{2}}{32}.$ **7.** (a) $\frac{1}{220};$ (b) $\frac{1}{22};$ (c) $\frac{7}{44};$ (d) $\frac{3}{44}.$ **9.** (a) $\frac{1}{216};$ (b) $\frac{1}{8};$ (c) $\frac{125}{216};$ (d) $\frac{91}{216};$ (e) $\frac{75}{216}.$

6-7 Odds and Mathematical Expectation

1. 1 to 7. **3.** 2 to 7. **5.** \$1.67. **7.** \$2.00. **9.** The probability that both of the bills drawn will be tens is $\frac{2}{5} \times \frac{1}{4} = \frac{1}{10}.$ The probability that both will be fives is $\frac{3}{5} \times \frac{2}{4} = \frac{3}{10}.$ The probability that one will be a five and one a ten is found as

$$(\tfrac{3}{5} \times \tfrac{2}{4}) + (\tfrac{2}{5} \times \tfrac{3}{4}) = \tfrac{3}{5}.$$

The mathematical expectation is then found to be

$$(\$20)(\tfrac{1}{10}) + (\$10)(\tfrac{3}{10}) + (\$15)(\tfrac{3}{5}) = \$14.$$

6-8 Pascal's Triangle

1. The entries for the first six rows are given in the text. Here are the entries for rows 7 through 10:

7th row: 1, 7, 21, 35, 35, 21, 7, 1
8th row: 1, 8, 28, 56, 70, 56, 28, 8, 1
9th row: 1, 9, 36, 84, 126, 126, 84, 36, 9, 1
10th row: 1, 10, 45, 120, 210, 252, 210, 120, 45, 10, 1

3.

Number of heads:	0	1	2	3	4	5
Probability:	$\frac{1}{32}$	$\frac{5}{32}$	$\frac{10}{32}$	$\frac{10}{32}$	$\frac{5}{32}$	$\frac{1}{32}$

5. The sum of the entries in the tenth row of Pascal's Triangle is 2^{10}, or 1,024. The probability of 0 heads is $\frac{1}{1024}$; the probability of 1 head is $\frac{10}{1024}$; the probability of having neither 0 nor 1 head (that is, of having at least 2 heads) is $1 - \frac{1}{1024} - \frac{10}{1024} = \frac{1013}{1024}$.

7. Both are the same, $\frac{1}{1024}$.

9. $1a^6 + 6a^5b + 15a^4b^2 + 20a^3b^3 + 15a^2b^4 + 6ab^5 + 1b^6$

Chapter 7

7-1 Numbers and Sets

1. 4. **3.** 1. **5.** 1. **7.** 1. **9.** $\{1, 2, 3, \ldots, 15\}$. **11.** $\{3, 6, 9, \ldots, 3n, \ldots\}$.
13. The set $\{1, 2, 3, \ldots, n, \ldots\}$ has the transfinite cardinal number $\aleph_0$; the set $\{\triangle, \square, 1, 2, 3, \ldots, n, \ldots\}$ has cardinal number $\aleph_0 + 2$, which is the same as $\aleph_0$. The equivalence of the two sets may be shown as follows:

$$\{1, \quad 2, \quad 3, \quad 4, \quad 5, \ldots, \quad n, \quad \ldots\}$$
$$\updownarrow \quad \updownarrow \quad \updownarrow \quad \updownarrow \quad \updownarrow \qquad \updownarrow$$
$$\{\triangle, \quad \square, \quad 1, \quad 2, \quad 3, \ldots, n - 2, \ldots\}$$

7-2 Prime Numbers

1. Any number that is divisible by 15 is also divisible by 3.

3. The set of numbers divisible by 3 and 5 is the set of numbers divisible by 15.

5. There are other possible answers in many cases. $4 = 2 + 2$, and

$$
\begin{array}{lll}
6 = 3 + 3, & 8 = 3 + 5, & 10 = 3 + 7, \\
12 = 5 + 7, & 14 = 7 + 7, & 16 = 3 + 13, \\
18 = 5 + 13, & 20 = 7 + 13, & 22 = 5 + 17, \\
24 = 7 + 17, & 26 = 3 + 23, & 28 = 5 + 23, \\
30 = 7 + 23, & 32 = 3 + 29, & 34 = 5 + 29, \\
36 = 7 + 29, & 38 = 7 + 31, & 40 = 3 + 37.
\end{array}
$$

7. **(a)** 13; **(b)** 19; **(c)** 31.

7-3 Prime Factorization

1. $68 = 2^2 \times 17$. **3.** $123 = 3 \times 41$. **5.** $1,425 = 3 \times 5^2 \times 19$. **7.** $819 = 3^2 \times 7 \times 13$. **9.** 2^2. **11.** 19. **13.** 5. **15.** $2^2 \times 17 \times 19$. **17.** $2^2 \times 3 \times 5^2 \times 19$. **19.** $3 \times 5^2 \times 19 \times 43$. **21.** $\frac{123}{215}$. **23.** $\frac{5}{12}$. **25.** $\dfrac{1,259}{3 \times 5 \times 41 \times 43}$.

7-4 Order Relations

1. $3 < 6$. **3.** $7 < 11$. **5.** $3 + 4 > 5$. **7.** $3 - 2 < 5 - 3$. **9.** $5 \times 6 = 6 \times 5$.
11. $\frac{720}{180} < \frac{720}{120}$. **13.** (1) $3 \neq 6$; (2) $11 \neq 17$; (3) $7 \neq 11$; (4) $7 \neq 3$; (5) $3 + 4 \neq 5$;
(6) $3 + 4 = 7$; (7) $3 - 2 \neq 5 - 3$; (8) $7 + 5 = 5 + 7$; (9) $5 \times 6 = 6 \times 5$; (10)
$\frac{120}{30} \neq \frac{120}{40}$; (11) $\frac{720}{180} \neq \frac{720}{120}$; (12) $17 \times 31 \neq 17 \times 29$. **15.** (1) $3 \leq 6$; (2) $11 \leq 17$;
(3) $7 \leq 11$; (4) $7 > 3$; (5) $3 + 4 > 5$; (6) $3 + 4 \leq 7$; (7) $3 - 2 \leq 5 - 3$; (8) $7 + 5$

$\leq 5 + 7$; (9) $5 \times 6 \leq 6 \times 5$; (10) $\frac{120}{30} > \frac{120}{40}$; (11) $\frac{720}{180} \leq \frac{720}{120}$; (12) $17 \times 31 > 17$ $\times 29$. **17.** 1, 2, 3, 4, 5. **19.** 1, 2, 3, 4. **21.** 6, 7, 8, 9, 10. **23.** 3, 4, 5, 6, 7, 8, 9, 10. **25.** 1, 2.

7-5 Integers

1. The empty set. **3.** (a) -2; (b) 5; (c) -8; (d) 7. **5.** $-a < -b < 0$. **7.** 4. **9.** 4. **11.** 12. **13.** 12. **15.** 32. **17.** 13.

7-6 Rational Numbers

1. Yes. **3.** (a) $\frac{1}{3}$; (b) $-\frac{1}{2}$; (c) $\frac{3}{5}$; (d) -2. **5.** $\frac{1}{b} < \frac{1}{a} < 0$. **7.** $\frac{6}{8}, \frac{15}{20}, \frac{75}{100}$.

9. $\frac{-4}{10}, \frac{-6}{15}, \frac{-10}{25}$. **11.** $\frac{-3}{16}, \frac{-9}{48}, \frac{3}{-16}$. **13.** $\frac{19}{12}$. **15.** $\frac{56}{25}$. **17.** $\frac{7}{6}$. **19.** $\frac{1}{5}$. **21.** $\frac{3}{20}$.

23. $\frac{-8}{45}$. **25.** $\frac{8}{3} \times \frac{3}{2} = 4$.

27. Any difference of rational numbers may be expressed in the form $\frac{a}{b} - \frac{c}{d}$ where a, b, c, and d stand for integers, $b \neq 0$, and $d \neq 0$. Then,

$$\frac{a}{b} - \frac{c}{d} = \frac{a}{b} + \frac{-c}{d} = \frac{ad + b(-c)}{bd} = \frac{ad - bc}{bd}$$

by the definitions of subtraction and addition of rational numbers and the properties of integers. Finally, $bd \neq 0$ and $\frac{ad - bc}{bd}$ represents a rational number since $(ad - bc)$ and bd each stand for integers. Remember that all sums, products, and differences of integers are integers.

29. Any rational number may be expressed in the form $\frac{a}{b}$ where a and b stand for integers and $b \neq 0$. Either $0 < b$ or $0 < (-b)$. If $0 < b$, our proof is complete. If $0 < (-b)$ then

$$\frac{a}{b} = \frac{(-1)a}{(-1)b} = \frac{-a}{-b},$$

which is in the desired form.

7-7 Odd Integers and Even Integers

1. Let $(2k + 1)$ and $(2m + 1)$ represent two odd integers. Then $(2k + 1) + (2m + 1) = 2k + 2m + 1 + 1 = 2k + 2m + 2 = 2(k + m + 1)$ where $(k + m + 1)$ is an integer; thus $2(k + m + 1)$ is an even integer.

3. Let $(2k + 1)$ represent an odd integer. Then

$$(2k + 1)^2 = 4k^2 + 4k + 1 = 2(2k^2 + 2k) + 1$$

where $(2k^2 + 2k)$ is an integer and $2(2k^2 + 2k) + 1$ is an odd integer.

7-8 Real Numbers

	(a)	**(b)**	**(c)**	**(d)**
1.	Yes.	Yes.	No.	Yes.
3.	Yes.	Yes.	No.	Yes.
5.	No.	No.	Yes.	Yes.
7.	No.	Yes.	No.	Yes.
9.	No.	No.	Yes.	Yes.

11. Terminating. **13.** Repeating. **15.** Terminating. **17.** Terminating. **19.** Non-terminating, nonrepeating. **21.** $0.166\overline{6}.\ldots$ **23.** 5.375. **25.** 5.5. **27.** $\dfrac{47}{9}$. **29.** $\dfrac{421}{99}$. **31.** $\dfrac{65,203}{999}$. **33.** $\dfrac{127,799}{99,900,000}$. **35.** $\dfrac{2,564,368}{9,999}$.

Chapter 8

8-1 Sentences and Statements

1. (a) Equality; (b) false. **3.** (a) Inequality; (b) true. **5.** (a) Inequality; (b) true. **7.** (a) Inequality; (b) true. **9.** (a) Equality; (b) true. **11.** (a) Equality; (b) false. **13.** (a) Inequality; (b) false. **15.** (a) Inequality; (b) false. **17.** $5 + n$ where n represents a positive integer. **19.** bh where b and h represent rational numbers. **21.** $4s$ where s represents a positive number. **23.** $2n - 1$ where n represents an integer. **25.** $0.05n + 0.08t$ where n and t represent nonnegative integers.

8-2 Solution Sets

1. (a) $\{x \mid 2x - 1 = 11, x \text{ a real number}\}$; (b) $\{6\}$;

(c)

3. (a) $\{y \mid y + 3 \geq 5, y \text{ a negative integer}\}$; (b) $\varnothing$;

(c)

5. (a) $\{x \mid x < -3, x \text{ a negative number}\}$;
(b) all real numbers less than -3;

(c)

7. (a) $\{x \mid -2 \leq x < 3, x \text{ a real number}\}$;
(b) all real numbers greater than or equal to -2 but less than 3;

(c)

9. (a) $\{x \mid |x| < 2,\ x \text{ a real number}\}$;
   (b) all real numbers between -2 and 2;

   (c)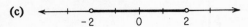
   $$-2 \qquad 0 \qquad 2$$

11. (a) $\{x \mid x^2 = 16,\ x \text{ a real number}\}$;
   (b) $\{-4, 4\}$.

   (c)
   $$-4 \qquad 0 \qquad 4$$

13. (a) $\{x \mid 5x \geq 10,\ x \text{ a real number}\}$;
   (b) all real numbers greater than or equal to 2;

   (c)
   $$0 \qquad 2$$

15. (a) $\{x \mid x + 2 < 5 + 2,\ x \text{ a negative integer}\}$;
   (b) all negative integers;

   (c)
   $$-6 \ -5 \ -4 \ -3 \ -2 \ -1 \ \ 0$$

17. (a) $\{r \mid 3 + r = r + 2,\ r \text{ a real number}\}$; **(b)** $\varnothing$;

   (c)
   $$0 \quad 1$$

19. (a) $\{x \mid x^2 < 9,\ x \text{ a real number}\}$;
   (b) all real numbers between -3 and 3;

   (c)
   $$-3 \qquad 0 \qquad 3$$

21.
   $$0 \qquad 11$$

23.
   $$0$$

25.
   $$0 \qquad 10$$

27.
   $$-3 \qquad 0$$

29.
   $$0 \qquad 2$$

31.
   $$0 \qquad 5$$

33. The solution set is the empty set.

35.
   $$-2 \qquad 0 \qquad 2$$

37.

39.

8-3 Classification of Statements

1. Conditional equation. **3.** Identity. **5.** Conditional inequality. **7.** Absolute inequality. **9.** Conditional equation. **11.** (1) Conditional equation; (2) conditional inequality; (3) identity; (4) conditional equation; (5) conditional inequality; (6) conditional inequality; (7) absolute inequality; (8) impossible equation; (9) conditional equation; (10) conditional equation.

8-4 Linear Statements in Two Variables

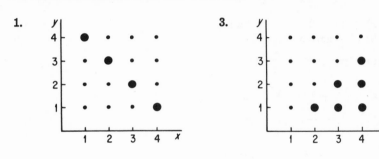

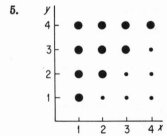

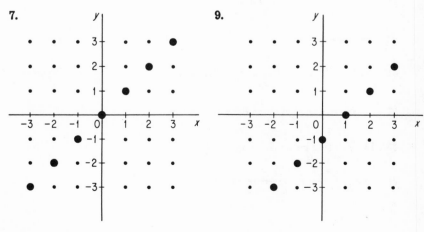

13. The solution set is the empty set.

11.

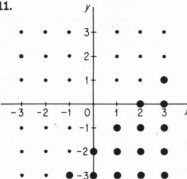

15.

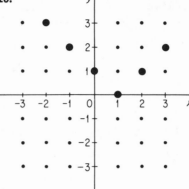

17. (1)

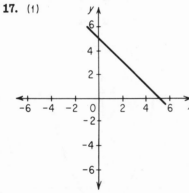

(2)

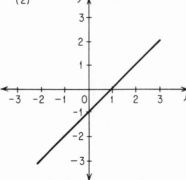

(3)

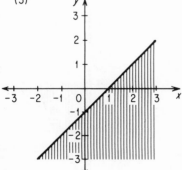

(4)

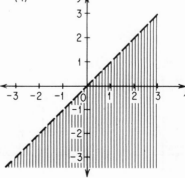

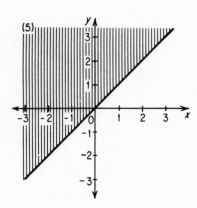
(5)

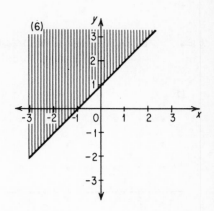
(6)

8-5 Other Statements in Two Variables

1.
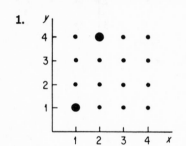

3.
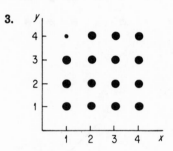

5.
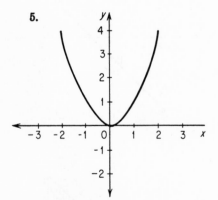

7.
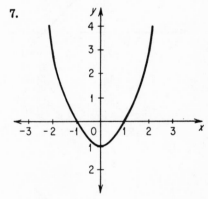

9.
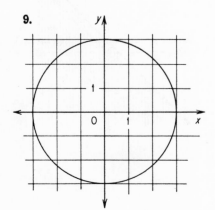

11.
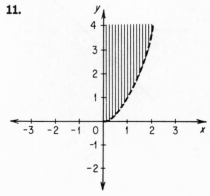

13.

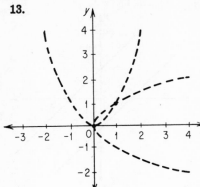

15.

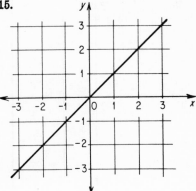

8-6 Relations and Functions

1.

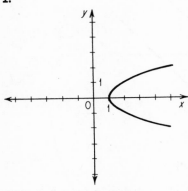

Not a function.

3.

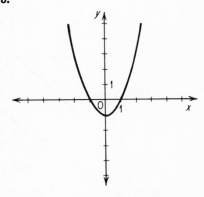

A function.

5.

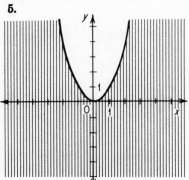

Not a function.

7.

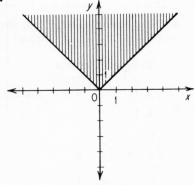

Not a function.

9.

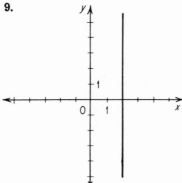

Not a function.

11.

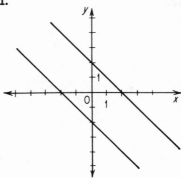

Not a function.

13.

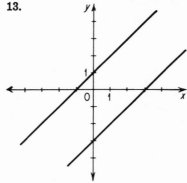

Not a function.

15. The graph consists of two straight lines parallel to the y-axis, namely: $x = k$ and $x = -k$.

17. The graph consists of two parallel lines with slope -1 and y-intercepts k and $-k$: $x + y = k$ and $x + y = -k$.

19. The graph consists of two parallel lines with slope 1 and y-intercepts $b + k$ and $b - k$: $y - x - b = k$ and $y - x - b = -k$.

8-7 Inverse Relations

1. $\{(2, 1), (2, 3), (3, 5)\}$; not a function.

3. $\{(1, 1), (2, 2), (3, 3), (4, 4)\}$; a function.

5.

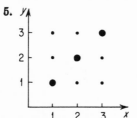

The graph of the inverse of this relation is the same as for the given relation. It consists of the set: $\{(1, 1), (2, 2), (3, 3)\}$.

7.

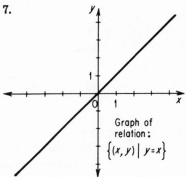

Graph of
relation:
$\{(x,y) \mid y=x\}$

The graph of the inverse of this relation is the same as for the given relation.

9.

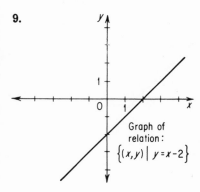

Graph of
relation:
$\{(x,y) \mid y=x-2\}$

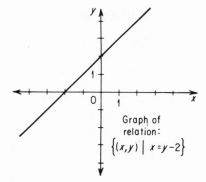

Graph of
relation:
$\{(x,y) \mid x=y-2\}$

11.

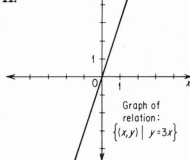

Graph of
relation:
$\{(x,y) \mid y=3x\}$

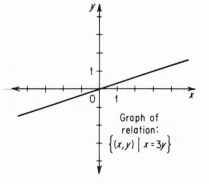

Graph of
relation:
$\{(x,y) \mid x=3y\}$

13.

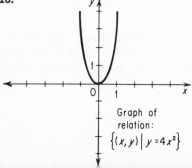

Graph of
relation:
$\{(x,y) \mid y=4x^2\}$

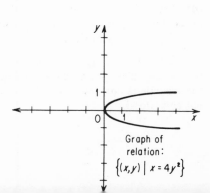

Graph of
relation:
$\{(x,y) \mid x=4y^2\}$

Chapter 9

9-1 Statements

1. (a) $(\sim p) \wedge (\sim q)$; **(b)** $(\sim q) \wedge p$; **(c)** $(\sim p) \wedge q$; **(d)** $(\sim p) \wedge q$; **(e)** $\sim [p \wedge (\sim q)]$; **(f)** $(\sim p) \vee q$; **(g)** $p \vee (\sim q)$.

3. (a) I like this book and I like mathematics. **(b)** I do not like mathematics. **(c)** I do not like this book. **(d)** I do not like this book and I do not like mathematics. **(e)** I do not like this book and I like mathematics. **(f)** I like this book or I like mathematics. **(g)** It is not true that I like this book and I like mathematics. **(h)** It is not true that I do not like this book and I like mathematics.

5. (b), (f), (g), and **(h)**.

9-2 Truth Tables

1. (a), (d), (e), and **(f)**. **3.** Contrary.

5.

p	q	$p \underline{\vee} q$
T	T	F
T	F	T
F	T	T
F	F	F

7. $\sim (p \wedge q)$.

9.

p	q	(a) $(\sim p) \wedge q$	(b) $(\sim p) \wedge (\sim q)$	(c) $\sim (p \wedge q)$	(d) $p \vee (\sim q)$	(e) $\sim [p \vee (\sim q)]$	(f) $\sim [(\sim p) \vee q]$
T	T	F	F	F	T	F	F
T	F	F	F	T	T	F	T
F	T	T	F	T	F	T	F
F	F	F	T	T	T	F	F

9-3 Implication

1. (a) If he has red hair, then the boy is a Johnson. **(b)** If the creature is a duck, then it is a bird. **(c)** If two angles are vertical angles, then they are equal. **(d)** If two angles are complements of a given angle, then they are equal. **(e)** If two angles are supplements of equal angles, then they are equal. **(f)** If two lines are parallel, then they are coplanar.

3. (a) If a triangle is equilateral, then the triangle is isosceles. **(b)** If a triangle is isosceles, then the triangle is equilateral. **(c)** If a triangle is not equilateral, then the triangle is not isosceles. **(d)** If a triangle is not isosceles, then the triangle is not equilateral.

5. *Converse:* If we buy a new car, then we can afford it. *Inverse:* If we cannot afford it, then we do not buy a new car. *Contrapositive:* If we do not buy a new car, then we cannot afford it.

7. *Converse:* If the triangles are congruent, then two sides and the included angle of one are equal to two sides and the included angle of the other. *Inverse:* If two sides and the included angle of one triangle are not equal to two sides and the included angle of another triangle, then the triangles are not congruent. *Contrapositive:* If two triangles are not congruent, then two sides and the included angle of one are not equal to two sides and the included angle of the other.

9. *Converse:* If $x = 1$, then $x(x - 1) = 0$. *Inverse:* If $x(x - 1) \neq 0$, then $x \neq 1$. *Contrapositive:* If $x \neq 1$, then $x(x - 1) \neq 0$.

11. The inverse is always true in Exercises 7 and 9. (Note that these answers are the same as those for Exercise 10.)

13. For any statement $p \rightarrow q$, the contrapositive is $(\sim q) \rightarrow (\sim p)$. The contrapositive of the contrapositive is $[\sim (\sim p)] \rightarrow [\sim (\sim q)]$; that is, $p \rightarrow q$.

15.

p	q	$(p \rightarrow q)$	$\wedge$	$(q \rightarrow p)$
T	T	T	**T**	T
T	F	F	**F**	T
F	T	T	**F**	F
F	F	T	**T**	T

[*Note:* The final results are in bold print.]

17.

p	q	$[(\sim p) \wedge q]$	$\rightarrow$	$(p \vee q)$
T	T	F	**T**	T
T	F	F	**T**	T
F	T	T	**T**	T
F	F	F	**T**	F

[*Note:* The final results are in bold print.]

19. *Converse:* $q \rightarrow (\sim p)$. *Inverse:* $p \rightarrow (\sim q)$. *Contrapositive:* $(\sim q) \rightarrow p$.

21. All five statements are equivalent. That is, all five are different ways of saying "if p, then q."

9-4 Necessary and Sufficient Conditions

1. **(a)** and **(b)** are both the same: If you like this book, then you will like mathematics. **(c)**, **(d)**, and **(e)** are all the same: If you like mathematics, then you will like this book.

3. **(a)** $p \leftrightarrow q$; **(b)** $p \rightarrow q$; **(c)** $q \rightarrow p$; **(d)** $q \leftrightarrow p$; **(e)** $(\sim p) \rightarrow (\sim q)$.

5. **(a)**, **(b)**, and **(d)** are true; **(c)** and **(e)** are false.

7.

p	q	$p \leftrightarrow q$	$[(\sim p) \rightarrow (\sim q)]$	$\wedge$	$[(\sim q) \rightarrow (\sim p)]$
T	T	T	T	T	T
T	F	F	T	F	F
F	T	F	F	F	T
F	F	T	T	T	T

9. The assertion is equivalent to saying: "If I marry your daughter, then you will give me \$10,000." The converse cannot be implied. That is, the young man did *not* say: "If you give me \$10,000, then I will marry your daughter." He should not be sued for breach of promise.

9-5 The Nature of Proof

1.

p	q	$p \rightarrow q$	$\wedge$	p
T	T	T	T	T
T	F	F	F	T
F	T	T	F	F
F	F	T	F	F

[Note that only in the first row are $p \rightarrow q$ and p both true, and that q is also true there.]

3. Valid. **5.** Valid. **7.** Valid. **9.** Not valid. **11.** You do not drink milk. **13.** If you like to fish, then you are a mathematician. **15.** If you like this book, then you will become a mathematician.

9-6 Euler Diagrams

1. Valid. In the diagram, S represents all students, M represents those who love mathematics, and H represents Harry.

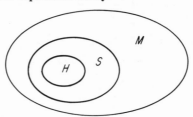

3. Not valid. In the diagram, G represents all girls, B represents all beautiful people, and L represents those who like this book.

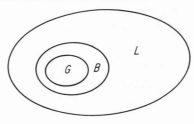

5. (a) Valid; **(b)** valid; **(c)** valid; **(d)** not valid. In the diagram, J represents all juniors, C represents clever people, and M represents males.

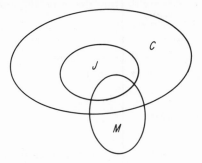

7. (a) Valid; **(b)** not valid; **(c)** not valid; **(d)** not valid; **(e)** not valid; **(f)** not valid; **(g)** not valid. In the diagram, I represents interesting people, M represents mathematics teachers, A represents attractive individuals, and K represents kind individuals.

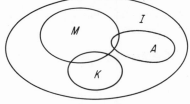

9. (a) Valid; **(b)** valid; **(c)** valid; **(d)** not valid. In the diagram the a's, b's, c's, and d's are represented by circles A, B, C, and D. Note the two possibilities D_1 and D_2 for D. The statement "Some d's are not c's" does not necessarily imply that some d's *are* c's.

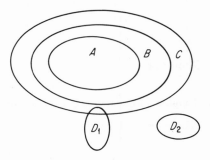

Chapter 10

10-1 Evolution of Geometry

1. The entire figure is equal to the sum of its parts. The early Greeks thought of the area $(x + 1)^2$ of the square with side $(x + 1)$ as the square on $(x + 1)$; they thought of the area $x \times 1$ of the rectangle with sides x and 1 as the rectangle contained by x and 1. Then the square on $(x + 1)$ is equal to the sum of the square on x and the square on 1 together with twice the rectangle contained by x and 1.

3. As in Exercise 1 the square on $(a - b)$ together with twice the rectangle contained by a and b is equal to the sum of the squares on a and b; that is,

$$(a - b)^2 + 2ab = a^2 + b^2$$

and thus
$$(a - b)^2 = a^2 - 2ab + b^2.$$

10-2 Euclidean Geometry

1. No; "point" is not classified and the definition is not reversible.

3. No; the definition is not reversible.

5. No; for most people, a general polygon is not a simpler figure than a triangle.

7. (a) Line to line; **(b)** line to line, line to plane, plane to line, plane to plane.

9. (a) Line to line; **(b)** line to line, line to plane, plane to line, plane to plane.

10-3 Non-Euclidean Geometries

	Euclidean	Elliptic	Hyperbolic
1.	Yes.	No.	Yes.
3.	Yes.	No parallels.	No.
5.	Yes.	No.	No.
7.	No.	Yes.	No.
9.	No.	Yes.	Yes.

10-4 Projective Geometry

1. Any two distinct points on the same plane determine a unique line.

3. Any two distinct lines on the same plane determine a unique point.

5.

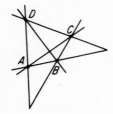

7.

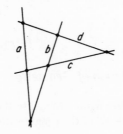

9.

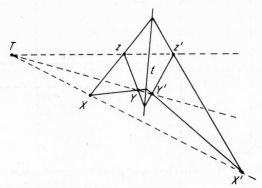

11. See the text.

10-5 A Finite Geometry

1. Postulate I. **3.** Postulate III. **5.** Postulate VI. **7.** Postulate II. **9.** Postulate V. **11.** Postulate II. **13.** Postulate V. **15.** Postulate V. **17.** Postulate V. **19.** Postulate IV. **21.** Postulate V. **23.** Postulates III and VII and Exercises 21 and 22. **25.** Postulate VII. **27.** Postulate V. **29.** Postulate IV. **31.** Postulate V. **33.** Postulates III and VII and Exercises 31 and 32. **35.** Postulate VII. **37.** Postulate V. **39**. Postulate III and Exercises 36, 37, and 38. **41.** Exercises 34 and 40. **43.** Exercises 1 through 41.

10-6 Coordinate Geometry

1, 3, 5, and **7.**   **9.**

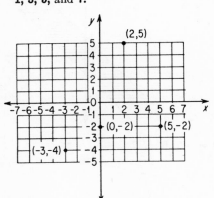 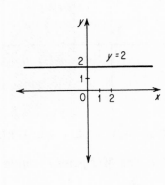

11.

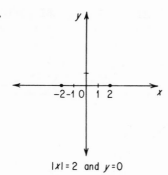

$|x| = 2$ and $y = 0$

13.

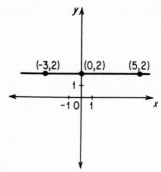

In Exercises 13 though 21, there are many possible correct selections of points satisfying the conditions.

15.

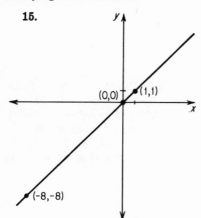

17.

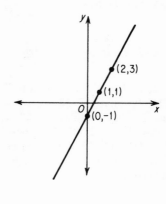

19.

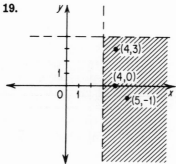

21.

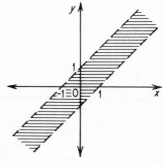

23. $x = -3$; 5. **25.** $y = 2$; 4. **27.** $y = -3$; 6.

10-7 The Mid-point Formula

1. $(2, 5)$.   **3.** $(-1, 1)$.

5. Let ABC be any right triangle, $\angle C = 90°$, $\overline{BC} = a$, and $\overline{CA} = b$. The triangle on a coordinate plane with vertices C': $(0, 0)$, A': $(b, 0)$, and B': $(0, a)$ has

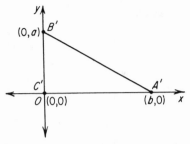

$\angle C' = 90°$, and thus, by *s.a.s.* = *s.a.s.*, is congruent to the given triangle. In other words, we may use such a triangle $A'B'C'$ to represent any given right triangle ABC on a coordinate plane.

7. Label the points A': $(0, 0)$, B': $(a, 0)$, C': (a, a), and D':$(0, a)$. Then $A'B'C'D'$ is a rectangle (Exercise 6) with a pair of adjacent sides equal ($\overline{A'B'} = \overline{A'D'}$) and thus is a square. Any square may be represented in this way by taking a as the length of a side of the square.

9. Label the points A': $(0, 0)$, B': $(a, 0)$, C': $(a + b, c)$, and D': (b, c). Notice that $\overline{A'B'} = \overline{D'C'} = a$, $\overline{A'D'} = \overline{B'C'} = b$, $A'B' \parallel D'C'$ and $A'D' \parallel B'C'$, and c may be selected to make angle A' equal to any angle A of a given parallelogram. Since the two sides $\overline{AB}$ and $\overline{AD}$ and $\angle A$ suffice to determine any parallelogram, any parallelogram $ABCD$ may be represented by a parallelogram $A'B'C'D'$ with vertices of the given form.

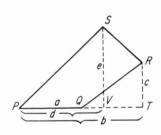
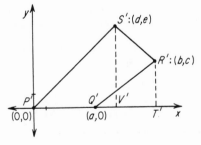

11. Any quadrilateral has at least one angle $\leq 90°$. Given any quadrilateral $PQRS$ with $\overline{PQ} = a$, we may take P': $(0, 0)$ and Q': $(a, 0)$. Draw altitudes $\overline{RT}$ and $\overline{SV}$ to the line PQ. For $\overline{PT} = b$ and $\overline{RT} = c$, we take R': (b, c); for $\overline{PV} = d$ and $\overline{VS} = e$, we take S': (d, e). For P' at $(0, 0)$, PQ along the positive x-axis, and R in the first quadrant (that is, with both coordinates positive), the points Q', R', and S' are uniquely determined by the given figure and themselves determine with P' a quadrilateral which may be used to represent the given quadrilateral $PQRS$ on a coordinate plane.

13. A quadrilateral $PQRS$ is a trapezoid if $PQ \parallel RS$. We may represent the trapezoid on a coordinate plane with $P'Q'$ on the x-axis, P' at $(0, 0)$, Q' at $(a, 0)$ where $\overline{PQ} = a$, and R' with a positive y-coordinate. Since $SR \parallel PQ$, the altitudes $\overline{SA}$ and $\overline{RB}$ onto PQ are equal; suppose $\overline{SA} = h$. Then S' and R' have y-coordinate h; they may have any distinct numbers b and d, respectively, as x-coordinate, where $b < d$ for a convex figure. We take S' at (b, h) and R' at (d, h). Any trapezoid $PQRS$ may be represented on a coordinate plane in this manner with vertices at $(0, 0)$, $(a, 0)$, (d, h), and (b, h) for suitable choices of values for a, b, d, and h. Let M' be the mid-point of $\overline{P'S'}$ and N' be the mid-point of $\overline{R'Q'}$. Then we have

$$M': \left(\frac{b}{2}, \frac{h}{2}\right) \qquad \text{and} \qquad N': \left(\frac{a+d}{2}, \frac{h}{2}\right).$$

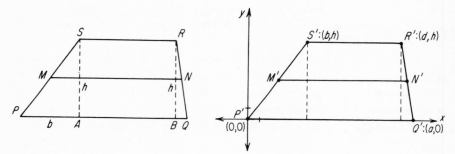

The line $M'N'$ is parallel to the x-axis and, thus, to $P'Q'$, since the y-coordinates of M' and N' are equal. The length of $\overline{M'N'}$ is $\left|\dfrac{a+d}{2} - \dfrac{b}{2}\right|$, that is, $\frac{1}{2}[a + (d - b)]$. The length of $\overline{P'Q'}$ is a, the length of $\overline{S'R'}$ is $(d - b)$. Thus, the length of $\overline{M'N'}$ is one-half the sum of the bases of the trapezoid.

15. Any given quadrilateral $PQRS$ may be represented on a coordinate plane by $P'Q'R'S'$, as in Exercise 11, with $P': (0, 0)$, $Q': (a, 0)$, $R': (b, c)$, and $S': (d, e)$. The sides $\overline{P'Q'}$ and $\overline{R'S'}$ are opposite sides and have mid-points $\left(\dfrac{a}{2}, 0\right)$ and $\left(\dfrac{b+d}{2}, \dfrac{c+e}{2}\right)$, respectively. The line segment joining these mid-points itself has mid-point $\left(\dfrac{a+b+d}{4}, \dfrac{c+e}{4}\right)$. Similarly, the sides $\overline{P'S'}$ and $\overline{Q'R'}$ are opposite sides and have mid-points $\left(\dfrac{d}{2}, \dfrac{e}{2}\right)$ and $\left(\dfrac{a+b}{2}, \dfrac{c}{2}\right)$, respectively. The line segment joining these mid-points itself has mid-point $\left(\dfrac{a+b+d}{2}, \dfrac{c+e}{2}\right)$. Since the line segments joining the mid-points of the opposite sides of the quadrilateral have the same mid-point, they bisect each other.

17. $(8, -11)$.

10-8 The Slope of a Line

There are many possible answers in Exercises 1 and 3.

1. $(0, -5)$, $(1, -2)$, $\dfrac{y - (-5)}{x - 0} = \dfrac{-2 - (-5)}{1 - 0}$.

3. $(1, 4)$, $(2, 3)$, $\dfrac{y - 4}{x - 1} = \dfrac{3 - 4}{2 - 1}$.

5. (1) $y - (-5) = 3(x - 0)$; (2) $y - 2 = -\frac{2}{3}(x - 0)$;
(3) $y - 4 = (-1)(x - 1)$; (4) $y - (-2) = 0(x - 0)$.

7. (1) $\dfrac{x}{\frac{5}{3}} + \dfrac{y}{-5} = 1$; (2) $\dfrac{x}{3} + \dfrac{y}{2} = 1$; (3) $\dfrac{x}{5} + \dfrac{y}{5} = 1$.

[*Note:* In Exercises 9 and 11 other equivalent forms of the equations are also acceptable.]

9. $\dfrac{y - 3}{x - 2} = \dfrac{5 - 3}{4 - 2}$; that is, $y = x + 1$.

11. $y + 2 = \dfrac{3}{2}x$.

13. Given: Lines a, b, c, such that $a \parallel b$ and $c \parallel b$. To prove: $a \parallel c$. *Proof:* The line b is taken not parallel to the y-axis, so that it has a slope m. Then the line a has slope m, since $a \parallel b$; also, the line c has slope m, since $c \parallel b$. Finally, $a \parallel c$, since each has slope m.

15. Given: Lines a, b, and c such that $a \parallel b$ and b intersects c. To prove: a intersects c. *Proof:* As in Exercise 14, let m be the slope of the line b; the slope of a is also m; the slope of c is not equal to m; a and c have different slopes and thus intersect.

17. AB and CD each has slope $\frac{7}{5}$; AD and BC each has slope 3; $AB \parallel CD$ and $AD \parallel BC$; thus, by definition, $ABCD$ is a parallelogram.

10-9 The Distance Formula

1. 5. **3.** $\sqrt{73}$. **5.** $\sqrt{5}$, $\sqrt{5}$, $\sqrt{10}$; **(a)** yes; **(b)** no; **(c)** yes.

7. Given: Circle $x^2 + y^2 = r^2$, $x = p_1$ where $p_1 > r$, $x = p_2$ where $p_2 = r$, $x = p_3$ where $p_3 < r$. To prove: the line $x = p_1$ does not intersect the circle; $x = p_2$ is

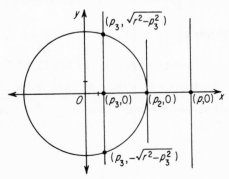

tangent to the circle; $x = p_3$ is a secant of the circle. *Proof:* Solving the equation $x^2 + y^2 = r^2$ of the circle simultaneously with the equation $x = p_1$ of the line, $p_1^2 + y^2 = r^2$, that is, $y^2 = r^2 - p_1^2$. But $p_1^2 > r^2$; therefore, $(r^2 - p_1^2)$ is negative and y is imaginary; in other words, this line does not intersect the circle. Using the line $x = p_2$, $y^2 = r^2 - p_2^2$. But $r^2 = p_2^2$ because $r = p_2$; therefore, $y = 0$ and the only point common to $x^2 + y^2 = r^2$ and $x = p_2$ is the point $(p_2, 0)$; hence, $x = p_2$ is tangent to the circle. Using the line $x = p_3$, $y^2 = r^2 - p_3^2$. But $r^2 > p_3^2$ because $r > p_3$; therefore, $(r^2 - p_3^2)$ is positive and y has two distinct real roots. Hence, $x = p_3$ cuts $x^2 + y^2 = r^2$ at $(p_3, \sqrt{r^2 - p_3^2})$ and $(p_3, -\sqrt{r^2 - p_3^2})$, and $x = p_3$ is a secant of the circle.

9. Given: Isosceles triangle ABC, $\overline{AB} = \overline{BC}$ with $\overline{AE}$ and $\overline{CD}$ as medians, $A: (0, 0)$, $B: (a, b)$, $C: (2a, 0)$. To prove: $\overline{AE} = \overline{CD}$. *Proof:* By the mid-point formula, we have $E: \left(\dfrac{3a}{2}, \dfrac{b}{2}\right)$ and $D: \left(\dfrac{a}{2}, \dfrac{b}{2}\right)$. By the distance formula,

$$\overline{AE} = \sqrt{\left(\frac{3a}{2}\right)^2 + \frac{b^2}{4}} = \frac{\sqrt{9a^2 + b^2}}{2}$$

and

$$\overline{CD} = \sqrt{\left(2a - \frac{a}{2}\right)^2 + \left(-\frac{b}{2}\right)^2} = \sqrt{\left(\frac{3a}{2}\right)^2 + \left(\frac{b}{2}\right)^2}$$

$$= \frac{\sqrt{9a^2 + b^2}}{2};$$

hence,

$$\overline{AE} = \overline{CD}, \text{ since each equals } \frac{\sqrt{9a^2 + b^2}}{2}.$$

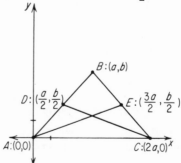

10-10 Perpendicular Lines

1. Given: $a \parallel b$, $r \perp a$, slope of a is m. To prove: $r \perp b$. *Proof:* Slope of b is m, since $a \parallel b$ and parallel lines have the same slope. Slope of r is $-\dfrac{1}{m}$, because $r \perp a$; hence, their slopes must be negative reciprocals. The slope of b and the slope of r are negative reciprocals; hence, $r \perp b$, because two lines whose slopes are negative reciprocals are perpendicular.

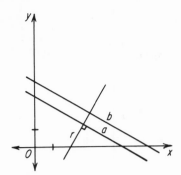

3. Given: Intersecting lines a with slope m and b with slope n, lines $r \perp a$ and $s \perp b$. To prove: r intersects s. *Proof:* The slopes m and n are not equal, since the lines a and b intersect. Thus,

$$\frac{1}{m} \neq \frac{1}{n} \qquad \text{and} \qquad -\frac{1}{m} \neq -\frac{1}{n}.$$

The slope of r is $-\dfrac{1}{m}$; the slope of s is $-\dfrac{1}{n}$; r and s intersect.

5. Given: $\triangle ABC$ with altitudes CD, AE, and BF, A: $(0, 0)$, B: $(b, 0)$, C: (a, c). To prove: AE, BF, and DC are concurrent. *Proof:* Since $CD \perp AB$, $CD \parallel y$-axis and the equation of CD is $x = a$. The slope of AC is $\dfrac{c}{a}$ and the slope of BF, the altitude to AC, is $-\dfrac{a}{c}$; in the same manner, the slope of BC is $\dfrac{c}{a - b}$ and the slope

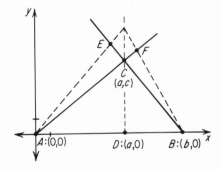

of AE, the altitude to BC, is $-\dfrac{a - b}{c}$ or $\dfrac{b - a}{c}$, because an altitude is perpendicular to the side to which it is drawn, and the slopes of perpendicular lines are negative reciprocals. By the point-slope formula, the equation of AE is $y = \dfrac{b - a}{c}x$ and the equation of BF is $y = -\dfrac{a}{c}(x - b)$. Solving these two equations simultaneously,

$$\frac{b - a}{c}x = -\frac{a}{c}(x - b),$$

that is, $x = a$ and $y = \dfrac{ab - a^2}{c}$. Thus, the coordinates of the point of intersection of AE and BF are $\left(a, \dfrac{ab - a^2}{c}\right)$, which is also a point on $x = a$; therefore, AE, BF, and DC are concurrent.

10-11 The Conic Sections

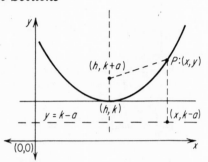

1. A parabola is defined as the locus of P such that the distance from P to the focal point is equal to the distance from P to the directrix. Using this definition and the distance formula,

$$\sqrt{(x - h)^2 + (y - k - a)^2} = y - k + a.$$

Squaring both sides of this equation,

$$(x - h)^2 + y^2 + k^2 + a^2 - 2ky - 2ay + 2ak = y^2 + k^2 + a^2 - 2ky + 2ay - 2ak.$$

Collecting terms,

$$(x - h)^2 = 4ay - 4ak,$$

or $(x - h)^2 = 4a(y - k)$, as in (7).

3. If the center of the ellipse is at (h, k), then the foci will be at

$$(-\sqrt{a^2 - b^2} + h, k) \qquad \text{and} \qquad (\sqrt{a^2 - b^2} + h, k).$$

Use the definition of an ellipse which states that an ellipse is the locus of a point

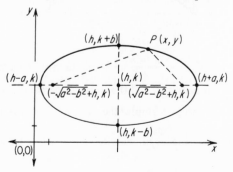

$P: (x, y)$ the sum of whose distances from the two foci is constant. Then substituting in the distance formula gives:

$$2a = \sqrt{(x + \sqrt{a^2 - b^2} - h)^2 + (y - k)^2}$$
$$+ \sqrt{(x - \sqrt{a^2 - b^2} - h)^2 + (y - k)^2}.$$

Then

$$4a^2 + (x + \sqrt{a^2 - b^2} - h)^2 + (y - k)^2 - 4a\sqrt{(x + \sqrt{a^2 - b^2} - h)^2 + (y - k)^2}$$
$$= (x - \sqrt{a^2 - b^2} - h)^2 + (y - k)^2,$$

which simplifies to

$$a^2 + x\sqrt{a^2 - b^2} - h\sqrt{a^2 - b^2} = a\sqrt{(x + \sqrt{a^2 - b^2} - h)^2 + (y - k)^2}.$$

Squaring both sides of this equation and simplifying, we have

$$-b^2x^2 - b^2h^2 + 2b^2hx = -a^2b^2 + a^2(y - k)^2;$$

dividing through by $(-b^2)$,

$$x^2 - 2hx + h^2 = a^2 - \frac{a^2}{b^2}(y - k)^2;$$

and dividing through by a^2 and simplifying,

$$\frac{(x - h)^2}{a^2} + \frac{(y - k)^2}{b^2} = 1,$$

as in (2).

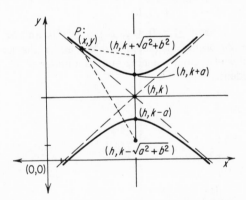

5. This exercise is set up in the same manner as Exercise 4. The initial equation is:

$$\pm 2a = \sqrt{(x - h)^2 + (y - k + \sqrt{a^2 + b^2})^2} - \sqrt{(x - h)^2 + (y - k - \sqrt{a^2 + b^2})^2}.$$

Following the same algebraic processes as in Exercise 4,

$$k\sqrt{a^2 + b^2} - y\sqrt{a^2 + b^2} + a^2 = \pm a\sqrt{(x - h)^2 + (y - k - \sqrt{a^2 + b^2})^2};$$

$$b^2y^2 - 2b^2ky + b^2k^2 = a^2(x - h)^2 + a^2b^2;$$

$$(y - k)^2 = \frac{a^2}{b^2}(x - h)^2 + a^2; \qquad \frac{(y - k)^2}{a^2} - \frac{(x - h)^2}{b^2} = 1,$$

as in (5).

10-12 Linear Programming

1.

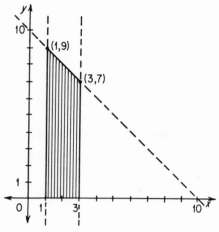

3. (a) The maximum value of $x + 2y$ is 19 and occurs at $(1, 9)$; **(b)** The minimum value of $x + 2y$ is 1 and occurs at $(1, 0)$.

5. (a) The maximum value of $x + y$ is 9 and occurs at $(6, 3)$; the minimum value of $x + y$ is 0 and occurs at $(0, 0)$.

7. The conditions are $0 \leq x$, $0 \leq y$, $x + y \leq 180$, and $5x + 3y \leq 750$. The maximum of $3x + 2y$ occurs at $(105, 75)$; thus under the assumptions of this exercise, 105 minutes of regular teaching and 75 minutes of TV instruction would be best for the students.

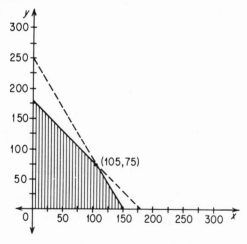

9. The maximum of $x + 2y$ occurs at $(30, 150)$; thus under the assumptions of this exercise, 30 minutes of regular teaching and 150 minutes of TV instruction would be best for the students.

INDEX